PRINCIPLES OF TREE HAZARD ASSESSMENT AND MANAGEMENT

Dr David Lonsdale

London: TSO

Department for Communities and Local Government
Eland House
Bressenden Place
London SW1E 5DU
Web Site http://www.communities.gov.uk

On 5th May 2006 the responsibilities of the Office of the Deputy Prime Minister (ODPM) transferred to the Department for Communities and Local Government (DCLG).

Published with the permission of the Department for Communities and Local Government on behalf of the Controller of Her Majesty's Stationery Office.

First published July 1999
Fourth Impression 2006

ISBN 0 11 753355 6

Printed in Great Britain on material containing 75% post-consumer waste and 25% ECF pulp.
N5389514 C7 07/06

Other reports available in the *Research for amenity trees* series

No.	Title
1	*Trees in Towns*, TSO, 1993 (Out of Print)
2	*Diagnosis of Ill Health in Trees*, TSO, 2nd edition 2000
3	*Urban Tree Strategies*, DoE, 1994 (Out of Print)
4	*The Body Language of Trees – A Handbook for Failure Analysis*, TSO, 1995
5	*Urban Woodland and the Benefits for Local Air Quality*, TSO, 1996
6	*Arboricultural Practice, Present and Future*, DETR/TAT/AA, 1997
7	*Principle of Tree Hazard Assessment and Management*, TSO, 1999
8	*Tree Roots in the Built Environment*, TSO, 2006

(Please contact DCLG for DoE & DETR titles)

Foreword by Caroline Davis MBE

Principles of Tree Hazard Assessment and Management

"Principles of Tree Hazard Assessment and Management" is the third handbook to be produced in the Research for Amenity Tree Series to assist practitioners to make better informed decisions on the health and safety of trees. Two were initially envisaged, the first concentrating on diagnosis of pests and diseases ('Diagnosis of Ill Health in Trees' published in 1994), and the second to cover in greater detail decay and other causes of failure, drawing in work on biomechanics. However, because biomechanics had rapidly become a large and significant subject in its own right, 'The Body Language of Trees', a new English edition of the original German text by Claus Mattheck and Helge Breloer was published as a handbook in 1995 to make this available to the UK profession.

David Lonsdale has played an increasingly important role as this series of handbooks has developed. He contributed to 'Diagnosis of Ill-Health in Trees', was a meticulous technical editor of 'Body Language of Trees', and has single-handedly authored this, the final handbook in the set. The objective of this handbook is to provide practical guidance on the recognition, evaluation and management of hazards in trees. To do this it has been necessary to bring together state-of-the-art knowledge from a broad range of subjects. This has been a demanding interdisciplinary undertaking, which might have daunted someone with less determination and tenacity. The result is that this book contains a unique combination of tree biology, mycology, arboriculture, forestry, biomechanics and law. It has only been made possible by the depth and breadth of David Lonsdale's knowledge and understanding which he has brought to bear in distilling relevant information from the literature and input from arboriculturists worldwide. Following an objective and critical analysis, this has been skilfully synthesised into a comprehensive and practical work written in a clear and accessible style.

The quantum leap forward in knowledge in some of the contributing disciplines has focused the pressing need for a comprehensive re-appraisal of much accepted wisdom and deeply ingrained views. Principal among these is the view that infection, disease and decay are, axiomatically, detrimental and life-threatening to trees and consequently a threat to human safety. This now naive view, along with others, is challenged and comprehensively laid to rest in this book. It is opportune, at a time when the recognition of the value of decayed and dead wood is being realised and included in 'Habitat Action Plans', that we have this book to help tree managers distinguish when decay and other factors do represent risk necessitating removal, from the many situations when other options should be considered. This book is a major contribution to the development of management practices which take into account the needs of trees, people and the wider ecology.

I would like to add my grateful thanks to all those who participated at the Arboricultural Association conference session, gave feedback at the meeting at Marsham Street or who have otherwise contributed knowledge and experience to the final product. Although this has lengthened its gestation and added to the complexity of David's task, it was always considered paramount to have the widest possible involvement of arboriculturists. I hope that the close contact between researchers and practitioners that has been achieved will continue in the future to capture and pass on the great wealth of knowledge that exists within the profession.

It has been my privilege and pleasure to have been involved with the commissioning and publication of these handbooks. The aim of all three has been to assist arboriculturists and others who have responsibility for trees by providing comprehensive and up-to-date information on which to base management decisions relating to the health and safety of trees in a readily used format. I believe that this has been achieved, in no small measure, due to David's unstinting efforts.

Preface

One of the more difficult tasks in writing this book was the choice of a title. I included the word 'hazard' because it was central to the content of the book, but I was aware that it could convey an unduly negative message about trees. Such a message might encourage owners or managers to play safe by unnecessarily cutting trees which show the merest sign of suspected 'defects'. The sad truth, however, is that this already happens because of an inability to distinguish between features which represent significant hazards and those which do not. On the other side of the same coin, there have been occasional instances in which people have died or been maimed due to negligence. I hope very much that this book will go some way towards saving trees as well as people.

Trees, like many things in the world, are essential to our lives but also contribute to the hazards of life. In particular, their potential to fall or to shed limbs may put people at risk of being injured or of having their property damaged. We have the ability to control these risks in various ways but we could not entirely eliminate them without destroying nearly every tree in the world. Thus, rather than seek absolute safety, we need to manage trees so as to keep risks within limits acceptable to the judiciary, the insurance companies and society in general.

The risks that we face from trees are generally very small, but site owners and managers need to recognise individual situations where the risks may be considerable and where harm to people or property might be deemed foreseeable in the eyes of the law. If, in this context, a mechanical defect has contributed to the mechanical failure of a tree, one of the key questions is whether or not the defect could have been identified beforehand by a competent person.

Competence in tree hazard assessment is acquired through experience, as well as through training and keeping up with 'the literature'. It is hoped that the present book may aid the learning process by bringing together a body of relevant information and ideas. It is certainly not designed to turn the reader into a tree hazard expert in 'ten easy lessons'. A prescriptive approach is all very well for telling people how to work with predictable things such as lawnmowers, but there are dangers in trying to adopt such an approach where trees are concerned. This is not to imply that we are dealing here with a 'muck and mystery' subject, but to make it clear that practitioners need to understand and apply principles, as distinct from operating like quality control staff on a production line.

It is difficult to learn about the limits of mechanical strength in trees from first-hand experience of the kind that everyone has with breakable man-made objects like pieces of crockery or furniture. A more objective approach is to apply the principles of mechanics, and this has become increasingly possible by virtue of recent advances in research. Of particular importance in this regard has been the work of Prof. Claus Mattheck at the Karlsruhe Research Institute following the earlier contributions of others in Europe and the USA, including Dr. Willis Wagener. Prof. Mattheck's diagnostic methods, together with many other aspects of understanding the 'body language of trees', are presented in detail within a book of that title which has been published in the 'Research for Amenity Trees' series.

The insights which are now being provided through an understanding of tree biomechanics may help our appreciation of the amazing natural 'engineering' of trees. I do not suppose that any human architect or sculptor would dare to construct anything so mechanically outrageous as a mature broadleaved tree. Widely spreading heavy branches, great height and a huge sail area look like a recipe for disaster, and yet disaster rarely strikes except in cases when exceptionally severe weather conditions occur, or when trees have serious mechanical defects.

Among the things that can contribute to mechanical failure, decay has often attracted particular attention. Its spatial development within trees and the factors which influence its initiation and extent have become increasingly well understood by arboriculturists, thanks in particular to the work of Dr. Alex Shigo and his colleagues in the USA. There is also a growing body of information on different types of decay induced by various fungal species and the consequent weakening of wood. Recent research in this area, especially the work of Dr. Francis Schwarze and co-workers at Freiburg University, Germany, is adding to our ability to assess the mechanical integrity of trees. There is also a growing realisation that old, decaying trees have great ecological importance and deserve protection, subject to hazard management being duly considered.

One of the problems of writing a book on a fast-developing subject is that it will be slightly out of date even before it is printed. One area of continuing research which deserves future attention is the evaluation of diagnostic devices for the assessment of wood quality in standing trees. Yet another emerging area of potential progress is the improvement of methods of risk assessment, led by various arboriculturists, including Jim Clark and Nelda Matheny in the USA and Rodney Helliwell, Mike Ellison and Neville Fay in the UK.

This book has been enhanced considerably by information and advice provided by many individuals. Not all their observations and opinions have been subjected to scientific rigour, but they are nonetheless valuable. I have, where appropriate, indicated where information is based on observation, rather than on scientific investigation. It has been something of a challenge to write a book on a subject in which no-one – and certainly not I – can claim expertise in all its aspects, but it has also been a privilege to try to bring a number of different disciplines together. I hope that my own need to understand more of those disciplines has helped me to write about this fascinating subject in a language which others can understand.

David Lonsdale
September 1998

Acknowledgements

This book was written as part of a contract placed with the Forestry Commission Research Agency* by the Department of the Environment, Transport and the Regions† (DETR). I am grateful for the support and encouragement of both organisations; to the Forestry Commission for providing me with the means to develop my knowledge of trees and to the DETR for sustaining a programme of research and publications for arboriculture.

This book could not have been written without the help, both direct or indirect, of many individuals. Much of the information that I have used was gleaned from research papers and other writings of other workers in the fields of tree biology, mycology, arboriculture, forestry, biomechanics and the law. I have also drawn heavily on the advice of many members of the arboricultural and other professions who kindly agreed to comment on an early draft of the book, even to the extent of attending a special meeting. I regarded their advice as very important because no individual, and certainly not I, could have written with authority on all the many issues that were relevant.

A list of the arboriculturists who played a significant part in the main review of my first draft, and/or who provided information for Appendix 2, is shown below. In addition, my colleagues Dr. John Gibbs and Mr. Robert Strouts commented most helpfully on substantial sections of the draft. As indicated in the text, the section on fungal identification was provided by Mr. Strouts. I also received comments on specific chapters from the late Dr. Ray Pearce of Birmingham University and from legal experts Messrs. Charles Mynors and Steve Clark.

In acknowledging those who have commented on drafts of this book, I must make special mention of Mrs. Caroline Davis, MBE, who has worked closely with me throughout this project, even following her early retirement from DETR. Indeed, it has been very largely through her commitment to the provision of information to the arboricultural industry that this book and others in this series have come into existence. I am also most grateful to those who have worked subsequently on the book; to Caroline's successor at DETR, Mr. Peter Annett for many very helpful comments and suggestions, and to Mr. Neil Richardson of DETR and Mr. Ian Carter and his colleagues at The Stationery Office for their work on the various stages of production.

To the extent that some of the information in this book comes from my own research, I acknowledge the help that has been provided by various former and present members of staff at Alice Holt Research Station, especially Mrs. Sarah Brown and Messrs. Ian Hickman, Colin Palmer and Martin Lipscombe. I have also greatly valued my discussions with others who have worked or advised on tree decay or safety, especially Prof. Claus Mattheck, Dr. Alex Shigo, Dr.

Francis Schwarze and the following present and former colleagues: Brian Greig, Dr. Peter Mercer, Derek Patch, Jim Pratt, David Rose, Robert Strouts and the late Bill Young.

The photographs in this book come from many sources, including the collections at Alice Holt research station, and I acknowledge the help of Miss M. Trusler and Mr. George Gate in providing copies of these. I am also very grateful to all those outwith the Forestry Commission who lent me their photos, and who were so patient during the protracted process of choosing those that were to be selected for use. The sources of the various photos are listed below.

Finally, I would like to thank those who allowed use of copyright material in Appendix 3: The International Society of Arboriculture and Mr. Mike Ellison.

* formerly, the Forestry Commission Research Division
† formerly, the Department of the Environment

Arboriculturists who contributed significant comments and/or who attended the editorial review in London, May 1996.

Peter Annett
David Archer
Jeremy Barrell
Giles Biddle
Peter Bridgeman
Jon Capel
Brian Crane
John Cromar
Chris Davies
John Dolwin
Dave Dowson
Mike Ellison
Alan Engley
Roy Finch
Henry Girling
Dick Grainger
John Harraway
Jim Harrisson
Peter Holloway
Conrad Jørgensen
Ian Keen
Jim Keyes
Tony Kirkham
Bill Kowalczyk
Margaret MacQueen
Bill Matthews
Simon Pryce
Les Round
Keith Rushforth
David Thorman
Chris Yarrow

Contributors of photographs, showing relevant plate numbers

(N.B. The individuals named below retain the copyright for all the photographs which they kindly contributed from their private collections)

Caroline Davis: 12, 13, 17, 21, 27, 53, 70, 81, 114, 125, 149, 150, 151, 154

Gordon Dickson: 49, 64, 69, 84, 101

Mark Finch: 126

Roy Finch: 1, 3, 7, 9, 15, 20, 34, 37, 54, 117, 118, 119, 120, 121, 122, 123, 132, 135, 137, 139

Forest Research: DETR-contract collection 4, 5, 6, 10, 14, 23, 28, 33, 35, 36, 38, 39, 40, 78, 97, 110, 113, 128, 129, 130, 131, 133, 134, 143, 144, 145, 147, 148

Forest Research: photographic collection 11, 41, 42, 44, 45, 46, 47, 48, 50, 52, 55, 56, 59, 61, 63, 65, 66, 67, 68, 72, 73, 77, 79, 80, 85, 86, 87, 88, 89, 90, 92, 93, 94, 98, 100, 104, 105

Ted Green: 83, 91

John Harraway: 108

David Lonsdale: 2, 8, 16, 18, 19, 22, 24, 25, 26, 32, 57, 109, 111, 115, 116, 127, 136, 138, 142, 146, 152, 153, 155, 156

Claus Mattheck: 107

Graham Mattock: 51, 58, 60, 62, 71, 82, 96, 99, 102, 103

William Moore: 140, 141

Klaus Schröder: 124

Francis Schwarze: 29, 30, 31, 74, 75, 76, 106, 112

Robert Strouts: 43, 95

Principles of Tree Hazard Assessment and Management

CONTENTS

Foreword by Caroline Davis

Preface

Chapter 3 Decay: its development in trees

Chapter 4 Principal decay fungi

Chapter 5 Tree inspection procedures and reporting

Chapter 7 Prevention of hazards

Chapter 8 Environmental implications of hazard and disease management

Chapter 1 Introduction

1.1 Hazard and risk

According to definitions proposed by a UK government agency [202], a hazard is "the disposition of a thing, a condition or a situation to produce injury", whereas risk is "the chance of something adverse happening". We instinctively avoid risk when the hazards are very obvious, as in the case of fire or flood, and we have the capacity to learn about more subtle hazards, such as those associated with poisonous substances and ionising radiations. Our modern-day desire to avoid hazards may, however, obscure the fact that they are to some extent an intrinsic part of life, and indeed have been essential in the evolution of living species. We walk a tightrope merely by being alive, as can be illustrated by the fact that vitally important substances such as potassium or oxygen are deadly if their concentrations within living cells are not very accurately regulated.

Philosophical arguments about the nature of hazards are not necessarily very helpful to someone who has been crushed by a falling tree, but they provide a basis for understanding that we cannot achieve a completely risk-free existence. In effect, they indicate the need for a pragmatic approach, whereby we try to identify hazards and consequent risks which are serious enough to require preventive action, or at least some form of insurance policy. To this end, we need to ask two questions. The first of these concerns the **magnitude** of the observed hazard; in other words, what is its capacity to cause harm? The second question concerns the risk; i.e. the **probability** that harm might occur. Both magnitude of hazard and the probability of occurrence can to some extent be quantified and then combined so as to provide a **risk assessment**.

Among the hazards that may be associated with trees, their capacity to fall on people or property is perhaps of the greatest concern. Mechanical failures in trees are often attributable to recognisable 'defects', but even an apparently sound specimen can fail if the wind is exceptionally strong. There is one means of achieving absolute safety from tree failure; that is, the removal of every tree that might conceivably fall on someone or someone's property, given sufficiently extreme weather conditions. Such an approach would clearly detract so much from the immense contribution that trees make to our environment that the results would be unacceptable to most people. On the other hand, people and property must be protected, and this can be achieved through various forms of preventive and remedial action which provide an acceptable margin of safety.

The reduction of risk where it cannot be totally eliminated is an accepted practice in many aspects of life and work [203, 204]. Indeed, on grounds of cost or general acceptability, there are instances (for example, in transportation) where certain safety measures are not implemented despite being theoretically possible. By taking all relevant factors into consideration, it is possible to define the maximum degree of risk that is acceptable.

For the purposes of risk reduction, safety policies are formulated for industry and for everyday life. In the UK, the Health and Safety Executive [203] has suggested that, for workers, a risk of death of 1 in 1,000 per annum should be the maximum acceptable limit, whereas the corresponding limit for members of the public could range between 1 in 10,000 and 1 in 1,000,000 per annum. The value of 1 in 10,000 applies when an identifiable risk is imposed upon people in "the wider interest", and is perhaps appropriate as far as risks and benefits from trees are concerned.

It is instructive to consider tree-related hazards alongside others which arise with man-made things. For example, chimneys, roof tiles and advertising hoardings can, like trees, cause serious harm if they fall. Like trees, they can fall as a result of exceptional weather conditions even if they are in good condition. Trees should therefore be seen in perspective alongside other everyday things which are desirable or necessary but not hazard-free.

In reality, far fewer people are killed by trees than by many other everyday things which are valued for their benefits despite the associated risks. The motor car is one such example, although perhaps we need to reconsider the balance between its benefits and risks. Although the benefits from trees generally outweigh the risks very greatly, there are particular cases where individual trees, by virtue of their condition and location, pose an unacceptable risk to people or property. Assessment of risk in such cases involves considerable uncertainty, as there are no precise methods for calculating the magnitude of the hazard and the probability of harm occurring. The underlying factors comprise the following:

- the probability of mechanical failure
- the severity of impact in the event of failure
- the probability of one or more persons or particular items of property being present at the time.

Despite unavoidable subjectivity, experienced practitioners are able to assess risk within broad categories. Potentially more sensitive methods for risk assessment are currently being developed [e.g., 49].

In considering safety standards for trees, we can make some comparisons with buildings and other man-made structures. Architects and engineers usually work to specifications which give assurance that the structures they create are very unlikely to fail under a given range of conditions. Thus, for example, a bridge may be deemed to be 'safe', within a stated maximum working load. Similarly, a trunk or branch of a tree is able to withstand loads within certain limits, although the limits may be less well defined than in a man-made structure. In either case, we are dealing with a margin of safety; not absolute safety, which is not achievable for any kind of structure.

Trees have an inherent margin of safety or 'safety factor', as they are usually able to withstand much stronger mechanical loading than occurs under average conditions (see Section 1.3). Thus, provided that they are free from significant mechanical defects, they can withstand quite severe winds. If, under exceptionally severe conditions, the safety factor of a tree is exceeded, failure is of course possible. It must, however, be accepted that conditions such as these are potentially hazardous whether or not trees are present. On the other hand, trees with mechanical defects sometimes fail under weather conditions which could be reasonably expected to occur from time to time. If such a tree is so placed that it could harm people or property, there is a need to decide whether it represents an unacceptable hazard. If so, some form of remedial action should be considered.

1.2 Legal considerations and insurance

In the UK, as in many other countries, the occupier of a site has a duty of care to take reasonable steps to prevent or minimise the risk of personal injury or damage to property arising from the presence of any tree on the site, or from its breakage or uprooting. This duty is defined in law, in particular by the Occupiers' Liability Act (1957 and 1984) [207, 208] in the case of England and Wales. The earlier Act concerns the duty of care which occupiers have towards their visitors, while the later Act concerns their duty towards other persons. Duty of care has also been a consideration in various court cases involving harm caused by trees [e.g. 182, 184, 185, 188].

In the event of a claim arising from personal injury or other damage involving a tree, the occupier will in most cases be liable and could be found negligent if he or she had failed in the above duty of care [e.g. 186]. For proof of negligence, it will usually have to be shown that the occupier, within reason, had been in a position to foresee that the tree might do damage, and to have taken steps to prevent such damage [e.g. 190].

The question as to whether personal injury or other damage is foreseeable depends partly on the siting of the tree. If, for example, the risk involved the possibility of poisoning, a poisonous tree within the reach of children might be considered dangerous. The possibility of mechanical failure is of particular concern if the tree is near a road or other place where people are often present (see Chapter 5). Even in an area where there is no lawful public access, personal injury from a mechanically defective tree could be deemed foreseeable if the occupier knew that people were in the habit of gaining unauthorised access and had not tried to prevent this by maintaining good walls or fences.

If a tree is so placed that it (or part of it) could fall on someone, the occupier is expected to ensure that it is subjected to expert inspection [e.g. 186]. The purpose of such inspection is to determine whether the tree could foreseeably cause harm by virtue of its size and physical condition. The courts recognise that the occupier may not have the necessary expertise to make such a determination [e.g. 183]. It is therefore accepted that the occupier's duty of care to inspect trees can be fulfilled by employing an expert to do this work.

It is important that tree inspections are carried out competently, and that appropriate work is carried out if necessary to remove or minimise any risk. It is, however, not feasible to lay down exact requirements either for inspection or for remedial action. The legal requirement is generally that occupiers should take 'reasonable steps' to carry out these procedures. On this basis, the practicability and cost of the work involved are taken into consideration by the courts. Under UK law, an occupier who fails to carry out remedial action could be required to do so if people or property would otherwise be at risk of harm. This power could be exercised either through a Court Injunction or through a Notice served on the occupier by the local authority under the Local Government (Miscellaneous Provisions) Act [192] or Highways Act [209].

In the event of legal proceedings arising from the mechanical failure of a tree, importance would normally be attached to any evidence of the presence or absence of features which might have contributed to the failure and which would have been detectable in an expert inspection. Nevertheless, the comments of a judge in a 1985 court case [189], cited by Griffin [65], may reflect the fact that there is no tree for which the possibility of mechanical failure can be completely ruled out. He is quoted as follows:

"*....a tree planted at a roadside may by its very size be judged to have become dangerous in the sense that in a high wind it, or part of it, may fall across the road to the danger of traffic*."

In the months and years following an inspection, the condition of trees inevitably changes. It is therefore essential that trees should be inspected regularly and also after any event such as a storm which may have caused a sudden change. If an expert has inspected a particular tree and found that it is safe enough to be retained for the present, but requires special monitoring, the resulting advice regarding the frequency of future inspections should be followed. A tree owner could be found negligent if a tree involved in a claim had developed a defect since it was last inspected. It is advisable for an owner to maintain and to abide by a written safety policy, in which the need for regular inspection is stated.

As pointed out earlier in this chapter, exceptionally severe weather conditions may result in the snapping or uprooting of any tree, even if it is free from recognisable defects. To some extent, the law allows for the fact that extreme and unforeseeable events occur. In any particular case, however, there may be a need to establish whether personal injury or other damage from a tree was caused by such an event, and not by a hazardous condition of the tree. In practice, this means that experts who examine trees for potential defects need to be aware of the range of weather conditions that can reasonably be expected to occur at the site.

Clearly, the degree to which a potentially serious accident is foreseeable could be a matter for argument. Nevertheless, the ownership of trees ought not to give rise to any more fear of liability for injury or damage than the ownership of buildings, motor vehicles or other potentially hazardous things. Provided that owners take reasonable steps to inspect trees and to carry out any remedial action that may be appropriate, there will usually be very little risk of a foreseeable nature to people or property. If an accident nevertheless occurs, the owner will have a basis for demonstrating that he had not failed in his duty of care.

Tree owners need to be aware that inappropriate remedial action, and indeed any sort of unsuitable tree work, can make trees hazardous. Any resulting injury or damage could be the subject of legal action. For example, the removal of a tree may increase the exposure of neighbouring trees to the wind and so lead to their failure. Also, the removal or shortening of branches on one side of a tree crown could lead to failure by altering the distribution of loading on the trunk and root system.

Although we are concerned here mainly with hazards associated with the mechanical failure of trees, it should be noted that buildings can be damaged as a result of the growth or activity of tree roots. Such damage may result from the growth in diameter of large woody roots or the shrinkage of soil from which fine roots are extracting moisture. Site occupiers are accordingly under a duty of care to take reasonable steps to prevent or minimise these types of damage to neighbouring property. They should, however, also comply with any local or national regulations which control the felling or lopping of trees.

In some countries, the authorities are empowered to protect designated trees or groups of trees from inappropriate felling or wilful damage. In the UK, such controls are exercised through Tree Preservation Orders [195, 200], which are issued by the local planning authorities. There are also powers for the designation of Conservation Areas [196], within which owners must give a specified period of notice to the local planning authority before carrying out tree work. Additionally, there may be controls over the felling of trees for timber [191] or in areas designated for their scientific or heritage value [210, 211].

Although a Tree Preservation Order normally prohibits the felling, uprooting or lopping of the tree or trees concerned, there are exemptions which allow work on specific classes of trees, such as those which have become dangerous [195, 213]. It is, however, highly advisable for the owner to obtain prior agreement from the local planning authority. If it is not practicable to inform the local authority, the next best course of action is to obtain ample photographic evidence of the state of the tree or trees, together with the written report of an expert, before the work is done. Such evidence could be important if the local authority subsequently seeks to prosecute the owner on the grounds that unjustified work appears to have been carried out. In a recent case, cited by Dolwin [47], a tree with basal decay was felled on the pretext that it was dangerous, but was later shown to have contained sufficient sound wood to provide adequate support.

In addition to carrying out tree inspections and, if necessary, remedial action, site owners should have adequate insurance. The terms and the amount of the insurance should be appropriate for the usage of the site concerned. In the event of an insurance claim, it will be helpful if the owner is able to produce written records to show that the tree or trees concerned had been properly inspected. Experts employed by tree owners should also have adequate professional indemnity insurance, since they may be held liable for damage caused by trees on which they have previously given advice.

1.3 Some general principles for the recognition, assessment and management of hazards

As mentioned above, trees generally have a considerable mechanical safety factor. It has been estimated that, in diverse species, main stems and root systems can generally withstand about 4.5 times the average of the mechanical forces to which they are subjected from their own weight and from loading by wind, rain and snow [106]. In this context, the purpose of a hazard assessment is to identify any mechanical defects in the tree or features of the site which could significantly lessen the safety factor.

Certain characteristics which can be regarded as distinct defects from a mechanical point of view are outlined briefly in this introductory chapter and discussed in more detail in Chapters 2 and 5. When such a defect is detected, there is a need to take account of the size of the tree, or part of the tree, that would fall in the event of failure at the defect. Its size, together with the height from which it would fall, provides a basis for assessing the magnitude of the hazard associated with the defect. For example, a twig cannot usually represent more than a slight hazard, whereas a large branch could cause serious injury, even if falling from a modest height.

In addition to 'defects' which may be evident in a tree, certain features of the site may also constitute a hazard. For example, the recent felling of another tree or the removal or erection of a building may have increased the exposure of the tree to the wind. This particular problem is important, as the strength of a tree develops in response to the range of windspeeds to which it has previously been exposed, and may be inadequate under the altered conditions. Many years of growth might have to elapse before a previously sheltered tree can regain its original safety factor, if ever.

The rigour with which safety inspections need to be carried out may seem to vary according to legal test cases [106, 183, 186]. A reasonable expectation is that, at any site where tree failure could harm persons or property, all trees should be regularly viewed from ground-level so as to identify any potential signs of serious defect. If such an inspection gives any indication of a potentially serious defect that is too high in a tree to be viewed from the ground, there may be a need to make a closer inspection by climbing or using an hydraulic hoist. The same need may apply if a potential defect is obscured, for example by ivy or other vegetation.

Relatively simple training is needed for the initial recognition of the most obvious types of mechanical defect, but the assessment of possible weakness is usually a job for a specialist consultant, who may need to use detailed methods of investigation. Such an assessment should identify any need for remedial action such as felling the tree, removing defective branches or modifying the site so as to move 'targets' such as pedestrian or vehicular routes (see Chapter 5). In many cases, it will be found that trees which initially give cause for concern can be retained without undue risk for many years.

If there are indications both of foreseeable tree failure and of unacceptable risks to persons or property, some form of remedial action is appropriate. As explained in Chapter 6, this may necessitate work on the tree or trees concerned, but it can often be achieved through other means, such as the re-siting of paths or other facilities. Remedial action should be carried out promptly, but it may be considered reasonable to attend first to the most hazardous individuals if a number of trees on a site require attention. The question of whether a tree is legally protected, for example by a Tree Preservation Order, must also be considered.

In areas where persons or property are not significantly at risk from the mechanical failure of trees, it is often desirable to allow some trees to die and decay naturally since they can provide very valuable habitats for plants and animals dependent on dead wood or ancient bark surfaces. The natural shedding of branches, together with the eventual break-up or fall of the main stem, is a natural process which is important in the recycling of carbon and mineral nutrients within forest ecosystems.

1.4 Different kinds of hazard and their causes

As mentioned above, most tree species can withstand the normal range of windspeeds and other external loads. For defect-free parts of the structure, failure tends to occur only when the loads are great enough to overcome a tree's safety factor. Also the woody structure of trees tends to develop in such a way as to distribute stresses evenly and to prevent the formation of weak points [106]; in other words it is mechanically 'optimised'. In some cases, however, the existing structure suffers damage so that weak points develop. In other cases, factors which interfere with wood formation, either inherent or external, can impair the natural process of optimisation.

The most common inherent cause of weakness above ground is the formation of a fork or weak branch junction in which the wood of the two members is incompletely united due to the presence of a bark-to-bark contact zone (included bark) in an acutely angled crotch (Plate 1). Such unions split apart more easily than those with a complete woody connection, especially in certain species such as Horse chestnut, *Aesculus hippocastanum* [56]. Bark inclusions and other defects that can develop inherently within trees are described in more detail in Chapter 2. Another frequent cause of purely structural failure is the inability of the root system to develop sufficiently to resist strong winds. This in turn is often caused by restricted rooting conditions due to compaction or waterlogging.

The existing woody structure can become locally weakened due to sudden trauma, or as a result of gradual deterioration of wood quality from decay or physical or chemical changes. Traumatic injury can be accidental, as with vehicle impacts, or it can be the result of arboricultural work. One example of the latter is the excessive pruning of the lower branches on a trunk, which alters the pattern of wind loading and increases the chance of breakage [137] (Plate 10). A similar problem can arise from the removal of adjacent trees or other shelter, which alters the exposure to wind and may thereby create concentrations of mechanical stress. Trees can adapt to such changes by laying down new wood in a pattern which eventually redistributes excessive stress away from these points [106], but breakage sometimes occurs before this can be achieved.

Fungal decay is the best recognised cause of gradual deterioration of wood, and is explained in Chapter 3. There are many species of decay fungus, and they differ in their effects on wood strength. In some cases, a given fungus has different effects on the wood of its various host species [152]. Even in the absence of decay, branches and leaning trunks can undergo a deterioration in their load-bearing capacity due to the phenomenon of 'wood creep', which is an effect of prolonged bending stress [106]. The tree can compensate for the resulting downward bending by laying down new wood with sufficient thickness and with appropriate mechanical properties to help maintain the overall strength of the structure. In some cases, however, the local food supply to the cambium may be insufficient to maintain enough compensatory growth, so that failure becomes increasingly likely.

It is hard to assess the relative importance of different causes of failure, since 'casebook' observations do not provide sufficient information for a reliable analysis of data. One large data set has been provided by trees damaged in the Great Gale of October 1987 in south-east Britain [56]. These data showed that windthrow (i.e. uprooting) was a commoner cause of total tree failure than trunk breakage. Some of the uprooted trees had extensive decay in their root systems, but 72% did not. Indeed many unhealthy-looking trees, whose roots were probably affected by extensive decay, remained standing, perhaps because they had thin or stag-headed crowns which presented a relatively small 'sail area'. On the other hand, declining trees do eventually break up or fall over, and this probably explains why overall ill-health was the best predictor of failure in a study of oak trees in California [81].

Above-ground failures in the 1987 post-gale survey involved extensive decay in some cases, but the most common type of failure point was the weak fork or weak branch junction [56]. Thus, both in the below-ground and the above-ground failures, decay was a less important factor than the presence of growth-related defects. Although, as has been indicated, these data may be to some extent atypical because of the exceptional windspeeds involved, they place a large question mark over any supposition that decay is the most important factor in tree failure.

The recognition and assessment of defects can be aided by illustrated guides, but there is also a need for understanding of their causes and their effects on tree safety. For this reason, this book sets out to explain the principles of hazard assessment, as well as providing some practical guidance.

Chapter 2 Causes of hazard

2.1 Inherent strengths and weaknesses

For a tree to survive within a forest stand, it generally needs to keep pace with the growth of its neighbours. Otherwise, it could probably not absorb enough energy in the form of sunlight to maintain itself and to grow. An energy budget that stays 'in the red' or merely 'breaks even' is a sentence of death in the face of competition. Competitive pressure has stimulated the evolution of the tree habit, characterised by a permanent woody skeleton which provides a framework for an increasing height and spread. This skeleton must be strong enough to resist major breakage or uprooting, which could instantly lose a tree its place in the sunlight. Such damage would inevitably occur if trees were 'designed' merely to stay upright under average weather conditions. To survive, they must be able to withstand all but the most exceptional extremes of weather that occur in their native habitats.

A tree can be compared with a man-made structure which is designed with a considerable margin of strength beyond normal requirements. In engineering terms, the 'safety factor' of a component is the ratio between its breaking stress and the highest stress estimated to occur under normal working conditions; this ratio is often set at a value of four or more. For trees, Mattheck & Breloer [106] have defined the safety factor as the ratio between the breaking stress and the average stress. These workers suggest that this ratio is generally in the region of 4.5, as derived from various field studies both on stems and root-plates.

Another formula for calculating the safety factor is the ratio between the critical buckling height and the actual height of the stem. Niklas [119] found that this ratio was close to 4.0 in 111 plant species studied. Yet another formula, as applied by King [91], is the ratio between the actual stem diameter and the diameter required to keep the tree erect in the absence of wind. He found values in the range 2 to 6 among forest canopy stems of Sugar maple (*Acer saccharum*) in Wisconsin, USA. Trees at the lower end of this range may have developed under conditions relatively sheltered from the wind.

The safety factor of any part of a tree depends both on the diameter of its woody cylinder and on the mechanical properties of its wood cells. Its diameter increases with each seasonal increment, but unequally within different parts of the woody cylinder. Variations in incremental growth occur because cambial activity is influenced by the local availability of food materials and also by the magnitude and duration of mechanical stress. Wood quality is largely under genetic control, but within the genetic repertoire there is a capacity to produce special types of wood – known as reaction wood – which have the function of withstanding stresses which are predominantly of one type; either compressive or tensile. Reaction wood tends to form when the cambial cells are orientated other than vertically.

The term 'adaptive growth' has been used to describe the growth responses of the cambium to mechanical stresses and to its orientation within the gravitational field [106]. For the tree as a whole, adaptive growth helps to bring about a condition in which no part is either under-loaded nor over-loaded; i.e. there tends to be a uniform distribution of mechanical stresses. This has to some extent been recognised for many years, principally in relation to the effects of wind-induced flexure on stem taper; open-grown trees of a given species develop a more pronounced taper than those sheltered within forest stands. There is now a wider understanding of this principle, as expressed by the **axiom of uniform stress** [106], which applies to living things in general; not just to trees.

Although a local concentration of stress stimulates cambial activity, there may not always be enough food material available to allow optimal wood formation. Conversely, there is some evidence that surplus wood may be laid down in regions where carbohydrates accumulate in abundance. This has been observed in experiments involving the occlusion of wounds of different size and shape. In some situations, the relative importance of adaptive growth versus food supply is currently unclear. For example, the broad basal taper of a stem which is allowed to retain its low branches could be attributed partly to the load that it receives from these branches, and partly to the locally produced supply of food that it receives from them.

An understanding of mechanical optimisation – or the lack of it in some circumstances – helps to explain and predict mechanical failure. Failure becomes likely whenever the stresses imposed on the weakest part of a structure overcome its safety factor. It might be supposed that a perfect tree would not have any weak points, as every part of it could in theory be mechanically optimised by adaptive growth. In practice, however, it is usual for some parts not to be as well optimised as others. One reason for these differences in strength is that the anatomical structure of some parts, especially branch junctions, is not absolutely compatible with optimisation [106]. Also, the adaptation of some parts to withstand the types of stress to which they are usually exposed may be inadequate when unaccustomed stresses occur. Finally, as explained below, various things can interfere with adaptive growth and can therefore be regarded as causing defects.

2.1.1 The strength of different types of tree

It might be supposed that the safety factor would be relatively low in species whose wood is judged to be rather weak from everyday experience or from timber grading tests. This is not necessarily true, as a tree's safety factor depends on its biomechanical 'design', as well as on the properties of its wood. Some species, such as the tropical American tree *Ochroma lagopus* (balsa), have wood of such exceptional weakness that they can be suspected of having a relatively low safety factor. There are also some temperate trees, such as members of the genus *Populus*, which fail more often than others in high winds, even in the apparent absence of obvious defects. It can be argued that such trees have a strategy for rapid growth at the partial expense of wood strength. Further work is, perhaps, required to determine safety factors in a wider range of tree species and also within different parts of the tree.

2.1.2 Strength in different parts of the tree

The adaptive growth of wood enables its mechanical properties to meet local requirements in the tree. Within much of the root system, tensile strength to resist tearing is important, whereas considerable compressive strength is needed in many above-ground parts, especially on the sides of stems that face away from prevailing winds or on the undersides of large branches and of leaning stems. Apart from differences in the types of strength required in various parts of the tree, the overall requirement for strength is greatest in the parts most essential for survival; the main stem and the root-plate. The possibility that branches can be more easily 'sacrificed' is discussed below.

2.1.2.1 Reaction wood

Some parts of a tree, such as a vertical main stem, undergo both tensile and compressive stresses, although tension may predominate on the side of the structure facing a prevailing wind. For other parts, such as the upper and lower sides of branches and leaning stems, one or other of these types of stress strongly predominates. Progressive bending and cracking would occur in such parts of the tree, were it not for the localised production of a special type of wood, known as **reaction wood**, which differs from ordinary wood in its mechanical properties. Reaction wood is usually laid down in wider annual increments than occur elsewhere around the stem or branch circumference, so that the cross-section is often asymmetric or elliptical. The function of reaction wood is to help maintain the angle of the bent or leaning part by resisting further downward bending. Mattheck and Breloer [106] have suggested that, as reaction wood forms, it can exert enough force to help correct the angle of lean in stems which are still slender enough to remain fairly flexible.

Reaction wood resists progressive downward bending in either of two different ways, depending on the type of tree. In conifers, it forms on the underside of the bent or leaning part, and is strong in compression so that it helps to resist the compressive stress in this region. This type of reaction wood, which is termed **compression wood**, has a higher-than-average lignin content and the helical winding of the cellulose microfibrils in the S_2 layer of the secondary cell walls is at a flatter angle than normal (see Section 3.2.1). In broadleaved trees, reaction wood forms on the upper side of the part, and functions rather like a taut rope in helping to hold it up. This **tension wood** has high tensile strength and is more resistant to stretching than ordinary wood. This property comes from the arrangement of cellulose in the secondary cell walls of tension wood fibres. The wall consists largely or sometimes entirely of a thick layer of almost pure cellulose in which the microfibrils are almost parallel to the cell axes, and not wound at the more usual flatter angle which allows stretching as in the coiled flex of a telephone handset.

Reaction wood forms in place of normal wood as a result of the response of the cambial cells to gravity [69]. Cambial cells whose circumferential walls are aligned parallel to the force of gravity, as in a vertical stem or on the flanks of a leaning structure, give rise to ordinary wood cells. Deviation from this orientation stimulates the cambium to form reaction wood on the upper side of structures in broadleaved trees, or on the underside in conifers. Reaction wood is sometimes formed in vertical stems, probably in response to swaying movements in the wind. On the other hand it is generally absent from branches in certain species, mainly conifers. Such branches do not normally reach a very large size and invariably droop progressively under their own weight.

The presence of reaction wood does not represent any form of weakness in itself, provided that the part of the tree concerned is subjected only to the stresses that have predominated during its growth. If, however, a branch containing reaction wood is subjected to tension on its underside or compression on its upper side, the chance of failure is increased. This can happen during storms, when branches that normally bend downwards are forced upwards or twisted. Changes in moisture content can cause less sudden alterations in the distribution of stresses, due to differential shrinkage. It seems likely that this process is involved in summer branch drop (see below). The distribution of stresses can also be adversely altered by the heavy pruning of a leaning stem or a wide-angled branch, which reduces the forces acting on regions which had previously become adapted to load-bearing.

A sudden increase in exposure to wind is another factor that can lead to the failure of stems and branches whose support has been provided partly by reaction wood. This problem often arises when neighbouring trees are felled, or when tall buildings are erected or demolished. In some cases, the neighbouring trees may have also provided direct physical support. Unaccustomed wind exposure can of course also lead to the failure of any poorly adapted structure, even a vertical stem which may contain little or no reaction wood. There tends also to be a lack of reaction wood in leaning or horizontal formations which have been supported for many years by solid bodies such as retaining walls or branch-props. Removal of such support can lead to failure, sometimes immediately [106].

2.1.2.2 *Branch wood, as compared with stem wood*

It is not known whether the wood of branches is generally weaker than that of main stems, but the fact that failure usually occurs more readily in branches may suggest this. Branch failure may in some cases result from an unaccustomed force acting on reaction wood (see above), rather than from weakness *per se*. Branches sometimes fail by tearing out at their bases, rather than snapping, in which case their failure is related not so much to wood quality as to the anatomy of crotches. Another type of failure in heavy lower-crown branches sometimes results from progressive bending under their own weight (see Section 2.3.2.1).

Even in calm conditions, large branches can be shed due to the phenomenon known as summer branch drop [140], which has been observed in various types of tree, especially beech (*Fagus sylvatica*), Horse chestnut (*Aesculus* spp.) and elm (*Ulmus* spp.). This typically occurs in hot dry weather, and it seems likely that an altered moisture content disturbs the longitudinal pre-stressing of the wood which normally helps to support the load. This could explain why summer branch drop most often involves branches that are growing close to the horizontal and which therefore contain a high proportion of reaction wood (see Section 2.1.2.1). Drying could also reduce the circumferential pre-stressing, which acts like a corset in helping to hold a branch or stem together. It is known from timber technology that the natural pre-stressing of trees ('growth stress') is lost when the wood dries out during seasoning [61]. High temperature is another possible factor in summer branch drop, as it increases the tendency of wood to creep, i.e. to deform irrecoverably under its own weight.

Certain weather conditions may be a factor in the often higher rate of failure in branches, as compared with main stems. In many temperate regions, they are occasionally weighed down by heavy loads of snow or ice. They can also be broken as a result of strong wind turbulence which causes gyration or upward bending.

Although the mere presence of branches does not represent a significant hazard, it can be said that their safety factor is probably somewhat lower than that of main stems in many species. This probably reflects the ability of a tree to survive branch loss more easily than uprooting or the snapping of the main stem. Indeed, the shedding of branches may even protect the tree as a whole by reducing its wind resistance during severe gales. Quite apart from wind damage, all species shed dead branches in the course of their crown development and some also shed live ones of small size by the process of abscission.

2.1.2.3 *Junctions as potential points of failure*

It has been pointed out by Mattheck and Breloer [106] that the junctions in a branched structure render it more likely to fail than a simple unbranched one.

Thus, if it had not been important for trees to have a large photosynthetic area, they might perhaps have evolved without branches. Incidentally, certain tropical pines, such as *Pinus caribaea*, produce occasional genetic variants that have just such a form. Despite the inherent engineering problems represented by branched structures, branch junctions have an anatomical structure which confers remarkable strength [106, 156], as long as they do not contain large amounts of included bark.

Failures of living branches in high winds are sometimes sited at their bases, and it is stated by Mattheck & Breloer [106] that the centre of a crotch is the exact point where such failure tends to be initiated. At this point, the fibres of the parent stem diverge to pass to the left and right of the branch. These authors also suggest that the triggering of failure in the parent stem can also take place at this point. Basal failure usually results in the tearing out of the branch, so that a deep wound is left in the parent stem, with consequent decay being possible. Some species seem to undergo such failure more often than others; *Cedrus atlantica* var. *glauca* (Blue Atlas cedar) and *Aesculus hippocastanum* are said to be particularly affected.

A fork comprising co-dominant leaders is somewhat weaker than a junction between a main stem and a subsidiary branch [155]. In the region where a branch merges with the parent stem, its wood is partially enveloped by the latter due to its smaller annual growth in diameter. Shigo [156] has also pointed out that the formation of each annual increment within the main stem and branch begins asynchronously, so that overlapping layers of branch fibres and stem fibres are formed at the junction. The stem fibres also change direction abruptly around the branch base, so as to enclose it partially. In a co-dominant fork, the fibres of the two members meet symmetrically at a shallow angle and can be separated with relative ease. This can be demonstrated by trying to tear apart different twigs or small branches by hand, comparing co-dominant and ordinary unions.

The tendency for the wood fibres in a co-dominant union to split apart can be considerably increased if there is a bark inclusion (i.e. a zone of bark-to-bark contact) between the members (Plate 1). Bark inclusions, which occur commonly both in forks and in the crotches of acutely angled branches, come to occupy the region where there would otherwise be an anatomical union between the members. As a result, the strength of the structure can become increasingly compromised. Some crotches develop a sunken cup-like shape (Plate 2), which is probably more resistant to splitting than a union with a bark-to-bark contact, but is not as strong as an open U-shaped formation. The overflow of rainwater from the 'cup' may help to reveal its presence when viewed from below, but is not necessarily an indication of decay in this region as is sometimes supposed.

The term 'compression fork' has been used to describe a union in which the pressure between the two members diverts the flow of mechanical forces, stimulating an increased growth of wood on either side of the union [106]. The resulting broadening (Plate 1) does not fully compensate for the lack of

Plate 1 Fork with included bark in Fagus sylvatica, *showing lateral broadening of the junction and a crack developing from the crotch*

Plate 2 Fork with cup-like formation in Fagus sylvatica; *the co-dominant stems have been united for many years, following 'welding' of the cambium around an old bark inclusion*

Plate 3 Fork failure in Aesculus hippocastanum, *showing included bark*

attachment within the zone of bark-to-bark contact or the cup-shaped region that is usually present in compression forks.

A high proportion of tree failures are associated with unions containing included bark (Plate 3). For example, they accounted for 20% of all the above-ground failures amongst eighteen species in parkland sites surveyed after the Great Gale of October 1987 in south-east Britain [56]. For *F. sylvatica* alone, the corresponding figure was 52%, and the incidence was high also for *Aesculus* spp. (Horse chestnut). On the other hand, few such failures were observed in some of the other species, such as *Tilia* x *vulgaris* Common lime. Many other observations also indicate that there are large differences between species, and that it is therefore essential to have knowledge of such differences in making hazard assessments.

The incidence of failures associated with 'weak forks' varies not only among species, but also among cultivars of individual species. Cultivars such as *Fraxinus oxycarpa* 'Raywood' and various fastigiate trees, such as *Acer saccharinum* 'Pyramidale', have a reputation for failure at forks, although it is not clear whether most of the observed cases involved the splitting of the union, as compared with fracture across the grain. An example of a clonal stock that is prone to failure at forks is known in London plane (*Platanus x hispanica*), which otherwise has a very low incidence of failure of any type. The clone concerned appears to have been widely planted in England in the last 40–50 years.

It must not be supposed that all unions with included bark are likely to fail, as in many cases they are never subjected to forces strong enough to tear them apart. In particular, many trees containing such unions remain intact because they have a crown structure which is not easily penetrated by gusts of wind, or because they are well sheltered. Also, failure is generally unlikely if the forks themselves are more or less upright and do not carry heavy spreading branches. The types of acute union that fail tend to be those in which one or more members are subject to strong bending stresses because of their lean or their pattern of loading by branches. Such a situation may occur due to the splaying out of limbs in fastigiate trees (see above), even though trees of this growth habit more often have a good, cohesive crown structure.

Bark inclusions are associated not only with forks and naturally acute branch angles, but also with the acute branches or co-dominant stems which often form after trees are pollarded or coppiced. Moreover, the wood fibres of a pollard branch and the parent stem are at first held together rather weakly. They seem to show little or no pattern of asynchronous, overlapping growth as would occur in the junction between a primary branch and its intact parent stem. Although pollard branches and coppice stems are weakly attached when young, their unions later tend to strengthen when more carbohydrate becomes available for wood formation in the parent stem. Wood then still tends to form most rapidly near the unions, forming swollen regions known as pollard heads, bolling or knuckles. These are, however, relatively strong, and play a part in distributing mechanical stresses.

If a pollarded or coppiced tree is not cut again for many years, new bark inclusions may develop between adjacent branches, especially if they are crowded. There is then a renewed and increasing tendency for the branches to tear away, as they become heavier and spread more widely. Such failure can occur in practically any species, but it is most prevalent in those which tend to form numerous competing branches, or which appear to have weaker wood than most others. Thus, it appears that a very high proportion of pollard failures among amenity trees are accounted for by various types of poplar (*Populus* spp.) and perhaps also willow (*Salix* spp.). In other trees such as *F. sylvatica*, *Quercus robur* (English oak), and *Castanea sativa* (Sweet chestnut), such splitting is observed mainly in specimens that were last cut many decades ago, and which have developed very heavy branches. In the UK, these are usually lapsed rural pollards, unmanaged since the mid-19th Century.

On occasions when pollarded trees other than *Populus* spp. show branch failure, the affected branches are usually vigorous and are in tight competition so that they are long and slender and somewhat 'end-loaded' with twigs and foliage. The typical failure point then appears not to be at the branch junction, but some distance above it, where there is probably a concentration of stress, rather similar to the 'hot-spot' in a main stem (Section 2.2.1.2).

Although bark inclusions usually occur between the adjacent members of an acute union, the zone of bark-to-bark contact often eventually becomes encircled by a complete shell of sound wood. This happens when the surfaces are held tightly together without rubbing, so that bark formation gives way to cambial fusion; a form of self-grafting. In this way, a single woody cylinder is formed, albeit containing two centres separated by the original bark inclusion. A formation which has grown stronger by this process can be recognised by the structure of its branch bark ridge. If little or no fusion has occurred, the ridge appears like two slightly parted lips, betraying the presence of the bark inclusion (Plates 4–5). In zones where the 'lips' gape widely apart, there has been a substantial increase in girth following fusion (Plate 6). Fusion usually starts at the point of origin of the two members and progresses distally, but does not always occur all along the contact zone if the members are touching for a considerable distance.

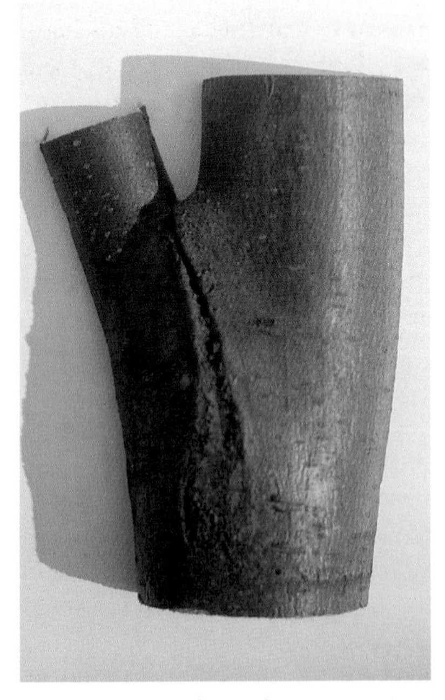

Plate 4 Branch base of Castanea sativa*: the lip-like zone of the branch bark ridge overlies included bark. Proximally, the zone where the 'lips' gape apart overlies complete annual increments which surround the bark inclusion*

Plate 5 As in Plate 4; internal view, longitudinal cut, showing the bark inclusion near the centre of the union

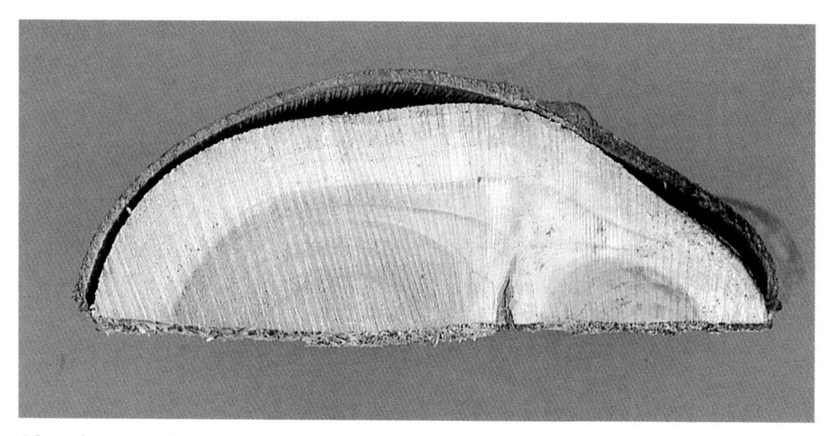

Plate 6 As in Plates 4 and 5; internal view, transverse cut, showing complete annual increments around the bark inclusion

2.1.2.4 Weakness at grafts

Grafts in trees have occasionally been known to fail (Plate 7), showing a straight fracture across the grain. In some, if not all, of these cases there appears to have been poor compatibility between the tissues of the stock and the scion. In the absence of any obvious failure, this may be externally visible from a distortion of growth above or below the graft line (Plate 8). Poor compatibility is not indicated merely by the faster growth in diameter of either the stock or the scion. Partial failure can occur deep within the tree, so that it is not directly visible, but the increased stresses that it causes are said to be responsible for the thickening of the stem that sometimes occurs both above and below a graft [106].

Plate 7 Failure at graft due to incompatibility in Sorbus *sp.*

Plate 8 External signs of graft incompatibility in Fagus sylvatica*; this is not necessarily a sign of a serious hazard*

2.1.2.5 The 'hazard beam'

Mattheck and Breloer [106] have drawn attention to the longitudinal splitting that occasionally occurs in upwardly curving stems or branches (Plate 9), as well as in the root flare region. In engineering terms, such structures have been described as hazard beams, on the grounds that they bear internal lateral stresses which, unlike stresses near the surface of the tree, do not induce a growth response in the cambium. These stresses sometimes induce cracking, but the cracks tend to be self-limiting in length due to the development of inward transverse pressure at their tips [106]. Although their origin is internal, they may extend to the outside so that adaptive growth of wood is then stimulated by an increase of mechanical stress in the cambial zone. Ribs of new wood may become apparent along the cracks, but there is often too much movement to allow occlusion of the cracks. The splitting of hazard beams can occur in almost any tree species, but is especially common in *A. hippocastanum* [59].

Plate 9 Partial splitting of upward-curving branch in Quercus robur*; hazard-beam failure*

Although branches that can technically be described as hazard beams occur very commonly, only a very small proportion of them actually fail. Even when failure does occur, the longitudinal splitting is rarely an immediate hazard in itself, unless the affected branch twists towards the ground instead of merely becoming slightly straighter. If, however, initial failure is not detected, the possible development of decay within the split region could eventually lead to complete fracture. Also, there are occasions when hazard beam failure in the root flare region or in the fibres encircling the base of a dead branch allows increased flexure of the main stem that may end in major failure [106]. Apart from the possible involvement of secondary decay, partly failed hazard beams with occlusion ribs often show no further failure, as has been observed in Wellingtonia (*Sequoiadendron giganteum*).

2.2 Impairment of uniform stress distribution

Although, in principle, the load-bearing structure of a tree develops so as to bear the increase in stresses that are brought about by its growth in height and crown-spread, this does not always happen. Sometimes the development of wood is affected by other organisms that kill areas of the cambium or induce the growth of abnormal wood cells. In other cases, trees which have previously been well adapted to the stresses acting on them are subjected to an alteration of stresses, so that they are no longer mechanically optimised. Such alterations can occur when the lower branches are removed from a stem, or when there is a change in wind exposure or direct support from neighbouring trees or other structures.

2.2.1 Distribution of loading on stems and branches

When a stem bends in the wind, the pattern of stresses within it is partly determined by the forces exerted by the weight of its branches. The same applies to a branch and its secondary branches. The effect is to damp down the swaying motion, thus helping to prevent fracture. A deficiency of lower branches tends to make snapping more likely, unless there is a relatively strong taper which can maintain a uniform distribution of stress.

2.2.1.1 End-loading

The branch structure of a stem influences its ability to withstand high winds. An extensive branch system represents a large 'sail area' but its correspondingly large leaf area is a plentiful source of carbohydrate for wood formation in the main stem. There is therefore a balance between the diameter of the stem and the load that it has to support. On the other hand, a stem which has few branches except near its top tends to have a non-uniform distribution of stress when it sways in the wind. This problem of 'end-loading' seems to be particularly serious if it has been brought about by the removal of middle and lower branches (Plate 10). This takes away the mechanical damping effect of the load previously exerted by the branches. Also, a long length of stem without branches may receive less carbohydrate from distant foliage than it needs for adaptive growth. End-loading can occur not only in main stems, but also in long branches which are deficient in secondary branches, giving rise to a formation which is sometimes known as 'lion tailing'.

Plate 10 End weighting of stems in Fraxinus excelsior *due to excessive branch removal*

Excessive swaying due to end-loading can lead to failure in gusts which coincide with the resonant frequency of the structure. It is therefore unwise to remove many low or middle branches at one time. Such action also tends to bring about the separate problem of exposing the wood excessively to the development of dysfunction and decay (see Chapter 3), especially if the branches are close together. Also, as branches are the source of food material for the parent stem, their removal will impair the tree's capacity to restore the distribution of mechanical stress by adaptive growth. If site usage demands the pruning of lower branches, this can be achieved through a programme of formative pruning whereby they are removed in stages while the trees are young. Provided that the branches are retained long enough for their foliage to produce the food materials needed to help build a sturdy main stem, the potentially adverse consequences of end-loading should not be very serious.

End-loading can develop due to the natural loss of lower branches when they become shaded, but this tends to occur gradually enough for compensatory growth of wood to occur. However, in such cases, the mechanical stresses are only optimised for the prevailing conditions. Thus, if end-loaded stems or branches become newly exposed to strong winds due to the removal of nearby tree crowns or buildings, failure can become more likely. A similar problem can arise within the crown of an individual tree if thinning exposes previously sheltered branches to increased windspeeds. Such exposure often occurs when the inner part of the crown is heavily thinned, while the outer parts are almost untouched. Instead, thinning should be done so as to produce a uniform crown density [193].

Another problem of end-loading may occur in long or heavy branches which are growing close to the horizontal. A reduction in the moisture of the wood can also disrupt the optimisation of mechanical stress in such branches, and this is thought to be a trigger for summer branch drop (see Section 2.1.2.2).

2.2.1.2 The 'hot spot' in the main stem

Even though the axiom of uniform stress [106] seems to apply generally to the structure of trees, there is observational evidence that a high proportion of failures of the main stem occur within a zone between a height of approximately one metre above ground and the lowest live branch. Albers & Hayes [2] refer to this zone as the 'hot spot'. It can be conjectured that the failure of some stems at the 'hot-spot' is related to end-loading (see above), in which the swaying motion of a tree is accentuated by a lack of branches except at its top. It is not clear whether hot-spots in trees are always created through branch removal or increased wind exposure, or whether there are other reasons why the axiom of uniform stress might not always apply in this region of the stem. In either case, it may be that defects such as target cankers are more likely to lead to failure when located at the 'hot spot' than elsewhere on a stem.

2.2.2 Perturbation of growth by living agents

A wide range of micro-organisms and certain insects can cause the formation of abnormal wood or of tumour-like growths which can disrupt the normal pattern of growth in which the distribution of mechanical stress is uniformly regulated. Examples are shown in Plates 11 and 12. Of particular importance

Plate 11 Target canker caused by Nectria cinnabarina *on* Quercus borealis

Plate 12 Tumerous cankers on Fraxinus excelsior, *caused by the bacterium* Pseudomonas syringae *subsp.* savastonoi *pv.* fraxini*; here associated with axial cracking*

are perennial cankers of the type known as 'target cankers', in which there are concentric target-like rings of occluding tissues that have been successively killed by a fungus such as *Nectria* sp.

No wood is formed at the face of a canker, so that there is in effect a hole within which no annual increments are laid down after the canker begins to develop. This hole interrupts the uniform distribution of stress, so that the canker becomes a focus for local concentrations of stress (notch stress). Also, barrier zones formed in the wood as a response to the infection are mechanically weak and can act like 'fault lines' along which shearing failure may occur [106]. If such a canker occupies more than about a third of the stem or branch circumference, there is often an increased chance that the part could snap at this point. Assessment of any potential hazard should, however, take account of experience with the tree species or cultivar concerned. There is observational evidence that some types of perennial canker are not generally prone to failure (e.g. the canker that frequently occurs on *Aesculus* x *carnea*). This particular canker, the cause of which has not been found, has the appearance more of a tumour than of a canker, as in the case of various conditions in other trees that are known to be caused by bacteria. Bacterial tumours contain abnormal wood with contorted grain, which might even resist failure by absorbing energy.

2.2.3 Inadequate root anchorage

An adequate knowledge of tree root systems is essential for anyone who assesses, manages or seeks to prevent hazards in trees. It is particularly important to be aware that tree roots usually spread very much further laterally than vertically. Another essential item of knowledge is that soil aeration is one of the most important factors influencing the development and survival of roots in most tree species. Several authors have provided useful information on root development and the 'architecture' of root systems, including Gasson & Cutler [53], Helliwell & Fordham [74] and Perry [131].

Anchorage depends partly on the extent and 'architecture' of the root system. It also depends on the strength of the roots themselves, and of cohesion; cohesion between roots and soil and between the soil particles. When the root anchorage of a tree undergoes major failure, the central part of the root system, together with adhering soil, is upturned in the form of a distinct 'root-plate'. In most cases, the spread of the roots is much greater than the root-plate diameter, as the outer roots tend to break and remain in the ground when failure occurs. The size and shape of the root-plate are determined by a boundary in the soil, at which the root density falls below a critical value. At this boundary, the cohesion between the roots and soil is stronger than that of the surrounding soil [34], so that the root-plate slides or lifts out of the ground as a discrete mass of soil and roots.

Inadequacies in root anchorage can perhaps be best understood by recognising three main types of root system and the respective mode of failure that each type tends to undergo, given a strong enough wind or a serious defect. Thus trees are classified as 'heart-rooters', 'flat-rooters' and 'tap-rooters' [43, 46]. (Most tree species produce a tap-root in the seedling stage but relatively few normally retain this into maturity.) The tendency for a particular kind of tree to form one or other of the three types of root system has a genetic basis, but it can also be influenced by soil conditions and cultural practices (see Section 7.2).

Mattheck and Breloer [106] have provided a detailed account of the mode of failure which can be ascribed to each of the three types of root system. The root-plates of heart-rooters are thought to rotate in the soil due to shearing between layers of soil, while tap-rooters tilt rather like crowbars. Flat rooters, such as the spruces (*Picea* spp.) and hemlocks (*Tsuga* spp,), which generally root only in the upper soil horizons, tend usually to have only shallow roots. Such a tree is uprooted rather like a toppling hat-stand, to use the analogy of Mattheck and Breloer [106]. Normally, this is counteracted either by mutual support in a woodland stand, or by a very widely spreading root-plate in open-grown situations. Such species are particularly liable to become unstable if their lateral root development is restricted.

Poor stability can occur in any kind of root system if its development is severely restricted, as can occur next to structures such as highways. Indeed, a kerb and the associated 'haunching' can act as a fulcrum for the uprooting of a tree. Root development can also be restricted by unfavourable soil conditions such as compaction, shallowness and waterlogging. Also, previously good anchorage can be impaired following a change in conditions or occurrence of disease that causes the dieback of fine roots, which form the link in the 'chain' between the larger roots and the soil particles. Similarly, the risk of failure can increase if larger roots are severed (see Section 2.2.3) or become decayed. Even when root systems have developed without serious restriction or subsequent damage, the chance of failure can become quite high if the soil becomes very wet, so that there is less friction between the soil particles and between the soil and the roots.

Sometimes, poor anchorage results from unsuitable cultural practices in the early stages of growth. These include long delayed planting out of containerised stock, the long-term retention of stakes and the failure to deal with girdling roots (see Chapter 7). A root is described as girdling if it crosses over the base of a major root, thus constricting its growth. Failure can occur at the point of girdling because mechanical stress is concentrated there. The management of neighbouring trees and other plants can also affect stability due to the restricting effects of root competition. In such cases, there may not be a problem until some of the trees are removed. Those that remain are then exposed to increased wind-loading and are liable to be uprooted. Also, the anchorage that may have been provided by the intertwined roots of neighbouring trees could be lost when these roots decay after felling.

As a tree increases in height, a stage may be reached when site conditions or root competition no longer allow the anchoring capacity of its root system to increase in proportion to the increasing leverage placed upon it. The leverage increases because of the lengthening lever arm of the tree, together with the tendency for windspeed to increase with height above ground. Thus although a tree is a self-optimising structure, at least in theory, there may be situations where height *per se* could be regarded as a hazard factor.

Restricted or impaired rooting due to site conditions or poor planting practices can lead to failure in any type of tree, but certain species or cultivars have a particular reputation for instability, irrespective of the growing conditions. Inadequate rooting capacity may perhaps occur naturally in species which have evolved in less windy situations than those where they are now frequently planted. In many cases, however, the problem is due to artificial selection or to the use of unsuitable rootstocks for grafted trees (e.g. *Sorbus* spp. grafted on to *Crataegus*). Artificial selection may be a contributory factor in the reputed instability of various ornamental cultivars, such as the golden form of the False acacia, *Robinia pseudoacacia* 'Frisia'. Clear evidence of the deleterious effects of artificial selection comes from clonally propagated trees, such as *Populus* spp. A comparison of clones shows that the poor 'track records' of some are not representative of the species as a whole.

2.3 Damage to existing support

The strength and stability of trees can be impaired by a wide range of agents which remove, injure or degrade wood. In the case of root-plates, support can be lost not only when roots themselves are damaged, but also when wet conditions cause a reduction in cohesion between roots and soil particles and within the soil itself. Damage can also occur when part of a tree is subjected to mechanical stress that is sufficient only to cause partial failure in the form of cracking or buckling. In some cases, this can considerably increase the likelihood of major failure in the future.

Trees have no known repair mechanism for damaged wood, but they can regain strength by adding increments of new wood, which can occlude damaged areas or add extra strength to regions weakened by decay. For this reason, the likelihood of failure associated with damage often decreases with each succeeding year of growth, provided that the tree retains sufficient vigour.

2.3.1 Direct physical injury

Wood can be removed, shattered or weakened by physical injuries such as impact from vehicles, lightning strikes and exposure to fire. Physical injury can also occur when the tree is subjected to a force that, despite being insufficient to cause obvious failure, results in cracking or localised buckling. Indeed, incipient failures such as these can develop progressively in a branch as its increasing weight bends it far below its original angle of formation.

Living agents such as gnawing mammals or boring insects can remove wood physically, while certain fungi can cause a different and very important kind of damage:- decay. A description of the manner in which different types of decay develop in trees is given in Chapter 3, which also provides general information about the weakening of the wood structure by decay fungi. Impairment of a tree's safety factor by decay is mentioned later in this section.

2.3.1.1 Above-ground impact damage or partial severance

The mechanical effect of removing or otherwise physically injuring wood is to create a point where stress becomes concentrated, instead of being uniformly distributed. The affected part of the structure can become overloaded and therefore more likely to fail. The deeper and more extensive a zone of physical injury, the greater will be the disturbance in the uniform pattern of stress distribution that had previously developed.

If a stem is deeply injured (e.g. by the tearing fracture of one of a pair of co-dominant leaders), the site of injury can become a local focus of stress (notch stress), at which there may be an increased risk of fracture. This situation can be caused either by the immediate damage done to the wood or the subsequent development of decay. Decay can also develop following superficial damage involving only bark tissues (e.g. squirrel damage or chemical injury), but in many such cases the decay is confined to the outermost layers of wood.

2.3.1.2 Injury to roots

Tree roots are often severed or otherwise injured as a result of site development or the laying of pipes and cables. Injury can also result from other activities such as deep ploughing, ditching and the use of heavy vehicles on soft ground.

Guidelines for the protection of trees on construction sites in the UK are given in British Standard 5837 [197]. This provides criteria for demarcating areas from which damaging activities and machinery should be excluded in the interests of the continued survival and stability of the trees within them (see Section 7.4). Special guidelines for the laying of pipes and cables have also been published [201], as mentioned further in Chapter 7. If, because of failure to observe such precautions, major roots are severed, a tree can immediately become liable to collapse. In such a case, the main stem may show a new lean or tendency to sway, and the rooting area will often show signs of soil movement.

On sites with high-value targets, an immediate remedy is needed for trees that have been made unstable (Chapter 6), as there would be legal implications and liabilities in the event of an accident. On development sites, new buildings may be not only targets, but also objects that create eddies of wind with unaccustomed strength. In such situations the remedy may have to be the felling of the affected trees, but it may be possible to retain them by judicious crown reduction, depending on the severity of the damage and the tolerance of the species to such treatment (see Chapter 8). As with wind-rocked trees, subsequent problems can arise due to the development of fungal decay in the damaged roots and extra vigilance is required during further monitoring.

As the spread of a tree's root system is typically between 1·5 and 2·5 times that of its crown spread, a significant proportion of it can be severed or damaged by site disturbance or compaction even if all guidelines relating to construction or trenching are observed. In such cases, stability is not usually threatened in the short term, as the root-plate area will have been safeguarded, but the loss of absorptive root area can lead to a deficiency of water and mineral nutrients. A rather different situation arises when the damage has been closer to a tree than should have been allowed under the guidelines, but not close enough to cause any obvious lean or wind-rock. A tree damaged in this way may be at an increased risk of uprooting in high winds, and the assessment of its safety requires an investigation to see how much of the root-plate is still intact and unrestricted by compaction or other obstructions (see Chapter 5).

Root severance is thought to provide a possible avenue for infection by decay fungi which can lead to a further impairment of water absorption and eventually to instability. It is not known whether such infection can start at the cut ends of small roots, but the general debilitation of trees due to root severance can make them more susceptible to invasion by some decay fungi, such as *Armillaria* species.

2.3.2 Partial failure from mechanical loading

Major failure, such as the snapping of a main stem or uprooting, sometimes, but by no means always, occurs after an earlier event involving partial failure. This may be visible at the surface in the form of cracking or distortion. It should not be supposed that such signs always indicate that major failure is likely to follow, as partial failure is often minor and localised. For example, longitudinal cracks at the surface sometimes involve bark and not wood (Plate 13). These 'growth cracks' can occur when the bark is stretched by a rapid expansion of the underlying woody cylinder, and have no effect on the mechanics of the tree. There are, however, some forms of cracking and other defects which may represent serious hazards.

When a crack forms in wood, it relieves stress but it thereby locally disrupts the uniform distribution of mechanical stress which has been maintained by the pattern of wood growth until that time. The initiation of a crack sometimes involves a trigger point, such as an old wound with inrolled occlusion tissues, known as a rams-horn (Plate 14). If a crack extends to the surface and thus breaks the cambium, it may become occluded by the formation of new wood from its edges. The occlusion of a crack usually produces a rib-like protrusion (Plates 15 & 20). After occlusion occurs, the

Plate 13 Expansion crack in bark of Fraxinus excelsior*; not affecting the underlying wood*

Plate 14 Cracking of occlusion roll (rams-horn formation) in Quercus robur

continued formation of wood increments may eventually restore the mechanical integrity of the structure. If, however, there is movement at the crack due to swaying or twisting in the wind, it may fail to become occluded (Plate 15). Even if occlusion occurs, the crack may re-open due to subsequent movements in storms or when freezing causes expansion of the tissues. Re-opening is more common in climates which are cold enough to cause frequent freezing of the tissues; hence the use of the term 'frost crack', even though the effect of freezing may be to propagate the crack, rather to initiate it [27].

The majority of cracks in the wood of a tree are longitudinal. Their formation involves the separation of fibres along the grain, which is known as delamination. Longitudinal cracking can result either from stress which pulls the wood apart (transverse tension stress), or from stress which causes a sliding effect, as in a fault-line (shear stress). Transverse cracks can also occur, but are comparatively rare except in wood affected by decay, for reasons explained later in this chapter.

2.3.2.1 Longitudinal cracks resulting from tension

The most obvious type of transverse tension occurs below a union when its members are pulled apart. If this results in a crack, further movement of this kind can easily extend it (Plate 1), resulting in a potentially major failure (see Section 2.1.2.3).

A less obvious form of tensile stress occurs within curving stems, branches or root bases when they are bent against the direction of curvature (Plate 9); this causes the type of cracking associated with 'hazard beams' [106], which are discussed in Section 2.1.2.5. The same kind of bending force also creates longitudinal compressive stress on the outer side of the curved structure, and this is accompanied by lateral tensile stress, which occasionally causes the fibres to split apart in this region, as in the skin of a banana which is being straightened. The resulting cracks have been described as 'subsidence cracks' by Mattheck & Breloer [106], as they tend to occur mainly on heavy branches or leaning stems that are progressively bending downwards under their increasing weight (Plate 16).

Plate 15 Cross-section through crack in Aesculus hippocastanum, *showing rib formation and absence of occlusion*

Plate 16 Downward bending branch of Fraxinus excelsior, *shown by gap in crown profile*

The progressive bending of branches or of leaning stems does not necessarily result in subsidence cracking, as the growth of new increments of wood may be able to keep pace with the changing curvature of the structure. The bark, however, may show signs of compression on the underside and stretching on the upperside (Plates 17–18) as described by Mattheck & Breloer [106]. If cracks are present, the structure of the associated 'callus' ribs is a guide to distinguishing between cracks that have been arrested and those which show signs of opening up again (see Section 5.2.1.3).

Heavy, low branches on old trees are particularly prone to progressive downward bending (Plate 19) and associated cracking, more so in some species (e.g. *A. hippocastanum*) than in others (e.g. *Q. robur*). If such a branch eventually breaks, it leaves a large wound which may become the seat of extensive decay, so that the safe retention time of the tree may be shortened. Forms of management which may lead to such problems are discussed in Chapter 7.

Progressive downward bending occurs quite normally in the relatively small branches of many excurrent species (especially conifers). Such branches do not usually fail by downward bending because the angle of growth in successive annual increments adjusts steadily to their increasing droop. The lower branches of species can, however, occasionally grow long and heavy and are then liable to bend down until they eventually snap under their own

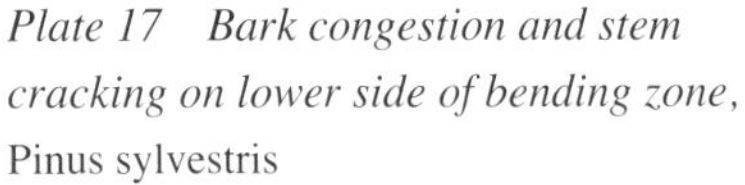

Plate 17 Bark congestion and stem cracking on lower side of bending zone, Pinus sylvestris

Plate 18 Bark stretching on upper side and crinkling on lower side of bending zone, Crataegus *sp.*

weight. Other conifers with a more decurrent habit produce long, spreading branches, whose foliage can become heavily laden with snow. The additional weight of the snow is sometimes enough to cause breakage, especially in the case of *Cedrus libani* (cedar of Lebanon) whose branches are characteristically horizontal.

In leaning stems, increased downward bending is less common than in branches; if it does occur, it tends to culminate in major failure. A lean is, however, not a cause for concern in itself. In some cases, a new or increased lean results from the movement of a damaged or unstable root-plate (Section 2.2.3), and urgent attention may be required. A lean may develop initially due to the movement of the root system in a planted tree, or the bending of a young stem deprived of a previous support. In other cases, the lean appears because of a phototropic response, and it may be for this reason that a leaning habit is common in some species such as Bhutan pine, *Pinus wallichiana*, [59] and White poplar, *Populus alba* [114].

Plate 19 Cracks in subsiding branches, with rib formation (arrows show tips of cracks), Q. x hispanica

2.3.2.2 Longitudinal cracks resulting from shearing

Like tension cracks, shearing cracks can develop in the radial plane (Plate 20), but they can also occur between or within annual increments, producing cylindrical cracks which are revealed only after felling. These are known as 'cup shakes' or 'ring shakes' and are common in some species, such as *Castanea sativa*. They sometimes form where there is a weakness due to the presence of a layer of abnormal wood cells (a barrier zone), laid down in response to wounding or other trauma [27]. Ring shakes are not in themselves regarded as a cause of hazard in standing trees, but they can contribute towards serious failure if other defects are present. Shearing in the plane of the annual increments can increase the likelihood of stem fracture at an open wound or canker. Such a wound concentrates tensile stress, which is further increased by the stretching of the freely sliding outermost annual increments [106].

Ring shakes, although concealed within the standing tree, are sometimes associated with radial cracks which can reach the surface. These are also shearing cracks, and their formation is triggered by the movement that can occur along the associated ring shake [27]. The radiating appearance of several such cracks as seen in cross-section has earned them the name 'star shakes'. Radial cracks sometimes appear to trigger major failure, mainly when two have developed on opposite sides of a main stem. Occasionally, a shearing plane passes right through a main stem, forming a 'diametral' crack (Plate 20), which does not owe its origin to a ring shake. In such cases, there is quite a high chance that the tree will eventually undergo major failure by sliding into two halves. Basal shearing cracks are especially likely to form if the stem base is largely hollow, in which case they sometimes occur on one side only.

Plate 20 A 'diametral' crack (i.e. right through the stem), with rib formation, in Fraxinus excelsior

Plate 21 Cracking due to partial failure of hollow stem of Quercus robur

Plate 22 Bottle butt at basal cavity, formed by locally increased radial growth around the zone of mechanical alteration

Plate 23 Horizontal bulge ('crease'), formed in response to fibre buckling in Betula pendula

2.3.2.3 *Helical cracks*

If a stem with a helical grain is twisted in the opposite direction by the wind, the resulting torsional stress can cause helical cracking. Mattheck & Breloer [106] liken this to the separation of the strands of a rope when it is twisted against the direction of its lay. Trees can be twisted the 'wrong way' during gales that come from unaccustomed points of the compass, and also following pruning which has altered the distribution of wind loading on the crown. The total collapse of stems with helical cracks does not appear to be very common, but it can happen if decay is also present, or if the crown is large and lop-sided.

2.3.2.4 *Transverse cracks*

Transverse cracks in wood can be caused by tensile stress stretching the fibres along their axes. This occurs in roots on the windward side of the tree and in the windward or uppermost sides of stems and branches. If failure occurs it tends to be complete, resulting in the snapping of the affected part as a sequel to fibre buckling on the opposite side. In such cases, especially in storm-damaged branches, the broken portion sometimes falls to the ground, but it may remain hanging by the buckled fibres on its underside. This near-complete failure may constitute an immediate hazard [97]. It is rare to find transverse cracking as a form of incipient failure, as most forces that are strong enough to overcome the tensile strength of wood will also overcome its compressive strength. Small transverse cracks are, however, often formed in wood which has previously lost tensile strength due to decay.

2.3.2.5 *Dents and bulges*

Unusual dents or bulges, usually accompanied by cracks, may indicate that a hollow structure has begun to collapse (Plate 21), and are thus a sign of decay, rather than being a type of defect in their own right. Bulges due to the partial failure of very thin-walled cavities must be distinguished from local thickening of the stem (e.g. bottle-butt; Plate 22) which can develop so as to counteract excessive flexure due to decay (see Section 3.2.2). Compensatory thickening also occurs in stems that have undergone partial failure in the form of fibre-buckling [106], and appears as a pronounced tyre-like bulge (Plates 23 & 152). After such thickening has developed, there is little or no increased risk of fracture. In some cases, the wood on the compression side of a stem or branch may show a wave-like deformation on the underside, rather than a distinct point of buckling.

2.3.2.6 *Partial uprooting*

Failure of root-plates is by no means always total (Plate 24). Partial failure sometimes leaves a tree leaning, with signs of soil mounding on the upward

Plate 24 Raised root-plate, apparently with freshly exposed root surface, possibly indicating recent movement, in Fagus sylvatica

Plate 25 Soil lift due to root-plate movement, long stabilised, in Crataegus *sp.*

side of the lean. The anchorage of such a tree is usually rather poor, at least in the short term, as some of its roots will probably have broken underground, and many others will have a poor cohesion with the soil. A subsequent storm may therefore complete the process of uprooting [97], but in many instances partially uprooted trees regain their stability by developing new roots. Such trees usually retain a leaning position at the stem base, but their leading shoots tend to grow back towards the vertical. Eventually the anchorage of a leaning tree may become just as good as that of an upright one, provided that the root system and the leaning portion of the stem are free to develop in proportion to the mechanical loading that they receive (Plate 25).

Although trees can often survive partial failure of their root-plates, it is difficult to assess their stability in the short term because much of the damage is hidden. There is also a longer-term possibility that a damaged root system might fail if it becomes affected by decay. On sites with high-value targets, wind-rocked trees must usually be regarded as hazardous and dealt with according to the same criteria as for trees with severed roots (Sections 2.2.3 and 6.5.5).

2.3.3 Decay as a hazard factor

Decay can take several forms, which differ in their effects on the strength of wood (see Chapter 3). For present purposes, the main distinction to be made is between brittle decay and non-brittle decay. In brittle decay, the tensile strength of the wood is lost, and this is particularly significant in those parts of the tree that are most strongly subjected to tensile loading, as on the upper sides of heavy branches and leaning stems and in roots on the windward side. Conversely, non-brittle decay mainly causes loss of compressive strength, which is more significant on the lower sides of leaning parts and in areas that tend to become bent strongly away from the direction of the prevailing wind.

Decay that is confined to the central area of the woody cylinder has comparatively little effect on the overall strength of the affected part of the tree unless it is very extensive. In this context, most arboriculturists have long been

Plate 26 Fracture of hollow stem base in hollow Fagus sylvatica *('Devil's ear failure')*

Plate 27 Dog-legged branch structure, formed following loss of original branch leader; investigation for decay at the junction may be advisable

aware that a hollow stem can be virtually as strong as a solid one, provided that the walls of the 'tube' are not too thin. The difficulty was in deciding how thin they could be allowed to become before safety was compromised. Evidence from field data suggested that the width of the 'residual wall' should not be less than approximately 30–35% of the stem radius [165, 175], and this has been confirmed for a range of tree genera on the basis both of large data sets and engineering theory [103, 106].

The significance of the 'critical' wall thickness of a hollow stem is that a stem with a thickness in excess of this value has almost as good a safety factor as a solid one, and tends to fail in the same manner if bent beyond its breaking strength. On the other hand, a hollow stem with a thinner wall is much more likely to fail, and will do so as a result of a buckling or flattening of the cross-section (Plate 26). The relevant criteria for hazard assessment are described in full by Mattheck & Breloer [106] and are summarised in Chapter 5 of the present book.

It may be asked whether wood that is partially decayed is 'safer' than a cavity. It may indeed be safer in some kinds of decay, since even a light filling material such as the pith in an elder stem is a good safeguard against the collapse of an outer shell of wood [106]. On the other hand, certain kinds of decay (such as that caused by *Ustulina deusta*) are very brittle, and can greatly reduce the bending strength of the structure even though the solid core may resist cross-sectional flattening.

Although criteria can be applied for the assessment of residual strength in decayed stems, there is always a need to take other factors into account. In particular, the presence of decay can increase the chance of failure due to another defect, such as a crack within the same part of the tree. Decay can also weaken a structure which is inherently subject to concentrations of stress, such as the abruptly angled formation that may develop after the pruning of a secondary branch. However, the example shown in Plate 27 has survived very impressively.

Factors that affect the incidence of decay and its influence on the strength of trees are outlined in the next chapter.

2.3.4 Hazards not related to mechanical failure

This book is primarily concerned with the prevention of injuries or damage that could result from mechanical failure, but it must be remembered that trees may be hazardous in other ways. Perhaps the most potentially serious of these is the possibility of poisoning by toxic foliage, berries or bark. Young children and domestic grazing animals may be especially at risk of poisoning if they have unsupervised access to low-growing branches of poisonous species, such as yew (*Taxus baccata*) and *Laburnum* spp. Occasionally, the falling of such a tree or of a branch results in poisoning, even though the foliage was previously out of reach. Another potentially serious hazard is electrocution from branches that are in contact with high tension electric cables, especially under wet conditions. Similarly, trees can attract lightning strikes which can injure nearby people or livestock. Leaves, heavy nuts or cones and other materials, such as honeydew [29], which commonly fall from trees can cause various kinds of damage, including injuries to people who slip on them or trip over them. Children collecting the nuts of *Aesculus hippocastanum* for conkers sometimes place themselves and others at risk, especially near roads [126].

Another tree-related problem is the subsidence of buildings with relatively shallow foundations, caused by the shrinkage of clays when these dry out because of water absorption by roots. Occasionally, the reverse process of 'soil heave' due to re-wetting causes damage after the removal or root severance of trees. A different type of displacement can occur when roots and buttresses expand near paved surfaces and lightweight structures with shallow foundations. Similarly roots can displace underground service ducts and pipes by their direct or indirect action, and they can also penetrate drains which have cracks or defective joints. Pavements which have been lifted by root growth can sometimes be re-laid after removing some of the soil and aggregate which has been pushed up. A more difficult situation arises if the root bases are protruding above the paved level; any attempt to 'shave' them could lead to serious disease or decay and will probably lead to renewed displacement due to 'callusing' of the wounds [117].

Chapter 3 Decay: its development in trees

Decay is one of the more important causes of hazard, as it commonly occurs in many tree species and can weaken wood enough to increase the chance of mechanical failure. Failure can occur even in the absence of decay and of other recognisable defects, given sufficiently extreme conditions. Equally, the mere presence of decay does not necessarily make failure more likely than it would otherwise be. In many instances, decay is not extensive enough to compromise the safety factor of the tree. Even if the mechanical characteristics of the tree have been affected, its safety factor may have been largely or wholly maintained by compensatory development of new wood around the affected zone. Clearly, hazard assessment involves more than the initial detection of decay; the extent and position of the decay within the tree must also be assessed. In some cases, it can also be very helpful to know which type of decay is involved.

The present chapter explains the different ways in which decay fungi can break down and weaken woody tissue. It also explains the balance of factors which determine the rate and extent of the development of decay within trees. The following chapter gives details of the principal decay fungi found in the British Isles, while Chapter 5 provides guidance on the detection, measurement and mechanical assessment of zones of decay.

3.1 The co-evolution of trees and decay fungi

Over the hundreds of millions of years during which woody plants and decay fungi have co-existed, there has been a sustained evolutionary race in which wood has been the main prize. For the fungus, wood represents a foodbase which is available in large volumes and which can therefore sustain the survival of an individual fungal colony in the long term. For the tree, living sapwood is essential for the conduction of water and mineral nutrients. Also, the long-term maintenance of the tree's woody framework is essential for the attainment of height and of longevity. These two attributes have enabled trees to become the dominant form of vegetation over much of the Earth's land surface.

If a micro-organism is to exploit wood as a food source, it must possess specialised enzymatic and other chemical systems which can break down the complex molecules of this material into simple ones, mainly sugars. Also, in order to exploit large woody stems or roots, the micro-organism must be able to penetrate deeply within them and to make efficient use of certain essential substances which are in short supply, particularly nitrogen compounds and free oxygen. This combination of attributes has evolved only within a few groups of micro-organisms. These are all fungi, and most of the fungi that cause decay in large trees belong to the major group known as the Basidiomycotina, or 'basidiomycetes' to use the anglicised term. Their fruit bodies mainly take the form of brackets or toadstools.

Although colonisation by decay fungi can cause physiological and mechanical damage to trees, they often survive in a partly decayed state for many years or even for centuries. In such cases, the fungi concerned exploit only the central part of the stem or root system, and do not develop very rapidly. In this way, the tree is able to maintain adequate physiological function and mechanical support through the continued development of radial increments and of its lateral roots. This relatively benign interaction is sometimes due to the combination of tree and fungal species, rather than to the 'non-aggressive' characteristics of the fungus. An example of this is the very different mechanical effect of decay by *Inonotus hispidus* on two of its most frequent hosts, *Fraxinus excelsior* (Common ash) and *Platanus* x *hispanica* (London plane).

It is thought that old trees probably benefit to some extent from the slow development of decay within their dead, central regions as well as being able to tolerate it. The basis of this idea is that the breakdown of the wood releases mineral nutrients, which can be re-absorbed by such trees. Indeed, it is quite common for them to produce adventitious roots which grow into their decaying cores to extract water and nutrients. On a wider scale, the breakdown of wood is an essential process in the cycling of nutrients and the maintenance of woodland ecosystems.

3.2 Decay processes and their effects on wood strength

3.2.1 The structure and mechanical properties of wood

Wood has to support trunks and branches so that neither the weight of the tree itself, nor the force exerted by the wind ('wind loading') are likely to cause structural collapse. In supporting the tree, wood has to resist both fracture and permanent deformation from bending. These requirements call for strength together with some degree of stiffness, but also enough flexibility to allow bending rather than snapping in a high wind. In the twigs and smaller branches, this flexibility allows considerable movement, helping to dissipate wind energy and to 'trim' the sail area of the crown. The mechanical properties that enable wood to perform so effectively as a structural material reside partly in the composition of the walls of its cells and partly in the pattern in which the various types of cell are orientated and fit together [181].

Most of the cells in wood are axially orientated tubes (i.e. with their long axes along the stem; Fig. 3.1), and this arrangement helps to provide tensile strength, which is required on the side of the stem facing the wind. The hollow-fibre design of wood allows relative lightness to be combined with strength. The tubular structure of these cells is also essential for the conduction of water within the tree. In a broadleaved tree, support comes mainly from narrow, rather thick-walled cells called fibres or fibre-tracheids, whereas water conduction takes place mainly through vessels, which are usually wider and thinner-walled. In conifers, most of the axial wood cells are of one type; i.e. tracheids, which both support the tree and conduct water.

Within the cell walls, tensile strength is provided mainly by cellulose, a carbohydrate whose long thread-like molecules are composed of sugar molecules joined end-to-end. The cellulose molecules are wound helically within the various layers of the cell wall in the form of 'microfibrils', with a different angle of helical winding in each layer (Fig. 3.1). Of the three layers which usually make up the secondary cell wall (i.e. those that are laid down after the initial formation of the cell by the cambium), the middle or S_2 layer contains the most cellulose and is the thickest.

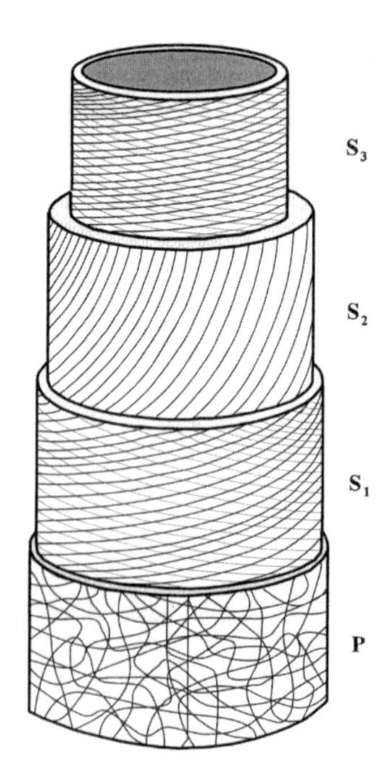

Figure 3.1 The main layers of a secondarily thickened cell wall: diagram showing some typical orientations of cellulose fibrils (P= primary wall)

If wood contained only cellulose it would be very flexible, like rope, and would not be able to support any weight or to resist compression on the leeward side of a stem. The relative stiffness of wood and its load-bearing capacity are provided by lignin, which is a hard matrix in which the cellulose microfibrils are embedded. This composite structure can be compared rather crudely to an artificial material consisting of fibres (e.g. glass fibres or carbon fibres) in a matrix such as an epoxy resin. The helical winding of the microfibrils at a number of different angles enhances the strength and toughness of the hollow cells that make up wood, and may also play a part in the development of growth stresses [4], the mechanical rôle of which is mentioned below. Also, as explained in connection with white-rots, the helical structure can also enhance the ability of wood to stretch without breaking when the cement-like lignin is degraded by certain kinds of white-rot fungus.

In addition to cellulose, other carbohydrates are present in wood; principally a matrix of hemicellulose, which binds the cellulose microfibrils together prior to lignification. The mechanical rôles of these other carbohydrates following lignification are uncertain, but their properties when moist may contribute to the ability of the tree to maintain an internal 'pre-stressing' system which helps to counteract wind loading and to hold the stem together rather like a corset. These 'growth stresses' are mentioned in Chapter 2 in connection with structural defects.

Another important component of wood is pectin, a jelly-like material which in effect glues the cells together while retaining some flexibility and so helps to resist splitting. The pectin is contained in a thin layer between the cells, known as the middle lamella. The middle lamella is closely associated with the adjacent primary cell wall and the first of the three layers that make up the secondary wall (the S_1 layer). Lignin is also present in the compound middle lamella, and is usually at a higher concentration there than elsewhere within the cell wall. It has been suggested that, in some tree species, the adhesive properties of pectin may have a rôle in helping to prevent the stem from bursting apart [146]. For example in limes (*Tilia* spp.), there are pectin-rich, tangentially elongated parenchyma cells which form circumferential bands within the wood and could thus help to hold the stem together.

Although most of the cells in wood are axially orientated, there are also many radially orientated cells; these make up the xylem rays (Fig. 3.2; Plate 74). The ray cells remain alive in sapwood, and can store and translocate food materials. Another of their functions, which is not mentioned in conventional botany textbooks, is to help hold the annual rings together and so prevent axial splitting. In some species, such as beech, *Fagus* spp., the larger rays are dilated at each annual ring boundary (Plate 28), and these dilatations are probably 'fastening' structures [106]. The strength of rays is much greater in some tree species (e.g. *Platanus* x *hispanica*), than in others (e.g. *Populus* spp., and most conifers), which appear to rely more on other features of wood structure to prevent splitting.

3.2.2 Different types of decay and their effects on wood strength

Intense decay in large volumes of wood is caused almost exclusively by fungi, although bacteria can cause a limited amount of degradation. The structure of

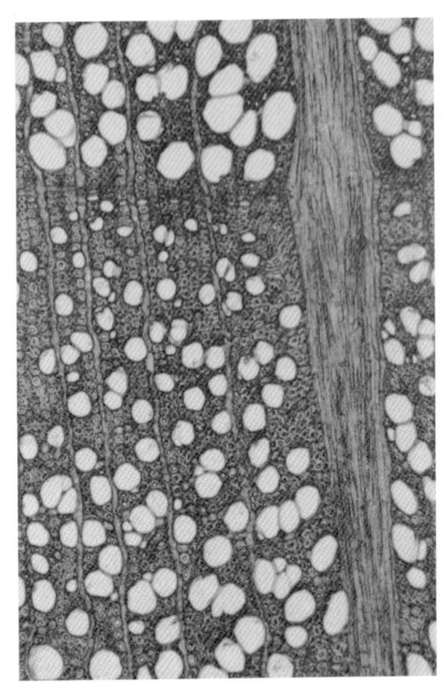

Plate 28 Fagus sylvatica *wood, transverse section showing dilatation of a large xylem ray at increment boundary*

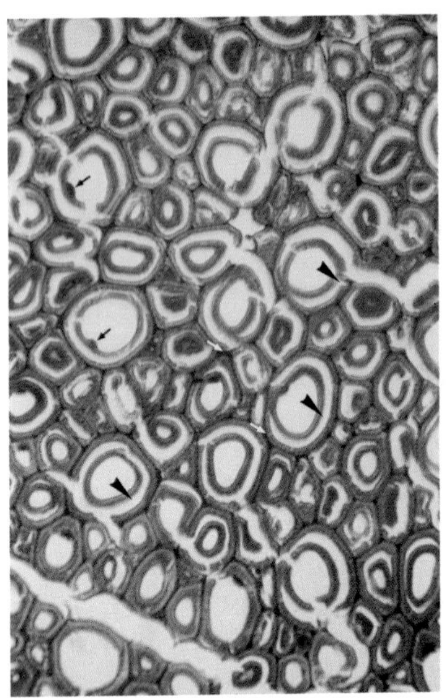

Plate 29 Brown-rot in heartwood of Robinia *colonised by* Laetiporus sulphureus *(small arrows indicate hyphae), showing degradation of S_2 layer (arrowheads) of cell walls*

fungi is well suited to development in wood, since they exist in the form of thread-like hyphae which can grow along the long channels that are provided by the hollow centres (lumina) of wood cells. The hyphae of some species can also grow within the thick secondary walls of the cells. Also, some species can bud in a yeast-like manner, forming single cells which can be transported in water columns.

Three main categories of wood decay are recognised; brown-rots, white-rots and soft-rots, and the type of decay produced by each species of decay fungus is conventionally assigned to one of these types. There are, however, important differences between the decay patterns induced by fungal species within each broad category, and there are many which can adapt their decay patterns according to environmental conditions [149, 152]. Some of these variations are explained in Chapter 4 in relation to particular fungi.

3.2.2.1 Brown-rots

Brown-rots principally involve the degradation of cellulose, while leaving the lignin largely undegraded. The remaining material is usually brownish in colour; hence the name. Although the lignin is not substantially degraded, it is often chemically altered in a way which helps to expose the cellulose to the enzymes and other 'digestive' substances which the fungus secretes. Indeed, enzyme molecules appear to be too large to diffuse into the tightly packed molecular matrix of the intact cell wall, so that non-enzymatic systems, involving iron and hydrogen peroxide, probably play an important rôle in the earlier stages of decay.

The cellulose molecules are broken at numerous points along their length in a brown-rot, so that their tensile strength is very rapidly lost. This effect is all the more drastic because degradation occurs diffusely within the cell wall, and is not localised close to the fungal hyphae, as occurs in other types of rot. Since the S_2 layer is the most cellulose-rich part of the cell wall, it is often completely dissolved while the other layers remain fairly intact (Plate 29). This selective degradation of the S_2 layer involves the diffusion of hyphal secretions through the S_3 layer, since the hyphae lie mainly within the cell lumina and enter the cell walls only at minute boreholes by which they pass between cells.

The mechanical effect of cellulose destruction in a brown-rot is to make the wood very brittle, for the same reason that a plaster cast would easily break if it were not built on a textile base. The affected wood cracks very easily, and does so like a biscuit; i.e. without bending beforehand and thus giving no warning sign [152]. Also, the wood retains much of its rigidity, so that adaptive growth in response to increased flexure is unlikely to be prominent. Flexure may, however, increase if the decay extends so much that a very thin sound shell of wood comes to surround a central core affected by shrinkage due to the loss of cellulose. This shrinkage leads to a pattern of cracking both along and across the grain, forming a cubical pattern (Plate 85). Cracks can also be found at a microscopic scale within the cell wall.

Wood that has become brittle can fracture suddenly [180], whereas wood affected by non-brittle decay tends to become more flexible before it gets to a stage when fracture is likely. Brown-rots and other brittle forms of decay do not produce warning signs (see below in relation to white-rots) except perhaps in extremely advanced cases. Also, as discussed in Chapter 6, brittle decay is virtually undetectable by tree-pulling tests [162], as these depend almost entirely on loss of stiffness [106].

There are some differences between brown-rots caused by different fungi in particular host tree species, and these are due partly to the rate of degradation, relative to that of fungal invasion. For example, *Fistulina hepatica* is reputed to cause brown-rot in oak trees (*Quercus* spp.), but causes serious strength loss only at a very advanced stage of attack, whereas many others (e.g. *Phaeolus schweinitzii* on various conifers) cause a rapid loss of strength. Also, there is some evidence that different brown-rot fungi have various degrees of tolerance to non-optimal conditions within the wood of living trees. These differences could explain why some species can degrade wood rapidly only within certain zones of the tree.

Brown-rots are more common in conifers than in broadleaved trees, perhaps because the wood of many of the latter is more highly lignified and therefore less accessible to brown-rot fungi, which cannot fully degrade lignin.

As such fungi are efficient at degrading cellulose, the relatively high cellulose content of conifer wood provides a favourable environment for them. Also, the lignin of conifer wood is generally more resistant to degradation by most white-rot fungi than the type of lignin found in the fibres of broadleaved species.

3.2.2.2 White-rots

White-rot fungi have the ability to degrade both lignin and cellulose, but the relative rate at which these major cell wall components are degraded varies greatly between the various fungal species. The ability to degrade pectin also varies amongst white-rot fungi, and is another factor in determining the nature of the strength loss that different species cause. As with brown-rot fungi, another source of variation lies in the tendency of some species to invade particular zones of the wood preferentially (e.g. late-wood or early-wood) in living trees.

Preferential attack on different parts of the wood structure results in many permutations in the types of decay caused by white-rot fungi, but two main types of white-rot can be recognised; simultaneous white-rot and selective delignification. In **simultaneous white-rot**, lignin and cellulose are decomposed at approximately the same rate. This causes the loss of both stiffness and tensile strength, so that the wood can be severely weakened. The resulting fracture tends often to be a little less brittle than in brown-rots, since the cellulose molecules are attacked mainly from their ends and therefore retain some tensile strength in the early stages of decay. In advanced decay there is often total destruction of wood, leading to cavity formation in the tree.

Selective delignification, as the term implies, involves the breakdown of lignin, while cellulose is degraded more slowly. The material that is left behind retains considerable tensile strength, while losing much of its stiffness. Indeed, the removal of the lignin matrix increases the ability of the helical cellulose microfibrils to be stretched like the coiled cable of a telephone handset, so enhancing the resistance of the wood to tensile failure. In some cases, for example in the tracheids of conifers colonised by *Heterobasidion annosum*, the earliest stages of delignification may occur locally within the cell wall, causing separation between layers of the wall or between adjacent cells (Plates 30–31). An interesting phenomenon that has recently been found in association with selective delignification is the formation of discrete cavities within the S_2 layer of the secondary cell wall [147]. This process involves the locally selective action of enzymes which diffuse from fungal hyphae lying in the cell lumina and is quite distinct from cavity formation due to hyphal tunnelling within the walls (see Section 3.2.2.3).

The term 'stringy white-rot' is often applied when lignin is selectively destroyed. The affected wood lacks much of its former stiffness, and its consistency can to some extent resemble that of a textile [152]. A rot of this type is, for example, often found in trees attacked by certain species of

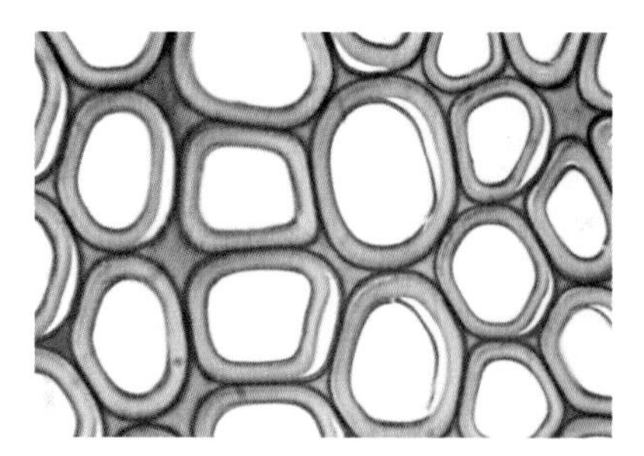

Plate 30 Selective delignification in wood of Pinus sylvestris *colonised by* Heterobasidion annosum, *with separation of layers of the cell wall*

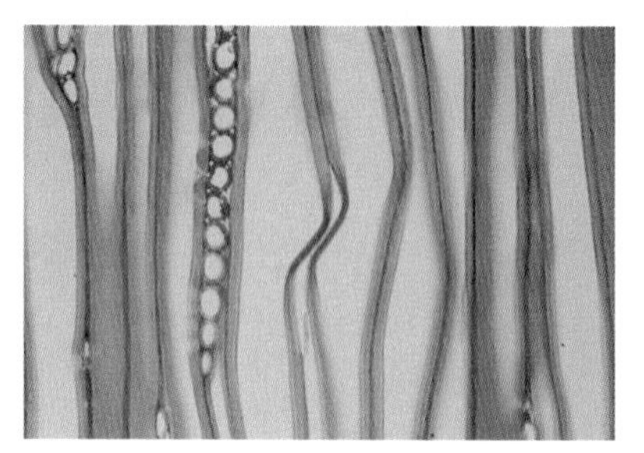

Plate 31 Fibre buckling due to cell wall separation in wood of Picea abies *colonised by* H. annosum

Ganoderma. The relative proportions of lignin and cellulose that are degraded depend both on environmental factors and the species of tree and fungus. In extreme cases, practically all the lignin is destroyed before the cellulose is much affected. This does not generally occur under British conditions, but is quite common in the temperate rainforests of South America, where fungi such as *G. applanatum* can reduce the wood of southern beech, *Nothofagus* spp., to a state where it has even been used as a fodder for cattle under the name '*palo blanco*' or '*palo podrido*' [1, 60].

The type of fracture caused by stringy white-rots tends to be ductile, as opposed to brittle, although this depends partly on the stage of decay that has been reached. At a very late stage, cellulose degradation can be completed, so that the wood is totally destroyed, leaving a cavity as in a simultaneous rot. When a large part of the stem cross-section is occupied by a stringy white-rot, the affected region flexes more in the wind, thereby altering the distribution of mechanical stress in the cambial zone. This can stimulate the cambium to lay down locally widened annual increments of wood, so counteracting the loss of stiffness. The resulting bulge in the affected part of the tree is an indication that a detailed safety inspection is advisable.

White-rot fungi are more common in broadleaved trees than in conifers, probably because of the chemical composition of their lignin, as mentioned in Section 3.2.2.1. Conifer lignin can, however, be selectively degraded very effectively by certain fungi such as *Heterobasidion annosum*.

It should be noted that the term 'white-rot' does not always seem to live up to its name. Although the decayed wood is often pale in colour, there is usually a dark region near its edge, where dark coloured phenolic substances are being produced by the tree's defensive responses or by the partial breakdown of lignin. These substances are usually degraded and bleached by the fungus if decay advances, but some fungi leave behind secretions which produce a persistent staining of the decayed wood. In such cases, the colour is often reddish, earning the term 'red rot'. Unfortunately, the same term is sometimes applied to brown-rots, which are fundamentally different but which may have a similar colour. Perhaps the term 'pigmented white-rot' would be more appropriate, albeit seemingly self-contradictory.

3.2.2.3 Soft-rots

Like brown-rots, soft-rots involve the selective degradation of cellulose, but the fungi involved invade the cell walls in an entirely different way. The fungal hyphae grow within the cell wall, following the helical path of the microfibrils [141], which they degrade by the local action of enzymes. Although this type of degradation was described in the 19th century [142], it was until recently believed only to occur in the surface layers of dead wood or timber. Such material can provide the combination of very wet and highly oxygenated conditions which are required by the fungi conventionally associated with soft-rots, which are microscopic members of the Ascomycotina. There were, however, a number of reports that decays resembling soft-rots could also be caused in timber by certain Basidiomycotina normally associated with white-rots [e.g. 37, 95, 120] or in one case a brown-rot [33].

It was later shown using high resolution light microscopy that some white-rot fungi can induce the formation of cavities of a soft-rot type within the fibre walls of living trees when conditions are not favourable for white-rotting [146, 152]. These conditions may include excessive wetness or dryness of the cell lumina, or the infiltration of the lumina by fungitoxic substances. A typical white-rot may ensue if the conditions are ameliorated, for example by drying of the wood so that the cell lumina are no longer completely water-filled.

The loss of tensile strength due to cellulose degradation of the soft-rot type results in a fairly brittle fracture in living trees [145], but the nature of the fracture also depends on the type of white-rot which the same fungus may be causing in the more advanced zones of decay. In trees colonised by the very common decay fungus *Ustulina deusta*, there may be a particular kind of brittle fracture in which the fracture surface is hard and smooth, like that of a ceramic [152]. This fracture occurs in wood which is extensively affected by soft-rot, according to microscopic criteria. This is perhaps consistent with the fact that *U. deusta* is a member of the Ascomycotina, which include typical soft-rot fungi. The rot in this instance is, however, clearly not soft in the literal sense.

3.3 Entry of decay fungi into trees

An intact covering of bark prevents the entry of most decay fungi, except perhaps for endophytes (see Section 3.4.1) and for a few species which can penetrate through the bark of roots. Breaks in this protective covering are caused in several ways, including breakage of roots or branches in storms (Plate 32), pruning (Plate 33), fire damage (Plate 34), vandalism, damage by

Plate 32 Stubs of broken branches on Fagus sylvatica *as sites of possible decay initiation*

Plate 34 Decayed base of Fraxinus excelsior, *previously damaged by fire*

Plate 33 Pruning wound as a site of long-established decay in Quercus robur; *note case-hardening of the surface, partly broken by woodpecker feeding*

animals and diseases or disorders that cause branches to die back. If the damage exposes only the surface of the wood, access for the spores of decay fungi is usually not easy. If, however, part of the cross-section becomes exposed, the open ends of the wood cells and the intercellular spaces can readily be colonised. Exposure of the cross-section may also allow conditions within the wood to become more favourable to fungal growth than within an intact woody cylinder, as will be explained in the next section.

Although decay often begins at points where external agents have exposed the wood, it can also occur where bark has been damaged mainly as a result of a tree's own pattern of growth. In particular, included bark within acute crotches (Plates 1–5) sometimes dies due to a pinching effect, so that decay may begin at these sites. Bark death and associated decay may also occur in a rather different type of crotch in which there is an upward facing cup-shaped region which periodically fills with rainwater. The death of bark in such crotches may be due to lack of oxygen beneath the water, but decay fungi may be inhibited for the same reason, unless the hollow dries out periodically or has been artificially drained. Decay associated with pinched bark can also develop within flutes at the stem base. Another reason for the presence of decay beneath bark inclusions is the exposure of wood due to cracking from incipient mechanical failure.

Many fungi cause decay in the roots of trees, and it is generally assumed that they enter through root injuries (whether natural or man-made) or areas of root dieback, analogous to entry points above ground level. This is, however, uncertain since infection processes in most species cannot be observed under entirely natural conditions underground. This difficulty is especially great because most cases of root decay in amenity trees occur in large old specimens. Infection is perhaps dependent on the occurrence of dieback in woody roots, which tends to occur in trees after they reach maturity. It is possible that infection of younger trees could follow the severance of major roots. The uninjured roots of young trees can, however, be infected by a few decay fungi, which have the ability to penetrate and kill the bark and cambium. This ability has been documented for *Armillaria* spp. and for *Heterobasidion annosum*. On the other hand, some fungi seem able to enter roots only as secondary colonisers, following other species. This has been observed with *Phaeolus schweinitzii*, which can follow *Armillaria* in coniferous hosts [8].

3.4 Factors determining the extent of decay in trees

3.4.1 Development of decay in relation to initiating events and tree anatomy

The decay process often follows the exposure of wood to the atmosphere. No tree remains entirely free from exposure of its woody tissues. At the very least, minor openings are created by the dieback and shedding of small twigs, which is a normal aspect of crown development. More significant exposures can occur from injuries such as lopping, vehicle impacts or branch breakage. Large areas of wood can also be exposed by the dieback of branches or roots as a result of environmental stress, disease or severe insect attack.

As well as allowing decay fungi and other micro-organisms to gain entry, the exposure of wood alters the internal environment in favour of microbial development. A particularly important feature of intact sapwood is that its hollow cell lumina are occupied by continuous water columns or gas mixtures low in oxygen. Under these conditions, most decay fungi cannot grow actively [16], but exposure results in partial drying and hence increased aeration. Some decay fungi, such as *Stereum* and its relatives, are able to colonise freshly created wounds, even before the tissues become sufficiently aerated to allow much decay to occur. Others, perhaps a majority, require older wounds in which aeration and microbial activity are well established. Yet others, known as endophytes or latent colonisers, occur sparsely within intact living sapwood and only cause decay or overt disease if the wood later becomes exposed to enhanced aeration.

For much of the year, injuries to woody tissues result in an immediate inrush of air into the water-conducting cells, owing to a strong tension in the water columns which causes them to retract rather like stretched elastic bands when they are cut. Fungal spores and bacteria can also be sucked in at this stage. After the retraction of water columns, there is a continued withdrawal of water from the damaged region due to the tree's transpirational pull. The resulting zones of drying extend as far as the ends of the vessels or other conducting cells that have been severed.

A zone of wood that has partially dried out cannot retain all its normal functions (especially the function of water conduction in the case of sapwood), and is therefore described as being dysfunctional. Loss of water-conducting capacity also occurs naturally in the older zones of sapwood as trees mature. The conducting cells are already dead while they are functional, but they are surrounded by living parenchyma cells which usually die at the same time that conductive function is lost due to the ageing of sapwood. As explained later, parenchyma cells have a rôle in the active defence of the tree against infection and decay, so that this type of defence largely disappears when they die. In

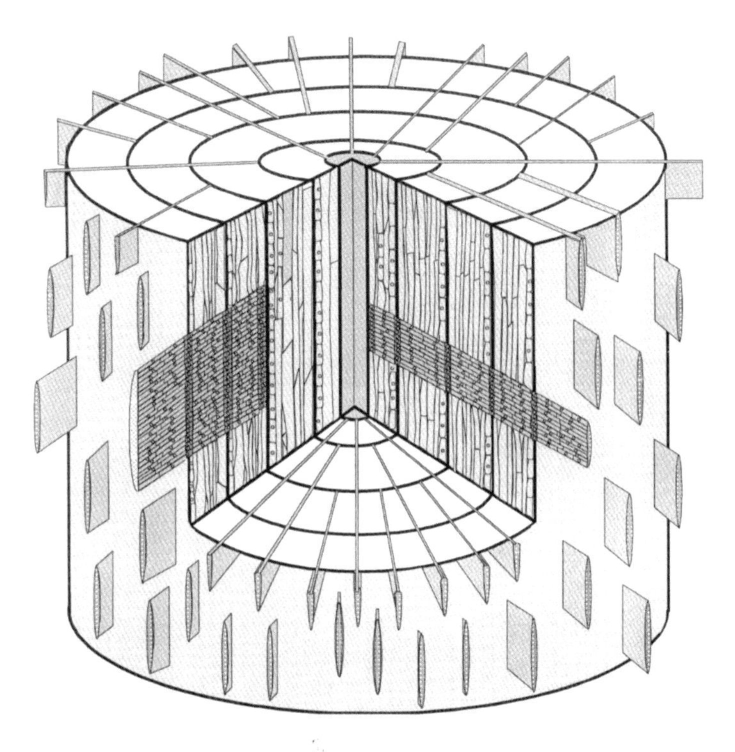

Figure 3.2 A portion of a young tree stem: a diagrammatic representation showing the anatomical boundaries which influence spatial patterns of dysfunction and microbial colonisation following damage to the xylem.

some tree species, however, the dying parenchyma cells release substances that impregnate surrounding cells and render the wood relatively resistant to degradation by at least some decay fungi. Thus, tree species differ considerably in the durability of their central wood (see heartwood and ripewood, later in this section).

When a zone of dysfunction develops within the wood of a standing tree, it tends to follow a shape that corresponds to the anatomical features of the wood. Any microbial development, including decay, also tends to follow the anatomy of the tree, so that it usually occurs most easily and extensively along the hollow lumina of vessels, fibres and tracheids which provide relatively easy pathways both for gas exchange and for microbial growth (Figs. 3.2 & 5.6). These dysfunctional zones therefore tend to take the form of elongated columns which are often bounded laterally by regions of the wood that provide a less easy route for microbial spread. These less easily colonised regions are of two main types, the sheets of parenchyma-like cells that occur at the annual ring boundaries in some species, and the xylem rays with their radially orientated cells (Fig. 3.2). However, some fungi such as *Ganoderma* species

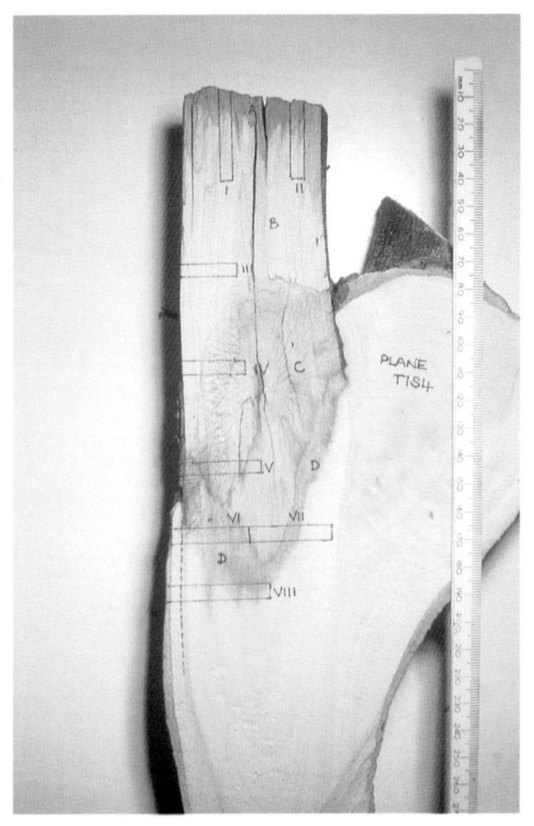

Plate 35 Discoloration and decay from a stub pruning wound in Platanus x hispanica*; the affected zone forms a discrete cone of decay*

can grow radially along the cells of the xylem rays, utilising their living contents as a nutrient source. In other circumstances, these living cells can take part in the tree's active defence systems as described in Section 3.4.2.

In hazard tree assessment, it is very important to appreciate the close links between the anatomy of the tree and the development of decay columns. Thus, for example, if a branch stub appears to be the origin of a decay column, the column is likely to form a cone-shaped zone tapering down into the branch-trace; i.e., the region where the former branch was 'plumbed in' to the main stem (Plate 35). If the infection court was a flush-cut pruning wound (see Chapter 7), the zone of decay might extend not only down into the branch-trace, but also upwards above the wound. If a very large wound is involved, or if there are a number of wounds on a single trunk, it is quite likely that the decay will not be confined to individual restricted cone-shaped zones; instead any such zones that originally formed might have coalesced to form a central column (Plates 36–37). Anticipation of the likely patterns of decay is never a reason for inadequate investigation, but it can greatly improve the efficiency of the job.

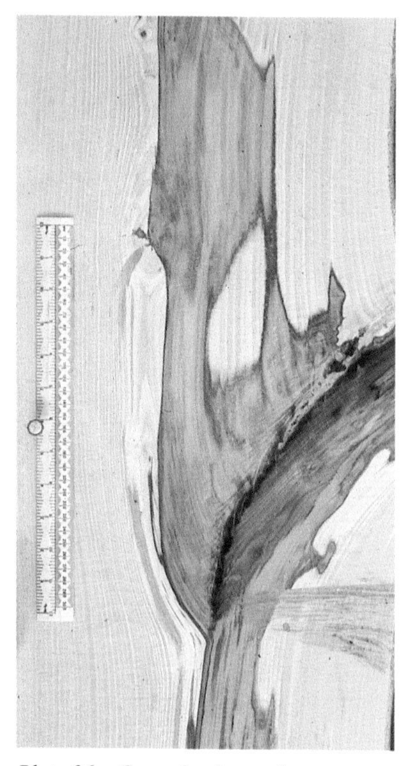

Plate 36 Central column of discoloration and decay, formed in Fagus sylvatica *from coalescence of dysfunctional zones associated with several pruning wounds*

Plate 37 Stem of Fagus sylvatica *showing multiple pruining wounds and signs of extensive colonisation by* Polyporus squamosus

The patterns of decay development in root systems are less well understood than above-ground patterns. Some information is available from exposed root systems but these usually become available only at an advanced stage of decay, when it is difficult to trace the points of origin and the directions of spread. On this basis, there is some indication that decay in old trees quite commonly begins in the central part of the root system. In such cases, the decay may be centred on the remains of a juvenile tap-root which had a limited life in the development of the tree. Within lateral roots, decay very often develops only on the undersides. This pattern may be related to the eccentricity of the anatomical centre, which is usually near the lower surface of the root [158]. If this decay pattern extends above ground level, it does so most often in the flute between adjacent root bases [158].

3.4.2 Factors restricting dysfunction and microbial colonisation within pre-existing wood

The extent of the dysfunctional zone that forms soon after damage depends to some extent on the type of tree. Some species, such as elms (*Ulmus* spp.) and many other ring-porous trees, have very long (and wide) early-wood vessels, which are highly efficient for water conduction, but which generally allow dysfunction to extend further than in diffuse-porous species such as *F. sylvatica* and *Acer* species (maples). However, even in some ring-porous species, such as *Quercus robur* (English oak), an injury that involves a branch wound tends not to lead to much dysfunction in the parent stem, since many of the vessels within the branch terminate in this region (Plate 38). There is a membrane at the end of every vessel, which allows water to pass but is a barrier to the movement of particles such as fungal spores. Even in the absence of injury, the large early-wood vessels of ring-porous species normally lose their water-conducting function after the first year, unlike the much smaller vessels of the late-wood.

Rapid drying does not happen during the rather brief periods (mainly in late winter and early spring) when the xylem sap is under positive pressure. Thus, the ‘bleeding’ that then occurs from a wound should not necessarily be seen as a bad thing. In some trees such as *Acer* spp., however, the leaking sap contains considerable amounts of dissolved sugars and its loss can therefore represent a depletion of the tree’s energy reserves.

Decay sometimes develops far beyond the region where it began, in which case the zone of partial drying continues to extend after the initial occurrence of a dysfunctional zone. Little is yet known about the movement of water that is involved in this continued process of partial drying. Obviously, some drying occurs at the surface of an injury, but it is uncertain whether this is sufficient to explain the drying of very large volumes of wood as decay develops, especially in view of the fact that the decay process itself generates additional water by oxidation. There is circumstantial evidence that some fungi improve conditions for active decay by actively ‘pumping’ water out of wood which is

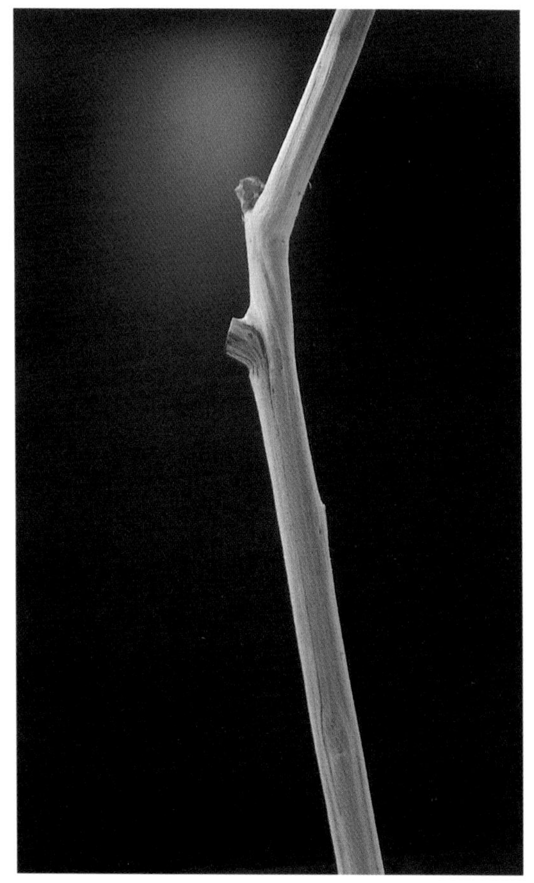

Plate 38 Twig of Quercus robur, *infused with Indian ink to show locations of vessel endings near a lateral twig junction*

initially too poorly aerated for decay to occur [146]. In particular, the moisture content in the vicinity of reaction zones is often greater than that of both the decaying wood and the adjacent sound wood, so that there is not a simple moisture gradient as might be expected if the drying process were purely passive. Similarly, wood blocks inoculated in the laboratory with *Ustulina deusta* sometimes exude water drops [75], as do the fruit bodies of various basidiomycetes such as *Inonotus* spp. on standing trees.

Although the development of dysfunction and decay sometimes becomes very extensive, it is usually 'walled off' within the tree by a variety of mechanisms in which living cells (parenchyma cells) in the sapwood react by forming plugs within the lumina of adjacent vessels and fibres at the margins of the damaged zone. These plugs sometimes consist of substances exuded in solution from the parenchyma cells and, in the case of vessels, the parenchyma cells themselves often form plugs by developing balloon-like extensions (tyloses), which protrude into the vessel via the inter-communicating pits in the adjacent cell walls. The effects of cell plugging are to reduce the permeability of the wood to the movement of water and gases and to deter the spread of invading micro-organisms. The barrier between sound and dysfunctional wood can often be seen as a band of dark discoloration, and has been described as the reaction zone [154]. It is important to distinguish the reaction zone from the **barrier zone**, which is formed in **new tissues** laid down after the wounding or other event which previously caused the zone of dysfunction to develop within the **pre-existing wood** [155].

The formation of a reaction zone helps to confine microbial development within the volume of sapwood that initially became dysfunctional due to wounding or other trauma. As mentioned above, this dysfunctional zone corresponds in shape to anatomical compartments within the tree. The process whereby this 'walling off' occurs within discrete anatomical regions of the wood is widely known as 'compartmentalisation' [158, 159]. This is presented as a model, in which the combination of pre-existing boundaries and the **reaction zone** is represented by three 'walls' (Fig. 3.2), limiting the spread of dysfunction and decay in different planes: 'wall 1' limits axial spread, 'wall 2' limits spread along the radius of the woody cylinder, and 'wall 3' limits spread parallel to its circumference. Distinct from 'walls 1, 2 and 3' is 'wall 4', which represents the boundary between pre-existing wood and the wood that forms after the initiating trauma. Near the site of damage, this 'wall 4' can be seen under the microscope as an anatomically distinct **barrier zone**.

Some reaction zones are much more effective than others in restricting the spread of dysfunction and microbial invasion. In the most favourable cases, the reaction zone is effective enough to restrict the zone of dysfunction close to the point of initial damage. This optimal response is believed to depend on the availability of ample carbohydrate reserves in the adjacent tissues, and on an adequate supply of water to balance transpirational loss, so that the tree is not under severe moisture stress. Such stress can cause the wood to dry out far beyond the region where the reaction zone might otherwise form. Both moisture stress and carbohydrate storage are strongly influenced by the season of the year (see Section 7.7.2.5). Further very important factors are the species of tree concerned and the genetic make-up of the individual [161]. If the reaction zone is ineffective, the zones of dysfunction and of microbial invasion progress beyond the boundaries that were set during the tree's initial response to damage.

Various types of fungal activity can be responsible for the 'breakdown of barriers'. Some fungi can degrade defensive materials that have been laid down by the tree. Others, like *Inonotus hispidus*, can bypass plugged cell lumina within the reaction zone by growing through the cell walls [152]. The relative success of host and pathogen in this kind of interaction is determined partly by the vitality of the tree and partly by the aggressiveness of the fungus concerned. In many such instances, the tree responds further by forming a new reaction zone deeper within the sapwood (Plate 39). Sometimes a series of microbial 'advances' and of successive phases of reaction zone formation can

Plate 39 Branch stub of Fagus sylvatica*; longitudinal cut, showing the faded remnant of a 'failed' reaction zone near the pruning cut on the right, and the dark current reaction further to the left*

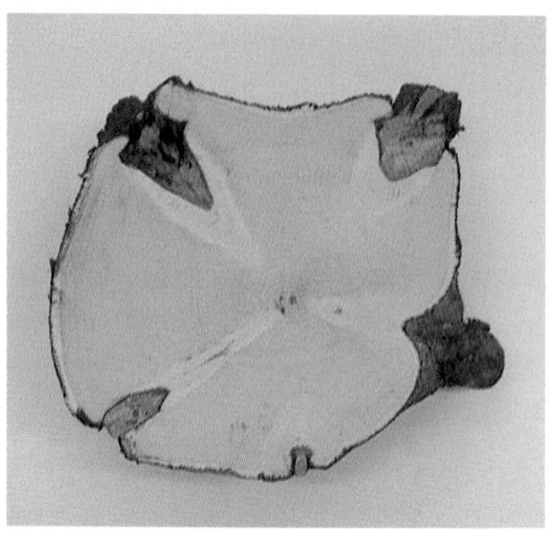

Plate 40 Stem of Ilex aquifolium *sawn across near branch pruning cuts: the sharpness of the dark reaction zones does not necessarily indicate that they are stable (note the pale zones of dysfunctional but sound wood)*

occur, perhaps in a seasonal cycle corresponding to periods of host activity and dormancy [152].

These considerations show that reaction zones (as distinct from barrier zones – see Section 3.4.3.) are not always effective barriers; they sometimes merely represent temporary invasion fronts. It has, however, been implied through various publications that any abrupt demarcation between sound and discoloured wood is a sign of successful 'compartmentalisation'. The appearance of a stem section such as that shown in Plate 40 could be interpreted in this way, but can equally be regarded as demonstrating that discoloration and decay nearly always tend to develop within sharply delimited zones of 'least resistance'. Such demarcations reflect the tree's anatomical structure and do not necessarily indicate whether or not the affected zones are going to extend beyond their present limits. Although the defensive rôle of reaction zones is often evident from the very restricted development of decay, it is wise not to rely too heavily on their long-term effectiveness when attempting a prognosis of tree safety (see Section 3.4.3). If, however, a reaction zone separates sound wood from a zone of advanced decay, as opposed to incipient decay or discoloration, it is probably very stable.

The older central wood in a mature tree lacks living cells and cannot therefore react to injury or microbial invasion as sapwood does. When, however, central wood is injured, the affected zone sometimes shows a colour change which might perhaps represent the formation of defensive substances formed through the oxidation of chemical precursors [160]. The main form of defence against decay in this region is a pre-existing one, represented by the formation of a durable heartwood. This is found in some species only (see Appendix 2) and is formed through a genetically determined process of ageing in the sapwood, in which the parenchyma cells die after giving rise to physical and chemical defences. The vessels become blocked by tyloses, although in some species the large springwood vessels are blocked long before heartwood formation.

In many tree species, heartwood formation also involves a general deposition of anti-microbial and plugging materials which are usually dark in colour. In timber technology these substances are known as extractives. In some species, one of the most important substances deposited is suberin [128]. Resins or gums also play an important part in heartwood formation in many species, especially conifers. Decay sometimes occurs in 'durable' types of heartwood, since certain decay fungi, such as *Laetiporus sulphureus*, are able to degrade or tolerate their defensive constituents. Some species, such as *Aesculus hippocastanum* (Horse chestnut) and *Fraxinus excelsior*, have a 'non-durable' heartwood and this can be readily decayed if exposed to partial drying and fungal infection. The same applies to some other species, such as *F. sylvatica* and *Acer* spp., in which there is no distinct heartwood; only a zone of 'ripewood', in which there has been gradual ageing and death of the sapwood.

To summarise, the main factors that can determine the eventual extent of a zone of decay are as follows:

- the nature and extent of the initiating wound or zones of dieback
- the species of tree
- the age, genetic make-up, moisture status and carbohydrate reserves of the individual tree
- the species of decay fungi present
- the interactions between decay fungi and other micro-organisms within the damaged wood
- the length of time over which the damaged wood remains open to the atmosphere.

The factors are considered in greater depth by Pearce [127] in an excellent review of antimicrobial defences in the wood of living trees. Another very useful source of reference is a book on defences of woody plants edited by Blanchette and Biggs [13]. Clearly, there are many permutations possible amongst the factors that can affect the extent of decay, with a very wide range of possible outcomes as far as the relative success of the tree and of the decay fungi is concerned. In some cases, as when a small area of bark is knocked off the base of the tree without serious damage to the underlying wood, there may be no more than a very shallow and localised area of discoloration. In other cases, such as the exposure of the entire cross-sectional area of a stem by 'topping', much of the pre-existing wood may be highly vulnerable to attack by decay fungi.

3.4.3 Rates of decay in different host/fungus associations

The factors discussed above, which influence the decay process, do not operate with equal effect in all tree species. Also, fungal species differ in their ability to tolerate or overcome adverse conditions, and this is not necessarily related to the rate at which they can decay wood under ideal conditions in the laboratory. Thus, the particular nature of the damage affecting the individual tree could have more effect on the decay rate than the characteristics either of the tree species or the fungal species. Climate, especially temperature, may also be important. For example, observations on *Quercus* spp. with basal fire damage show much faster development of associated decay in the south-eastern USA than in the north-east [77]. The *Quercus* species in those two geographical areas were not the same, but the authors regarded climate as more important than host differences in influencing the rate of decay.

The average annual extension rate of decay in a tree can be calculated by measuring the length or volume of the decay column and dividing this by the number of annual increments formed after the event that initiated the decay. There is, however, usually no means of knowing whether the fungus has been developing actively throughout the estimated period. It may well have grown rapidly for only part of this time, having been restricted by adverse conditions at other times. Also, such data as do exist from such studies are derived mainly from trees in forests rather than amenity sites. Despite these drawbacks, there is some evidence of inherent differences between fungi.

For amenity trees, there are anecdotal observations which indicate that some fungal species can cause especially rapid decay, but the ‘start’ time is often wrongly equated with the time when fruit bodies first appear. This event could occur after many years of unseen development. There is also some evidence that some host species, or indeed cultivars, are more rapidly decayed by a given fungus than others; this is particularly the case in species with a low wood density (e.g. *Populus* spp.) or with a poor ability to block their vessels as a defensive response (e.g. birches, *Betula* spp.). Otherwise, there is currently insufficient knowledge in this field to assist the diagnosis and prognosis of hazards.

3.4.4 The rôle of newly formed tissues in restricting the development of decay

Most of the above mentioned factors operate within the wood that is already present when a trauma initiates dysfunction and fungal development. At the very worst, as far as the tree is concerned, all this wood could eventually become decayed. Decay in this wood does not usually extend outwards into wood laid down after the trauma, although this new wood may of course be subject to decay arising from subsequent traumas. As outlined in the previous section, the immunity of the new wood appears to be conferred partly by the formation of a ‘barrier zone’, which is a sheet of especially modified living parenchyma-like xylem cells that are laid down by the cambium within the first annual ring formed after the trauma, and which represent 'wall 4' of the compartmentalisation model [158].

As the cells in the barrier zone are short and contain living contents, they are much more resistant to fungal invasion than normal fibres or vessels which can act as routes for rapid fungal growth up or down the axis of the stem or root. The barrier zone cells can lay down defensive substances similar to those found in durable heartwood; these include suberin [128, 129], which cannot be degraded by most decay fungi. The annual increment formed after the damaging event does not usually consist entirely of cells which can be visually or chemically categorised as barrier zone cells. These cells normally occupy an elliptical area, extending around the damaged area. Beyond the limits of this area, it might be supposed that decay could spread outwards into new wood. The reason that this does not happen is probably that, unlike the wood present before the trauma, the new wood is structurally and hydraulically intact and thus free from dysfunction [16].

Although barrier zones rarely fail, it is of course possible for fresh injuries to occur, thus exposing the new wood to decay fungi either from existing decay columns in the older wood or from outside sources. In some cases, such injuries can occur naturally when the new wood splits due to partial wind-induced failure or to localised stress caused by the formation of a 'rams-horn' in the tissues occluding an injury (see below). Also, certain fungi (e.g. *Inonotus hispidus*, Plates 71–73) can repeatedly kill the new tissues that develop around their entry points, and this provides them with a route for invading wood that is formed after the initiating injury. The killing of callus and cambial tissue induces a perennial canker, earning the term 'canker-rot' for this mode of attack.

It is not entirely clear whether wood formed after root damage is quite so resistant to the extension of decay as its counterpart in the above-ground parts of the tree. Roots can form barrier zones [174], but many root- and butt-rot fungi give the appearance of being able to develop outwards to the bark. The processes involved are not well documented, but studies on certain fungi have shown that breaching of the barrier zone need not be involved. For example, *Heterobasidion annosum* can grow through the bark so that it repeatedly reaches the cambium from the outside at fresh entry points [138]. Another possibility with various root-infecting fungi is that internal columns of decay, having extended upwards to the stem base, can continue developing outwards through ingrowing flutes in the buttress zone, where there is a bark-to-bark contact. Apparent extensions of decay columns are sometimes found in these ingrown regions, but their origin has not been studied in detail.

Another feature of the tree's continued growth after the trauma is that it can occlude wounds by the growth of new bark and wood around the edges of the damaged surface. If occlusion becomes complete, thereby preventing gas exchange in the damaged wood, existing decay tends to be arrested. Before total occlusion happens, however, (and this may never occur on a very large wound) partial occlusion can sometimes improve conditions for decay fungi by locking in moisture within regions of the wood which would otherwise become too dry for them to remain active [155]. Also, very rapid occlusion can involve the formation of a 'rams-horn', whereby the new tissues turn over upon themselves, with resulting mechanical stress and the risk of cracking and hence self-inflicted injury in the new wood (Plate 14).

The new tissues surrounding a wound or canker have traditionally been termed 'callus' although the term is confusing because it also describes other types of plant growth, including the undifferentiated cells which initially form around the edge of a wound. The term 'woundwood' has been suggested so as to help allay this confusion [158], but it does not convey the fact that the new tissues consist of wood, cambium and bark. Also, the original definition of woundwood ('Wundholz' in German), does not refer specifically to the occluding tissues, but to the anatomical characteristics of the new wood formed near a wound [68]. Perhaps there should be little objection to the use of 'callus' if its meaning is clear from the context. In the present book the term 'occluding tissues' is used in some cases to avoid confusion.

Chapter 4 Principal decay fungi

(incorporating information from Greig [63] and from Burdekin [25])

As indicated in Chapter 3, different fungi degrade woody cell walls in a variety of ways and differ correspondingly in the nature and severity of any weakening that they cause in their host trees. Many species also seem to show 'preferences' for particular parts of the tree, so that some are found only in the roots and stem base while others are confined mainly to the upper trunk or branches.

When decay or fungal fruit bodies are found during a tree hazard assessment, there is good reason to make an accurate identification of the fungus concerned if its typical pattern of spread within the tree and its effect on wood strength are known and therefore to some extent predictable. This knowledge can add to the ease and efficiency of assessing the extent and mechanical properties of the decayed zone, but it is not a substitute for such an assessment. In any case, there are unfortunately many fungi whose effects on wood strength are little known, and whose identification therefore remains a matter of academic rather than practical interest.

Preliminary guidance on identification is provided in a chart (Fig. 4.1), which places fungal genera into groups, according to general features of their fruit bodies. The following descriptions include individual species, selected on the basis of their ability to cause extensive decay in living trees. Also included are some which are usually confined to dead branches, stumps or fallen timber, but which are commonly found during tree inspections. Each description includes features by which the species concerned can be identified. There is also information, where available, about the typical manner in which the species concerned colonises its host trees and about the types of decay that it causes.

Many uncommon or less important species have been omitted for reasons of space, and the reader is recommended to consult one of the following books for a more comprehensive guide to identification. In the first two listed, the photographic illustrations are exceptionally good. A wide selection of tree decay fungi are well illustrated in the third book listed. The fourth on the list, which is now out of print, provides descriptions of a wide range of tree decay fungi and the decays that they cause.

- *Fungi of Switzerland* by J. Breitenbach & F. Kränzlin, 1991. 3 Vols., Verlag Mykologia, Lucerne, Switzerland. This edition is in English and includes most of the wood decay fungi that are likely to be found in Britain, central and western Europe.

- *Pilze an Bäumen* by H. Jahn, 2nd ed., revd. by H. Reinartz & M. Schlag, 1990, (Patzer, Berlin – Hannover) 272 pp. This is a specialist book on wood decay fungi, and there are photographic illustrations of particularly good quality. The accompanying written keys are currently available only in German.

- *Mushrooms and other Fungi of Great Britain and Europe* by R. Phillips (1981), Ward Locke, London, 288 pp.

- *Decay of Timber and its Prevention* by Cartwright, K.St.G., and Findlay, W.P.K. (1958). 2nd edn., HMSO, London.

For readers who want to learn more about the classification and biology of fungi, there are several standard textbooks, including the following:

- *Introductory Mycology* by C.J. Alexopoulos, 4th edn. revd. by C.W. Mims and M. Blackwell (1995), Wiley, USA.

- *Biology of Fungi* by C.T. Ingold, 6th edn. revd. by H.J. Hudson (1993), Chapman & Hall.

- *Introduction to Fungi* by J. Webster, 2nd edn. (1980), Cambridge Univ.

4.1 General features of decay fungi and of decayed wood

Like most other fungi, wood decaying species grow as microscopic branched, thread-like filaments known as **hyphae**. The hyphae grow through the wood and also collectively form a **mycelium** which is sometimes visible as a felty or woolly growth on moist surfaces of wood or bark. The appearance and growth rate of the mycelium and of individual hyphae can often help to indicate the identity of the fungus.

The hyphae of wood decay fungi secrete digestive **enzymes** which allow them to dissolve holes through or between the woody cell walls and to break down the chemical constituents of the wood into a soluble form which the fungus can absorb as a food source. The way in which a particular fungus invades and degrades the wood can help in its identification, as well as in assessing the hazard that it might pose by decaying the wood. Its ability to secrete various enzymes can be tested in the laboratory as a further indication of its identity.

Fungally invaded wood usually differs from sound wood both in colour and texture, and often has a different moisture content. In some cases the appearance of the wood is of value in fungal identification. In living trees that are undergoing decay there is often a band of dark or intense discoloration (a **reaction zone**) between the sound wood and the decayed wood, but the decayed wood can appear either pale or dark, depending on the type of decay and the stage that it has reached. The texture can be stringy, spongy, pasty, cheesy or brittle, or the wood may be destroyed so completely that only a cavity remains.

Wood decayed by certain fungi may contain thin, dark, sheets of material which have been produced by the fungus itself and which should be distinguished from the usually broader reaction zone at the edge of the colonised wood, although the two can coincide. These fungal sheets sometimes mark boundaries between zones of active decay and of early stages of fungal colonisation. In other cases, they delimit regions occupied by different fungal species or by different individuals of the same species. For some fungi, these sheets act as barriers against the diffusion of moisture and are known as '**pseudosclerotial plates**', indicating some similarity to sclerotia, which are hard, dark resting structures which enable some fungal species to survive adverse conditions. The fungally invaded wood enclosed within a pseudosclerotial plate is similarly a zone of protection for the fungus. As these sheets of fungal tissue enclose three-dimensional volumes of wood, it might be more accurate to refer to them as shells rather than plates. However, in sawn sections of wood, they appear as lines, and so the term **zone-line** is often applied.

The interactions between woody plant tissues and fungi, including the rôle of active host defences, have been described in an excellent review by Pearce [127].

4.1.1 Identification of fungi from their fruit bodies

For the majority of decay fungi, the most straightforward means of identification is by examining their fruit bodies, although these are by no means always found on trees affected by decay. Decay in living trees is mainly caused by basidiomycete fungi, whose fruit bodies usually consist of **brackets, toadstools** or **fronds**, and can sometimes be very large. There are also some that form sheet-like or lumpy masses of fruiting tissue, and there are a few (of very little importance in hazard tree assessment) whose fruit bodies are puffballs. The term **resupinate** is used for fruit bodies that form a layer on the host surface; such layers can intergrade with brackets in some species. The spore-bearing surface layer in these types of fruit body is known as the **hymenium**. It forms a simple covering on the sheet-like types, as in *Stereum* spp., but in most decay fungi it lines an intricate system of either **gills** or **tubes** which provide a much larger area than a flat surface. The openings of tubes are often referred to as **pores**. All features of the spore-bearing surface can be used in fungal identification, together with certain internal structures. The internal tissue of brackets and toadstools is known as the **context**, and the tissue immediately behind the hymenium is the **trama**. In this book, these internal tissues are described under the general term 'flesh'.

The function of fungal fruit bodies is to produce **spores**, which are microscopic, mainly airborne propagules by which the fungus can become established on new hosts, sometimes many kilometres away. In basidiomycetes, the main type of spore is the **basidiospore**. These are formed through sexual reproduction and are borne on microscopic peg-like structures known as **basidia**, which are in turn borne on the surface of the hymenium. The colour of the basidiospores, seen *en masse*, is of diagnostic value, as is their microscopic appearance. Some basidiomycetes additionally produce asexual spores within their mycelia.

The remaining decay fungi are ascomycetes, most of which form hard crust-like or domed fruit bodies, as in *Ustulina deusta*. These are generally rather small in size, ranging from pinhead-sized to several centimetres across but some species produce them in very large aggregations on the host surface. Their structure is different to that of basidiomycete fruit bodies, and consists of a mass of tissue (the **stroma**) in which small fruiting structures (**perithecia**) are embedded. Each perithecium contains microscopic sacs, called **asci**, in which the sexually produced **ascospores** are formed. Most of the wood-decay ascomycetes also form asexual spores on a fruiting surface which is later replaced by the mature stroma.

For identification in the field, the structure, size, texture and colour of fungal fruit bodies are very important, and these characters can show great variation between species. Closely related species may, however, have very similar fruit bodies, and so can only be separated on the basis of other characters. If the fungus cannot be accurately identified in the field, a fruit body or part of a fruit body may be collected for later observation. It is important to collect a sample which includes all the different parts of the fruiting structure, including the stalk (if present) and the upper and lower surfaces. For some species, microscopic examination of the fruit body tissue or of spores is needed for identification. If the sample is to be sent to a diagnostic laboratory, it should be carefully packed so as to avoid crushing, desiccation or wetting by condensation. Delivery should be arranged so as to minimise delay, especially in the case of soft fleshy species. High quality photographs, showing upper and lower surfaces, can also be of use.

4.1.2 Identification of decay fungi in culture

Fungal fruit bodies are often not found during tree decay investigations, but there are other means of identifying the causal organism. This can be done by isolating it from decayed wood in pure culture and carrying out laboratory tests which include microscopical examination of the mycelium, measurements of its growth rate and determining whether it can produce various enzymes. A key by Stalpers [167] provides a basis for testing all the wood decay basidiomycetes belonging to the group Aphyllophorales; i.e. those whose spores are formed on pores or flat surfaces rather than gills. A computer-based version of this key, known as "Rotters", has been developed by the Forestry Commission Disease and Diagnostic Advisory Service,

Farnham, Surrey, UK, and includes some gill-forming species, as well as revised information on species in the original key.

Specialised knowledge and experience is needed in order to carry out the tests needed for the Rotters key, but it is relatively easy to send wood samples to a diagnostic laboratory. All that is required is a piece of wood (or preferably several pieces) which includes the transitions between sound, discoloured and decayed tissue. Even if not all these zones can be sampled, the fungus can sometimes be isolated by placing chips of wood on to a growth medium (usually an agar jelly containing nutrients such as malt extract), following surface sterilisation to kill external contaminants. A simpler and often very effective method is to incubate the entire sample in humid conditions, which allow the mycelium of the fungus to appear on the surface.

The chances of successful isolation are improved if it is possible to saw the wood samples in the form of entire discs or, failing that, 2 – 3 cm-square battens, transecting the areas of interest, but this fully destructive sampling can be done only after the affected part (e.g. a branch) has already been removed from the tree. If the affected part has to be retained pending investigation, isolation of fungi can be attempted by extracting increment cores and taking wood chips from them for transfer to culture media. The cores must not be allowed to dry out in transit and the chips must be taken for fungal isolation before surface contaminant fungi have had a chance to penetrate. Another reason for extracting increment cores is that they can be used for assessing the relative extent of sound versus decayed wood, but the resulting holes can create avenues for the extension of decay within the tree. Now that this cause for concern has become widely known, other less damaging methods are often used. Some of these involve the use of long, narrow drill-bits, which can provide some opportunity of isolating fungi from the drill shavings.

4.2 Identification of principal wood-rotting fungi on standing trees

NB: *This guide works only for the genera mentioned in this chapter.*

Procedure for using the guide

- Make a short-list of possible genera using the chart in Fig. 4.1
- Turn to Appendix 2 and look up the entry for the host tree genus.
- Reduce the short-list by referring to the fungi (if any) which are named in the Appendix as being known to occur on the tree genus concerned. Also refer to the abbreviation which indicates the part of the tree in which the fungus is usually active; either '(B)' for bottom rots (i.e. root- and butt-rots), or '(T)' for top rots (i.e. originating from a point above ground).
- Check the descriptions of individual species given in this chapter.

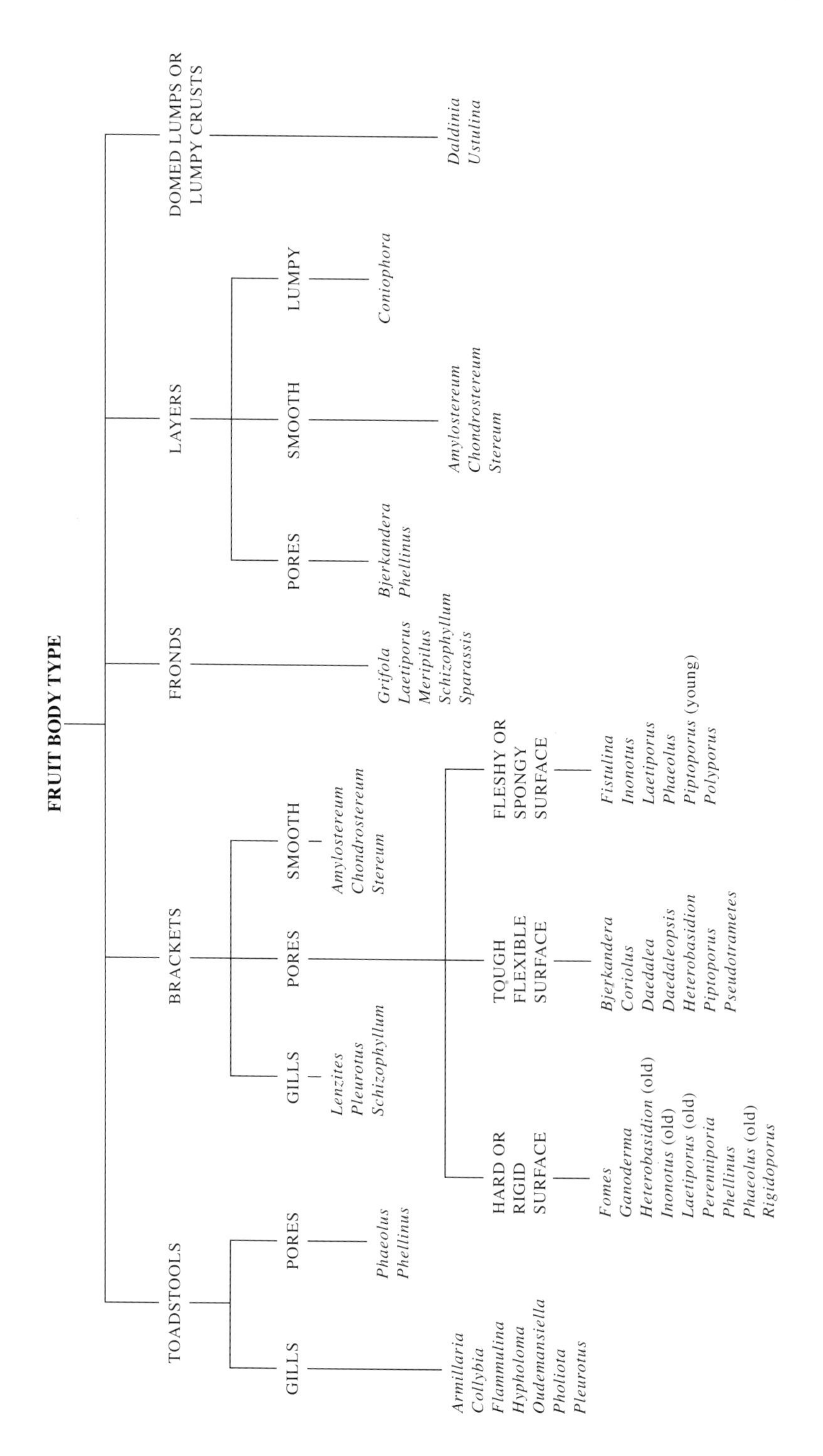

Figure 4.1 Key to principal genera of tree decay fungi, based on types of fruit body

The descriptions of individual species, which form the remainder of this chapter, can be used for further confirmation, but it must be appreciated that there are many other species – mostly rare or of little importance in tree hazard assessment – which can be identified only with the aid of a much more comprehensive guide, such as one of the books listed above.

4.3 Descriptions and significance of individual decay fungi

The fungi in the following descriptions appear in alphabetical order of their scientific names. Advances in fungal taxonomy have resulted in many name changes over the years so that for example there are now several genera, including *Bjerkandera*, *Laetiporus* and *Piptoporus*, that were once all grouped within *Polyporus*. The species headings in this chapter are based on the currently accepted names, but former names and synonyms other than decidedly obsolete ones are shown in brackets and are also included in the index to this book.

Each description includes, where relevant, the following information: range of host species, geographic occurrence in Great Britain, features of the fruit body, type of decay and significance for hazard evaluation. The most characteristic features of each species are shown in bold type. Host species and genera are identified here by their scientific names; their English equivalents can be found in Appendix 2.

Plate 41 Amylostereum laevigatum *on* Taxus baccata

Amylostereum laevigatum (Plate 41)

• *Hosts*

This fungus occurs on *Taxus* and *Juniperus* and also on *Thuja* and *Chamaecyparis lawsoniana*.

• *Fruit bodies*

The fruit bodies form an **inconspicuous skin-like layer**, on areas of bark which the fungus has killed. They can be found throughout the year.

• *Decay and disease*

This fungus enters through wounds, especially topping cuts, and occupies long strips of sapwood, causing a fibrous white-rot in which a light brown discoloration is present [173]. The fungus kills not only sapwood, but also bark and cambium and is thus the cause of a **canker-rot**.

• *Significance*

The death of branches or entire trees due to killing of the sapwood is more obvious than the decay caused by this fungus and is likely to draw attention to infected trees before the accompanying white-rot causes a hazard. These effects have been observed on *Thuja* and *C. lawsoniana* although it is uncertain whether *A. laevigatum* causes a similar disease in *Taxus* and *Juniperus*, which are perhaps its native hosts in Britain.

Plate 42 Armillaria gallica *fruiting around the stump of a tree killed by Dutch elm disease*

Plate 43 Armillaria gallica*; rhizomorphs on a stump*

Plate 44 Armillaria *butt-rot in* Picea abies*; cross-section of stem base*

Plate 45 Armillaria *butt-rot in* Picea abies*; longitudinal section of stem base*

***Armillaria* spp; honey fungus, bootlace fungus** (Plates 42–45)

• *Hosts*

Armillaria species all have a wide host range amongst trees and shrubs, but some occur mainly on conifers (e.g. *A. ostoyae*) while others occur mainly on broadleaved genera (e.g. *A. gallica* {syn. *A. bulbosa*}). They often begin their invasion of the host by killing the cambium of roots and thus causing disease before decaying the wood. Some species, such as *A. gallica*, are pathogenic only on stressed trees, while *A. mellea* and *A. ostoyae* can invade healthy individuals. A list of genera and species which appear to be resistant or tolerant to infection is available [64].

• *Fruit bodies and other fungal structures*

The fruit bodies are **brown or honey-yellow toadstools** which usually appear in clusters, sometimes singly, on stumps or on the ground over infected roots and at the bases of dead or windthrown trees. Occasionally, they can form some distance up a tree trunk. At first, they resemble 'button' mushrooms, but rapidly expand to reach **50 – 150 cm across the cap** and up to **150 cm high**. The cap often has **dark scales** on the upper surface, and its underside bears **pale cream gills** which usually run slightly on to the stem. The stem, which can exceed 2 cm in thickness, bears a collar-like **ring**, but no volva. The toadstools have a soft texture, lacking toughness, and rot away quickly. Species of *Armillaria* differ in some characters, such as the scaliness of the cap and the thickness of the stem, but they cannot be reliably distinguished in the field. Fruiting occurs mainly in the **autumn**, and the toadstools do not persist long as they are killed by the first frosts.

The fungus also produces bootlace-like structures, known as **rhizomorphs**, by which it spreads through the soil to new hosts or pieces of wood. These also vary in appearance between some of the *Armillaria* species, although they do not provide a reliable means of distinguishing between them. However, *A. gallica* is typified by an abundance of thick, black rhizomorphs with a circular cross-section. Thinner, flatter rhizomorphs with a red-brown colour and occurring sparsely in the soil are more typical of *A. mellea*. **The presence of rhizomorphs around the roots or stem base of a living tree is not proof of the presence of decay, nor of the cause of death**.

If *Armillaria* invades the cambium at the base of a tree, the resulting dead bark often conceals a characteristic fan of whitish mycelium. Rhizomorphs may also be present under the bark.

• *Decay*

The early stages of growth in the wood are shown by a **stain**, which forms irregular patches of a grey, pale brown or inky blue colour; these later darken to deep brown or blue-black. When **incipient decay** develops, the colour changes to mid-brown to orange-brown or yellow, often with thin black 'zone lines' (more properly called pseudosclerotial plates) at the junction of decayed and sound wood. A blue-grey stain may remain around the zone of incipient decay. The consistency of the incipient decay is dry and firm. In **advanced decay**, a stringy white-rot is evident, although the colour may range in different zones from white to yellowish or orange-brown. The stringy areas tend to be wet, and are often interlaced with thin black sheets of pseudosclerotial material.

• *Significance*

If decay by an *Armillaria* sp. is extensive in a root system, there is a high chance of windthrow. In such cases, the death of roots will usually produce symptoms in the crown of the tree. Sometimes the decay is most extensive in the stem base, so that above-ground fracture occurs, although it rarely extends more than 50 cm up the stem.

Sanitation is a major consideration with honey fungus, since it is known to spread below ground from tree to tree. For most other decay fungi, with the exception of *Heterobasidion annosum*, it is not clear whether this form of spread is significant. In cases where trees or shrubs are dying or have been killed due to invasion by honey fungus, it is likely that one of its more pathogenic forms, *A. mellea* or *A. ostoyae*, is involved and that neighbouring specimens may be at risk of invasion. This risk can be reduced by grubbing out the stumps and roots of the infected trees, so as to reduce the foodbase of the fungus. The stumps and roots of healthy trees that have been felled can also become infected by honey fungus, and are sometimes removed as a precaution when high value amenity trees are nearby. If grubbing out is not practicable, or is deemed inadvisable in the interests of conserving deadwood fauna and flora, a barrier can be inserted between vulnerable trees and nearby infection sources. This can take the form of a heavy-duty plastic sheet, which is inserted vertically into a trench extending well down into the subsoil. Other forms of control might become available in the future, such as the fumigation of stumps by trained operators or the use of other fungi as biological control agents. More information about species of *Armillaria* and their control has been provided by Greig, Gregory and Strouts [64].

Plate 46 Bjerkandera adusta *fruiting on stump of* Fagus sylvatica

Bjerkandera adusta syn. *Polyporus adustus* (Plate 46)

• *Hosts*

This fungus has a very wide host range among broadleaved trees, but is most common on *Fagus sylvatica* and *Carpinus betulus*. It occasionally occurs on conifers.

• *Fruit bodies*

The fungus forms small, thin, leathery brackets, which form in **dense tiers** on the dead bark or exposed wood of trunks, stumps and fallen trees. The brackets are often partly resupinate (i.e. lying flat on the surface of the host), and are very flexible so that they usually develop irregular wavy folds while expanding. The brackets individually measure **25 – 75 mm** across, and have a pale brownish grey to off-white colour on their upper surfaces, which bear very small hairs. The opposite surface, which bears **very small pores**, is white at first but becomes characteristically ashen-grey with age and black after death. A rapid test for *Bjerkandera* species is to cut or tear a bracket, which reveals a **blackish jelly-like** layer separating the **greyish-white** flesh from the tubes. The fruit bodies are annual, but can be found at all times of year. A similar but less common species, *B. fumosa*, is found in similar situations. Its brackets are somewhat larger, and are pale brown or greenish-grey above.

• *Decay*

The decay is a white-rot with a spongy consistency. It has not been studied in detail, but appears to be of the simultaneous kind, in which cellulose and lignin are both degraded, causing a relatively brittle fracture. The decay develops in sapwood, and can develop from pruning wounds, galleries of wood-boring insects, and broken branches. Occasionally, the fungus occurs in roots. The extent of the decay tends to be rather limited, either being confined to relatively small-diameter parts of the tree, or forming narrow pipe-like columns close to the surface of large trunks. There is some evidence that it can kill the cambium, thus causing a canker-rot.

• *Significance*

Decay by this fungus is not commonly associated with major mechanical failures in large trees, but it is a frequent cause of breakage in stems of *F. sylvatica* up to approx. 300 mm in diameter, typically following infection via areas of bark that have previously been killed by beech bark disease. The presence of the fungus on a tree is, however, an indication that a detailed inspection should be carried out. If fracture occurs, it is of a fairly brittle type.

Plate 47 Chondrostereum purpureum *fruiting, having killed a coppiced specimen of* Eucalyptus archeri

***Chondrostereum purpureum*; the silver-leaf disease fungus** (Plate 47)

• *Hosts*

This common fungus has a very wide host range among broadleaved trees and shrubs, and is an aggressive parasite on some of them.

• *Fruit bodies*

These are thin and **skin-like** fronds, with a **hard, tough texture**, which are often partly resupinate. Their slightly hairy upper surfaces are pale greyish-brown in colour. As with *Stereum* spp., their spore-bearing undersides carry no pores or gills. A distinguishing feature of the undersides of the young fruit bodies is their **lilac** or **purple** colour, but this fades to a dingy brown or grey with age. The fruit bodies can form at most times of year, except in dry summer periods. Although they are annual, they persist for many months and can re-imbibe moisture after becoming desiccated in dry weather.

• *Decay and disease*

Like *Amylostereum laevigatum*, this fungus is known more as a killer of trees than as a decay fungus. It enters through wounds and can rapidly invade and kill large volumes of sapwood in susceptible species or cultivars. This invasion does not involve any noticeable decay at an early stage, but it causes extensive loss of water-conducting function. This can result in the death of parts of the tree or of the entire tree. A toxin is involved in this process which, in some host species, is translocated to the leaves and causes them to develop a dull leaden lustre; hence the name silver-leaf for the disease caused by *C. purpureum*. The decay appears to be a slight white-rot of the sapwood, but this fungus is often replaced by others, such as *Coriolus versicolor*, which can cause a more complete decay.

• *Significance*

On its own, *C. purpureum* is not usually associated with structural failure, but it is very important as a pathogen on trees and shrubs in diverse taxonomic groups, including the Rosaceae, *Acer* spp., *Betula* spp. [110] and eucalypts. Structural failure from embrittlement of dry wood or decay by secondary invaders usually occurs only after the invaded parts have been killed.

Plate 48 Collybia fusipes, *fruiting near the stem base of* Quercus *sp.*

Collybia fusipes; the spindle shank (Plate 48)

• *Hosts*

The main hosts in the UK are *Quercus robur* and *Q. petraea*.

• *Fruit bodies*

These are robust **toadstools** which occur mainly in **small clusters** on the ground near the bases of host trees. They arise from blackish perennating masses of fungal tissue attached to the infected roots of the tree, but these are not easy to locate. When fresh, the caps are reddish brown above and can be almost liver-coloured in wet conditions, but they become a pale, dingy tan colour with age and often crack. They measure up to **50 mm** across, and are borne on grooved stems of similar colour which are approx. 100 mm high and 12 mm thick at the mid-point and which **taper markedly** towards their underground point of attachment. The gills are whitish at first, later acquiring the same colour as the rest of the toadstool. This species is sometimes mistaken for honey fungus but lacks the ring around the stem. It fruits at various times of year apart from midwinter but the toadstools remain alive for only a short time, although rotting only slowly when dead.

• *Decay*

The affected roots can become extensively decayed, but the decay rarely, if ever, extends above ground level. Little is known about the type of decay.

• *Significance*

It is not known from case history whether decay caused by *C. fusipes* ever leads to root-plate failure, but the infection can almost certainly impair root function enough to cause dieback in the crown of the tree [66].

Plate 49 Coniophora puteana

Coniophora puteana, syn. *Coniophora cerebella*; **wet-rot fungus, cellar fungus** (Plate 49)

• *Hosts*

Coniophora puteana grows on a wide range of broadleaved and coniferous species, but causes decay mainly in parts which are already dead and exposed to the atmosphere or in stumps, logs, and timber products. In the UK, it has been found causing extensive decay in a standing tree of *Cedrus* sp., [172] and is also known from heartwood decay in *Prunus nigra*, in North America [77].

• *Fruit bodies*

The fruit body is entirely **resupinate**; i.e. it forms a layer on the surface of the host. This fruiting layer is very variable in size and shape, though typically being roughly circular in outline and about 150 mm across. When young, it is whitish-yellow, later darkening to olive-green or bronze except at the margin, and has a soft leathery texture. Its spore-bearing surface is irregularly wrinkled or bumpy, and has **no pores**.

• *Decay*

The decay is a brown-rot, but the cracking is mainly longitudinal with only very fine transverse cracks, rather unlike the cubical shrinkage that is typical of brown-rots. The fungus rarely grows deeply within living trees, probably because it cannot tolerate the low concentrations of oxygen that usually occur beyond the immediate vicinity of wounds. It also requires moister conditions than tend to occur at the wound surface. Occasionally, however, the surface conditions are suitable for its development from latent sites of colonisation which are frequent on the bark of living trees. Once decay by the fungus is established, it can progress more deeply due to the ingress of air associated with shrinkage. The fungus also grows occasionally on the bark of healthy trees, causing the dead outer layers to slough off (a condition known as 'smooth patch') without any decay occurring in the underlying wood.

• *Significance*

The fungus is often found in the course of tree inspections, but rarely causes deep-seated decay in standing trees. Sometimes its fruit bodies are found on healthy bark, having spread from a nearby woody food source. Nevertheless, the presence of its fruit bodies indicates the need for detailed inspection. Even if it has only colonised the outer layers of the wood, other species may be present at greater depth. In keeping with the name 'cellar fungus', *C. puteana* is better known as the cause of 'wet rot' in moist timber products. Its economic importance in buildings is probably second only to that of the dry-rot fungus, *Serpula lachrymans*.

Plate 50 Coriolus versicolor

Coriolus versicolor, syn. *Trametes versicolor*, *Polystictus versicolor*; **the many-zoned polypore** (Plate 50)

• *Hosts*

This fungus is common on a very wide range of host species, especially *Fagus sylvatica* and rosaceous trees.

• *Fruit bodies*

These are **thin, leathery brackets**, which form in densely clustered tiers on stumps and on the surfaces of wounds of standing trees. Each bracket is semi-circular and flattened, reaching between **25 and 60 mm** across. A distinctive feature is the concentrically zoned colour pattern of the velvety upper surface. This consists of **alternating dark and light zones**, in which there may be various shades of grey, green-grey, yellow-brown and occasionally red or blue. The thin, **wavy or lobed margin** is the palest of the zones. Underneath, the **pores** are small and cream-coloured, becoming darker with age. Inside, the flesh is white, tough and is demarcated from the greyish or black tube layer. The brackets can be found throughout the year.

• *Decay*

The fungus causes a white-rot, but this is usually confined to fairly small volumes of the sapwood. In some cases, it occupies wood that has been initially invaded by *Chondrostereum purpureum*. On some occasions it appears to kill the cambium, as well as invading the sapwood.

• *Significance*

Due to the very common occurrence of this fungus, it is often found during tree inspections. It does not usually cause extensive rot in the trunks or main roots of large trees, but it can cause the fracture of small, dead limbs. Other fungi can sometimes replace it and cause more extensive rot, so that its presence on a large pruning wound or at the base of a broken branch indicates the need for a detailed inspection. A related white-rot fungus, *C. hirsuta*, occurs on sun-scorched trees, often together with *Schizophyllum commune*; its fruit bodies bear grey or yellowish stiff hairs above and have roundish, yellowish white pores beneath.

Plate 51 Daedalea quercina

***Daedalea quercina*; the maze-gill** (Plate 51)

• *Hosts*

This fungus occurs on *Fagus sylvatica*, *Quercus robur* and *Castanea sativa* and occasionally on other tree species.

• *Fruit bodies*

These are brackets with a **hard-leathery texture**, ranging from **50 to 175 mm** across. Their pale greyish-brown upper surfaces are relatively flat and smooth, but bear concentric zones. The pale brown under-surfaces bear pores which are **irregularly elongated** radially and some of these almost resemble gills. The pores are also contorted and some of them are cross-linked, giving a rather **maze-like** appearance ('daedaloid', pertaining to Daedalus of Greek mythology). The brackets are perennial and very persistent.

• *Decay*

This is an intense brown-rot and therefore causes a brittle fracture.

• *Significance*

Although *D. quercina* is common on trees, as well as on converted timber, it is largely confined to dead branches and stumps. It is therefore of limited significance for tree safety except as the cause of decay in already dead branches. For this reason, it has been noted as the cause of a safety hazard in amenity plantings of Red oak, *Quercus rubra* [26].

Plate 52 Daedaleopsis confragosa *fruiting on* Betula pendula

Daedaleopsis confragosa*, syn. Trametes rubescens* (Plate 52)

• *Hosts*

This fungus is very common on *Salix* and also occurs on many other broadleaved genera, such as *Fagus* and *Prunus*.

• *Fruit bodies*

The fruit bodies are hairless, tough or hard, **neatly semi-circular** brackets which develop on dead and broken branches and trunks. They measure up to **125 mm** across and are rather thin, having their greatest thickness, up to 15 mm, at the point of attachment. The upper surface of the bracket is zoned, with bands of off-white and reddish-brown, and the pore-bearing surface underneath is white or grey, **bruising blood-red** when fresh. When developing, the **pores** are roundish but later become **radially elongated**. The flesh has a hard leathery consistency and becomes somewhat brittle when dry.

The fruit bodies are not perennial but are found throughout the year, often remaining intact with darkened colour for many months.

• *Decay*

The decay has not been described in detail, but appears to be a white-rot with a rather brittle fracture. It is usually confined to parts of the tree that have previously died or that have been seriously damaged from other causes, and does not affect large volumes of wood in living stems.

• *Significance*

Due to its common occurrence, this fungus is likely to be found during tree inspections but its presence is not usually a cause for serious concern since it is not associated with failures in large living trunks. Dead branches and the trunks of small trees that have been extensively decayed by the fungus are liable to fracture, and should be cut down where this would represent a hazard.

Plate 53 Daldinia concentrica*; decay in* Fraxinus excelsior, *with fruit bodies*

***Daldinia concentrica*; King Alfred's cakes, cramp balls** (Plate 53)

• *Hosts*

This fungus is very commonly found on *Fraxinus* and occurs less commonly on other broadleaved genera, including *Fagus*.

• *Fruit bodies*

Unlike most well known decay fungi, which are basidiomycetes and therefore produce brackets, fronds or toadstools, *D. concentrica* is an ascomycete and produces **hard**, **black**, (initially reddish) **hemispherical** fruit bodies, **3 – 6 cm** across, with an almost smooth surface that is dotted with minute warts. These warts mark the openings of small chambers in which the black spores are formed. If a fruit body is cut open, it appears to be made up from a series of **concentric domes**, which have a **charcoal-like** consistency. Once mature, the fruit bodies do not develop further, but they are persistent and are found throughout the year.

• *Decay*

The decay has not been investigated in detail, but is currently classed as a white-rot. The fungus preferentially degrades certain zones of the wood, leaving others almost unaltered, so that a cross-section shows a characteristic pattern which in the past earned the name 'calico wood'. Within the decayed zones, white patches are present and often contain scattered black flecks and irregular brown or black stripes.

• *Significance*

This fungus, though common, is of relatively little significance for safety, since it is mainly confined to small trunks and branches which have in most cases died from some other cause.

Plate 54 Fistulina hepatica, *recently matured fruit body on* Quercus *sp. (see also Plate 65)*

Plate 55 Fistulina hepatica *decay in* Quercus *sp., with old fruit body*

***Fistulina hepatica*; beefsteak fungus** (Plates 54-55)

• *Hosts*

The most frequent hosts for *Fistulina hepatica* are *Quercus* spp. It also occurs on *Castanea* and occasionally on other broadleaved genera such as *Fraxinus*, *Juglans*, *Salix*, *Fagus*, *Carpinus* and *Ulmus*.

• *Fruit bodies*

The fruit bodies are **tongue-shaped or semi-circular fleshy brackets**, **5 to 30 cm** across, which develop either near the stem base or higher up on the tree at wounds or broken branches. They first appear as **creamy** soft swellings which become **purplish-red** or **brown** in maturity and may develop a stalk measuring 3 – 7 x 2 – 4 cm. The narrow tubes are **pale yellow** and can be separated from each other. They open as fine pores on to the under-surface, which darkens if bruised. The edible flesh is soft, yielding, reddish and **marbled (like raw steak)** and **exudes a blood-red juice** when broken. The brackets form from August to November, and soon decay after maturity.

• *Decay*

This fungus produces a brownish decay of the heartwood, but it is remarkable in that it produces extensive discoloration with little or no loss of strength until a late stage of degradation. The early stages of cell wall degradation have recently been found to be of the soft-rot type (F.W.M.R. Schwarze, personal communication). In *Quercus*, the rich brown colour of the discoloured wood ('brown oak') is highly valued by timber merchants. When advanced rot ensues, it is said to be a typical cubical brown-rot, but it never progresses to a soft and crumbly stage as happen with some other brown-rot fungi such as *Laetiporus sulphureus*.

• *Significance*

Due to the very slow development of advanced decay, the presence of *F. hepatica* does not signify a hazard unless it has been present in the tree for many years. The extent of weakening, as opposed to mere staining, can be ascertained if a hazard is suspected.

Plate 56 Flammulina velutipes *on* Ulmus *sp.*

Flammulina velutipes, syn. *Collybia velutipes*; **the velvet-shank** (Plate 56)

• *Hosts*

This fungus occurs on various broadleaved trees, including *Tilia* and *Ulmus* – on which it was the chief cause of the break-up of trees killed by Dutch elm disease in England [58] – and also shrubby genera such as *Ulex* (gorse).

• *Fruit bodies*

These are **toadstools** which occur in **clusters** either at the bases or stumps of host trees or higher up on trunks and branches. The **bright tawny cap** sometimes shows a reddish tinge in the centre and has a smooth, slimy, elastic skin. The cap diameter lies in the range **20 – 80 mm**, and the length and thickness of the **dark brown or blackish, velvety** stem are in the ranges **35 – 60 mm** and **5 – 10 mm** respectively. The gills are rather widely spaced and of unequal length and are **pale yellow**, darkening slightly in maturity. The toadstools can form at most times of year outside their peak period in late autumn and early winter. Although they die and wither after reaching maturity, they can withstand frost, unlike those of most other decay fungi.

• *Decay*

The decay develops near entry points such as pruning or other wounds on standing trees, but little is known about its type.

• *Significance*

It is not known whether the decay caused by *F. velutipes* ever becomes extensive enough to cause breakage in living trees, but its presence indicates the need for a detailed inspection.

Plate 57 Fomes fomentarius *on* Pseudotsuga menziesii

***Fomes fomentarius*; tinder fungus** (Plate 57)

• *Hosts*

This fungus has quite a wide host range in continental Europe, occurring mainly on broadleaved species, especially *Fagus sylvatica* which is also its most usual host at the relatively few sites in southern England where the fungus occurs. In northern Britain it is the most common decay fungus on *Betula* spp., whereas *Piptoporus betulinus* occupies this niche in the south.

• *Fruit bodies*

On *Betula* spp. the fruit body is a **hoof-shaped bracket**, **90 – 500 mm** across, and up to **200 mm** thick at its broad attachment to the main stem or major branch of the host. On other hosts, such as *Fagus*, the bracket can also be hoof-shaped, especially after several years' growth, but it often has more of the shelf-like shape of *Ganoderma adspersum*, which it resembles in size and texture, but does not have brown spores, nor dark brown flesh above the tubes. Continued growth of the fruit body or the appearance of new ones can occur for many years on the fallen timber of large trees. The **hard crust-like** upper surface of the bracket shows concentric zones which vary in colour from almost white to dark grey, sometimes with yellowish or brownish tints. The thin, tube-bearing under-surface is renewed annually in the spring, when it appears almost whitish due to the presence of spores. These cease to be shed after mid-summer, by which time the tubes and their **minute round pores** appear a **pale rusty brown**. The flesh, which is cinnamon-brown or **buff** with a **woolly texture**, was once used as tinder ('amadou'), as the common name implies, and has also been used as a styptic and for making poultices, surgical pads and various kinds of protective garment, matting and fancy goods. The brackets are perennial.

• *Decay*

The fungus enters the tree via broken branches or stem injuries and invades sapwood, ripewood and non-durable heartwood, depending on the tree species, and has also been reputed to kill the cambium on occasions, thus causing a canker rot. It destroys lignin and cellulose at similar rates, producing a simultaneous white-rot. A brownish stain develops in advance of the mottled creamy-white zone of decay which typically contains dark zone-lines.

• *Significance*

Since cellulose is degraded at an early stage of decay, the wood soon loses most of its tensile strength and therefore becomes liable to a brittle fracture. This means that the zone of decayed wood contributes very little to the support of the tree, and any strength that it might still have should be disregarded for the purpose of assessing the safety of any affected stems or branches. The rate of decay can be rapid, although large trees often contain enough residual sound wood to remain standing for many years before being seriously weakened.

Plate 58 Ganoderma adspersum *on* Populus *sp.*

Plate 59 Ganoderma adspersum/applanatum, *decay in stem of* Laburnum

Ganoderma applanatum and ***Ganoderma adspersum***, syn. *Ganoderma australe* (Plates 58–59)

• *Hosts*

These two fungi are common on a wide range of broadleaved hosts, especially *Fagus*, and also occasionally occur on conifers. They are described together because they can be distinguished with certainty only by microscopic examination. Recent records suggest that *G. adspersum* is the more common species, at least in southern England, and that the two have often been confused.

• *Fruit bodies*

In both species, the fruit bodies are hoof-shaped or shelf-like **brackets**, which are found most commonly between the buttresses of large trees, just above soil level. Additional, overlapping brackets often form directly above such positions of fruiting, sometimes occurring several metres above ground. More rarely, brackets are associated with aerial infections associated, for example, with pruning wounds. In both species, the brackets can reach **500 mm** across, and they can also be very thick, reaching up to **150 mm**, especially in *G. adspersum*. The upper surface of the brackets, which is rather lumpy and shows concentric growth increments, is covered with a hard, **brown crust** which is **matt**, and not varnish-like as in *G. pfeifferi* and *G. resinaceum*. In summer, this is often covered with a red-brown deposit of millions of spores which are released from the fine pores of the brownish tube layer underneath the bracket. When young, the pore surface is white and shows a dark brown mark if scratched, but it darkens to a dingy brownish-white with age. Successive pore surfaces develop with the incremental growth of the bracket, and appear as broad white margins during these periods of active growth. The flesh is thick and corky, with a silky texture when torn and is dark brown in colour. The brackets are perennial and can persist for many years. In many locations on the European continent, but only exceptionally in Great Britain, they develop warty or peg-like outgrowths developing from their undersides. These are galls produced by a fly, *Agathomyia wankowiczi*.

These *Ganoderma* species are sometimes confused with *Fomes fomentarius* which they resemble in general appearance, shape and texture, but the latter has pale flesh and white spores and is rather rare in southern Britain.

• *Decay*

In the early stages of decay, these species produce localised selective delignification as shown by a whitish mottling. This develops preferentially along the xylem rays, which in some host species can be delignified sufficiently to break up so that a radial cracking eventually develops. In very advanced decay, the lignin is almost totally degraded, leaving a spongy or fibrous mass of uniformly white, cellulose-rich material. The cellulose is also broken down to some extent, but in cases where the wood remains very moist, it can remain almost unaffected so that, in an extreme form studied in the temperate rainforests of Chile the resulting residue ('*palo blanco*') can contain as much as 97% cellulose and as little as 0.9% lignin [1]. The decay is surrounded by a dark coloured reaction zone, and this may in turn be surrounded by an irregular zone in which the wood appears sound but is somewhat drier than the adjoining functional sapwood. The zone of decay is often a central cone-shaped region, which extends upwards from the inner part of the root system. There may be narrow radial extensions outwards to points on the stem surface where fruit bodies are present.

• *Significance*

There is some evidence that living trees appear to be invaded more commonly by *G. applanatum* than by *G. adspersum*, but British records show no clear-cut difference between them in this respect [172]. On the European continent, however, *G. applanatum* is reported to occur mainly on dead stumps or on parts of trees previously invaded by other fungi [26].

As with any fungus that causes root- and butt-rot in living trees, decay by these *Ganoderma* species can cause mechanical failure of the stem base or root-plate. However, the partially decayed wood retains considerable tensile strength due to the fact that the decay involves selective delignification. For this reason, when failure occurs in stems infected by these fungi, the residual wall thickness of sound wood tends to be much less than the 30 – 35% of the stem radius which has been suggested as a minimum safety requirement for hollow trees [106]. It may take a great many years before the decayed zone becomes dangerously large in relation to the extent of sound wood, if ever, since the tree can produce compensatory growth of extra wood in response to the increased flexure caused by the decay. Some trees remain standing for many years while acting as hosts for these fungi, as shown by the considerable age of the perennial fruit bodies that they bear. Compensatory growth can result in a 'bottle-butt' symptom, and there may also be some distortion of the bark overlying the decayed zone.

Plate 60 Ganoderma pfeifferi, *young fruit body on* Fagus sylvatica

Plate 61 Ganoderma pfeifferi *decay in* Fagus sylvatica, *transverse section*

Ganoderma pfeifferi (Plates 60–61)

• *Hosts*

This fungus is quite common on *Fagus*. It has also been reported on *Quercus* but seems to be rare on that genus.

• *Fruit bodies*

The fruit bodies of *G. pfeifferi* are **woody, hoof-shaped or shelf-like brackets** which occur on stems and stumps, and which reach up to **300 cm** across and up to **80 mm** thick. The upper surface is **chestnut-brown** and **furrowed**, and is covered with a distinctly **varnish-like resinous layer** which melts in a match flame. This is, however, sometimes coated with a brownish spore deposit. The margin and lower surface, as in other *Ganoderma* species, are white while actively growing but turn **yellow** and resinous while maturing and then brown with **yellowish patches**. The flesh is woody in consistency, dark brown in colour and zoned towards the margin. As with *G. adspersum*, the brackets are **perennial** and grow by increments, so that well established specimens sometimes show a freshly formed whitish margin.

• *Decay*

The decay appears to involve localised selective delignification at first, as with other *Ganoderma* species, since it produces pale pockets of decay within areas of relatively sound wood. There is, however, a considerable amount of dark brown discoloration throughout the colonised region, in which the decayed pockets show up as straw-coloured spots and streaks.

• *Significance*

Although the fungus causes selective delignification, which generally has fairly mild effects on the strength of trees, it has been associated with windthrow of trees and with the breakage of limbs in cases where it has caused an aerial rot. There is also evidence that it can kill extensive areas of bark around places where it is present at the surface of the tree, and that it can even kill entire trees.

Plate 62 Ganoderma resinaceum

Plate 63 Ganoderma resinaceum, *decay*

Ganoderma resinaceum (Plates 62–63) and ***G. valesciacum***

• *Hosts*

In Great Britain, *G. resinaceum* occurs almost exclusively on *Quercus*. A rather similar species, *G. valesciacum*, occurs occasionally on conifers, including *Taxus*.

• *Fruit bodies*

Ganoderma resinaceum produces soft shelf-like brackets, **100 – 400 mm** across, at the bases of stems or on stumps. The upper surface is at first yellow and becomes **chestnut or blackish** with a distinctly **varnish-like resinous crust**, which cracks when pressed with the tip of a knife and melts in a match flame like that of *G. pfeifferi* but is less hard. The resinous surface may be obscured by a brown deposit of spores. The tubes, up to **30 mm** long, open on the underside via fine pores which are white when young. The tubes and the **thick corky flesh** are initially white, but soon become **pale brown** or **cinnamon-coloured**; not dark brown as with *G. adspersum* and *G. applanatum*. As with other *Ganoderma* species, there may be an actively growing whitish margin, but this usually seems not to be a perennial species even though it is reported to be relatively long-lived.

In the literature, reports of a *Ganoderma* species with a soft bracket-shaped fruit body with a varnished crust have often been attributed to another species, *G. lucidum* (Plate 64). However, *G. lucidum* is rare on standing trees and its

Plate 64 Ganoderma lucidum

bracket differs from that of *G. resinaceum* in having a distinct lateral **stalk**. It is also usually much smaller (50 – 280 mm across). Another stalked species with a varnished crust, *G. carnosum*, occurs mainly on conifers in continental Europe.

• *Decay*

The details of the decay process are not very well known for *G. resinaceum* but, like others of the genus, it can probably cause selective delignification. However, the destruction of the wood, including the cellulose content, appears to be more complete, since the residue is reported to consist largely of a soft plastic mat of white fungal material. However, in view of possible confusion with *G. lucidum*, this description of the decay may refer to the latter species, authenticated specimens of which have been associated with decay of a meringue-like consistency.

• *Significance*

The effects of decay by *G. resinaceum* on the strength of trees are probably rather more severe than in the case of other *Ganoderma* species, owing to the more complete degradation of cellulose. As the decay often extends from the roots some way into the trunk, either windthrow or stem breakage can result.

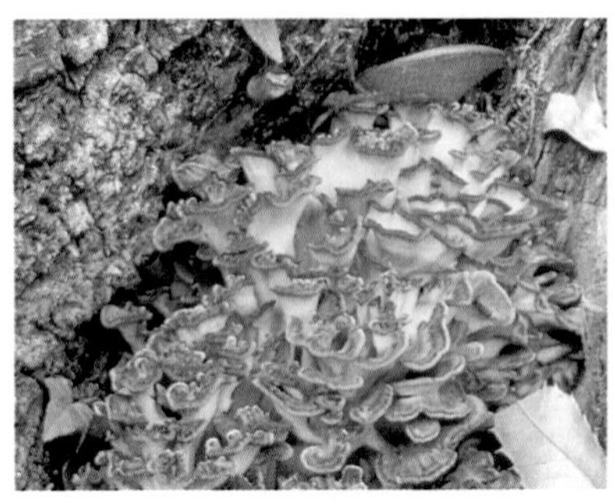

Plate 65 Grifola frondosa *at base of* Castanea sativa *(a young fruit body of* Fistulina hepatica *is also present above)*

Plate 66 Grifola frondosa, *decay in* Quercus *sp.*

Grifola frondosa, syn. *Polyporus frondosus* (Plates 65–66)

• *Hosts*

Grifola frondosa is virtually confined to *Quercus*.

• *Fruit bodies*

The fruit bodies are narrow, lobed, fan-like **fronds**, usually in a basal flute of the tree, which form dense tufts up to **260 cm** across. The individual fronds have a **grey-brown** colour above, often with a white margin, and are about 100 mm long, 50 mm wide and 20 mm thick at their smooth basal stalks. They broaden towards their tips, and are lobed and intricately recurved. Their pore-bearing under-surfaces are white, and **do not bruise dark** as in the sometimes rather similar *Meripilus giganteus*. The flesh is white, rather soft, and has a **mousey odour**. The fronds are not perennial and they soon decay after maturity. Another fungus which can be confused with *G. frondosa* is *Polyporus umbellatus*, but this has its fronds attached at a common point of origin, which is sometimes a black resting structure (a sclerotium).

• *Decay*

This is a stringy white-rot with orange lines, but recent work suggests that, like various other white-rot fungi, *G. frondosa* may invade the cell walls in a soft-rot mode during the early stages of decay [150]. It may therefore cause some loss of tensile strength before destroying the lignin. The affected wood is usually near and below ground level, and therefore rather inaccessible.

• *Significance*

Decay caused by *G. frondosa* appears to be seated in the central part of the root-plate and stem base, and this could weaken the anchorage of the tree.

Windthrow is, however, a rather uncommon type of mechanical failure in *Q. robur* and *Q. petraea*, and there is little case history which seems to implicate *G. frondosa*. If the fungus is found fruiting at the base of a tree of *Quercus* sp., the roots and stem base should be examined as far as is practicable to help determine the extent of the decay. If remedial work is required, crown reduction rather than felling may be a satisfactory option.

Plate 67 Heterobasidion annosum

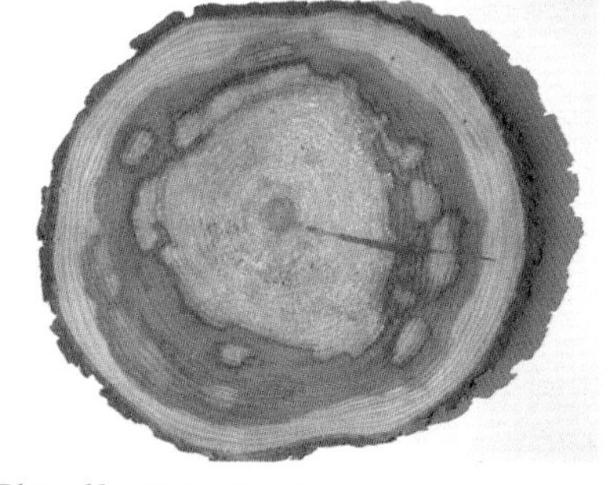

Plate 68 Heterobasidion annosum, *decay*

Heterobasidion annosum, syn. *Fomes annosus* (Plates 67–68)

• *Hosts*

This fungus occurs on a wide range of coniferous and broadleaved genera. In forests it is particularly common on *Pinus* and *Picea*, but in amenity plantings it has most often been reported on *Betula* and *Fagus*.

• *Fruit bodies*

The fruit bodies are tough, **rubbery or leathery brackets**, typically **10 – 20 cm** across, though sometimes ranging between 2 and 40 cm. Their upper surfaces are **brown and corrugated**, often with a zonate pattern. Their under-surfaces are **creamy white** and bear fine, closely spaced pores. The brackets are found at the base of the stem or on superficial roots, and are often covered by leaf or needle litter which they sometimes envelop as they expand. They are perennial.

• *Decay*

The decay begins in roots which have first been killed by the parasitic action of the fungus on the bark and cambium. Infection of the roots occurs via close contact with those of a neighbouring infected tree or stump. Initially, stumps of still-living trees are almost always the source of the infection, as their freshly cut surfaces provide the main sites for entry of the fungus in the form of germinating basidiospores. Progression of the fungus into the roots of the stumps allows subsequent root-to-root transmission.

The decay is a selective delignification in which cellulose is not degraded until a fairly advanced stage. Thus, the tensile strength of the wood is preserved for a considerable time, during which there is a loss of stiffness and a delamination (ungluing of cell wall components) due to the degradation of lignin. The delamination begins either between the S_2 and S_3 layers of the secondary cell wall, or between the individual cells, depending on the conditions within the wood [152]. At this early stage, the infected wood shows a grey to violet streaking, followed by the formation of reddish brown patches of decay containing small, scattered, white, spindle-shaped pockets as delignification progresses. Black flecks, which are deposits of an oxide of manganese, may also appear as a by-product of enzymatic activity, as in selective delignification by various other fungi [14]. Later, when cellulose is degraded, the wood disintegrates into a fibrous decay, and the destruction can become total, perhaps due to the activity of other micro-organisms, so that the stem can become hollow except for rot-resistant resinous knots in the case of certain coniferous hosts.

Active sapwood or highly resinous wood has some resistance to invasion [54] and invasion by the fungus within the living tree is restricted mainly to zones of ripewood or non-durable heartwood. The resulting shape and extent of the resulting decay columns vary according to the species and age of the tree concerned. For example, Scots pine (*Pinus sylvestris*), in contrast to spruce species, rarely shows extensive decay in the stem unless the tree is quite old, even when many of the roots have been killed due to parasitic invasion by the fungus.

• *Significance*

The delamination and loss of stiffness that occur in the early stages of decay produce a stringy rot which can result in a ductile bending fracture of the stem base. If decay progresses to extensive cavity formation, the stem may buckle due to cross-sectional flattening [106], but this still results in a ductile fracture owing to the stringy texture of the partially decayed zone surrounding the cavity. This kind of fracture gives advance warning in the form of bark distortion due to increased flexure, and occurs much less abruptly than brittle fracture. In open-grown situations, a bottle-butt symptom may develop in response to the increased flexure, and there may be sufficient extra wood laid down to provide an acceptable safety margin. This fungus is more troublesome as a killer of trees (or as a degrader of coniferous timber) than as a cause of windthrow or stem failure.

Plate 69 Hypholoma fasciculare

Hypholoma fasciculare*; the sulphur tuft (Plate 69)

• *Hosts*

This extremely common fungus has a very wide host range, especially among broadleaved trees, but is mainly confined to dead or dying trees and stumps.

• *Fruit bodies*

These are rather fragile **toadstools** which develop in clusters. Individual caps can measure **65 mm** or more in diameter, but more often measure less than **50 mm**, and are thus much smaller than those of honey fungus with which this fungus is often confused. Also, the cap colour is a **pale yellow**, often with a darker centre, and the gills are sulphur-yellow, maturing to **green**, later purplish brown. The stem, unlike that of honey fungus, does not bear a distinct collar-like ring, but sometimes shows a faint ring-like zone. The similar *H. capnoides* has a brownish-yellow cap and is mainly restricted to conifer stumps. The soft, non-persistent toadstools are most common in the autumn, but also occur at other times of year.

• *Decay*

Little is known about the type of decay, but *H. fasciculare* is capable of occupying large volumes of wood in dead root systems.

• *Significance*

In living trees, these *Hypholoma* species are not usually associated with serious decay, but they can cause windthrow of dead trees.

Plate 70 Inonotus dryadeus *on* Quercus ilex

Inonotus dryadeus syn. *Polyporus dryadeus, Phellinus dryadeus* (Plate 70)

• *Hosts*

The hosts of this fungus are various species of *Quercus*, and it is common on the native British members of this genus.

• *Fruit bodies*

The fruit body is a **soft, thick, lumpy bracket**, and its site of occurrence is almost invariably at the base of a large, old tree or stump. It measures up to **300 mm** across and **80 mm** thick. A few brackets sometimes occur together in an overlapping group. The upper surface has a thin cuticle, which is initially **yellowish** and wrinkled and later becomes smooth and rusty brown. The underside bears small whitish pores, and the flesh and tubes are **rusty brown**. The consistency of the flesh is soft at first, later becoming corky and then brittle with age. When fresh, the margin of the fruit body invariably exudes drops of a **watery golden liquid** from small round depressions on its surface. These dry up when the fruit body ages, but the depressions may persist. The bracket is not perennial, and several years may elapse before a new one appears on an infected tree. Fruiting occurs from May and December and the bracket gradually decomposes during the winter.

• *Decay*

The early stages of decay have not been described in detail, but appear to involve a localised selective delignification, as indicated by the formation of irregular yellowish stripes within a surrounding zone of dark water-soaked wood. The yellowish stripes gradually enlarge and become paler, until the whole zone of decay becomes a soft, filamentous or flaky mass containing thick sheets of white mycelium. The decay seems to start in the inner part of the root system and can extend into the stem base, though never more than 2 metres above soil level, and remaining confined to the central wood.

• *Significance*

In the most advanced stages, the wood is seriously weakened, although it probably retains some of its tensile strength for a considerable time in the earlier stages, due to the relative preservation of cellulose in the process of selective delignification. If the zone of advanced decay becomes extensive, windthrow can occur, but there is little 'casebook' evidence to suggest that this is common. On the other hand, it can be very difficult to detect decay caused by this fungus, even when the innermost roots are severely affected. This difficulty arises when, as is often the case, the decay extends only slightly if at all into the stem base or into the buttresses. The absence of fruit bodies is also a cause of the decay being overlooked. If decay is detected in a 'high risk' location, then every effort should be made to determine its extent, and to carry out remedial action such as crown reduction if significant anchorage has been lost [106].

Despite concern over the tendency for decay caused by this fungus to be overlooked, some trees affected by it have remained standing for many years, even when the stem base and central roots have decayed to the stage where the tree is supported only on a shell of stilt-like peripheral roots. It is, however, very important at high-risk sites to investigate the condition of the apparently sound roots, in case they are decayed below ground level only.

Plate 71 Inonotus hispidus, *fresh fruit body on* Fraxinus excelsior

Plate 72 Inonotus hispidus, *old fruit body on* Fraxinus excelsior

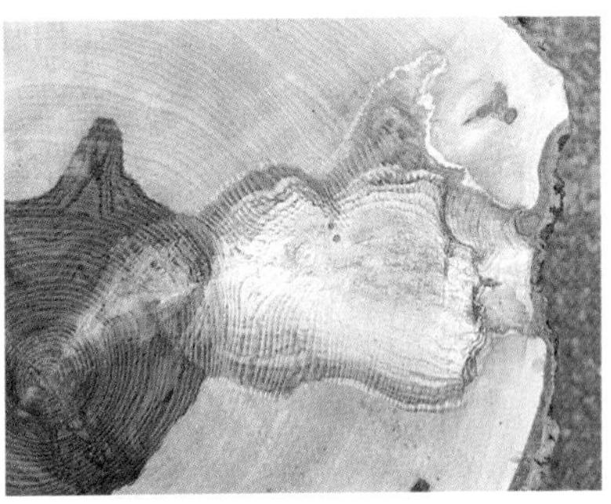

Plate 73 Inonotus hispidus, *decay in stem of* Fraxinus excelsior, *showing extension into younger wood and cambium (canker rot)*

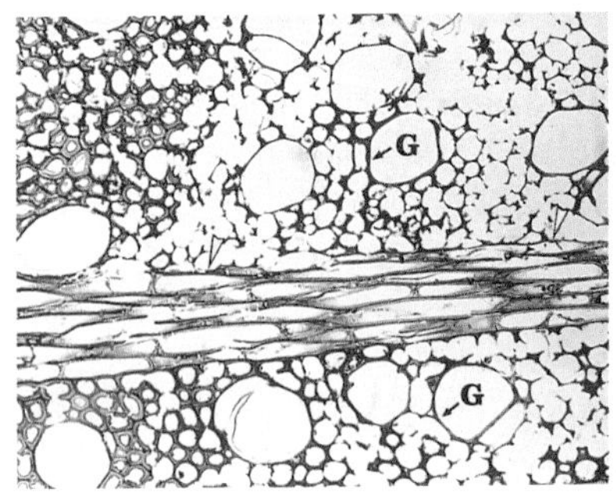

Plate 74 Inonotus hispidus *in wood of* Platanus x hispanica *(transverse section); walls of vessels ('G') and fibres are partly degraded, xylem ray cells (running across picture) remain intact*

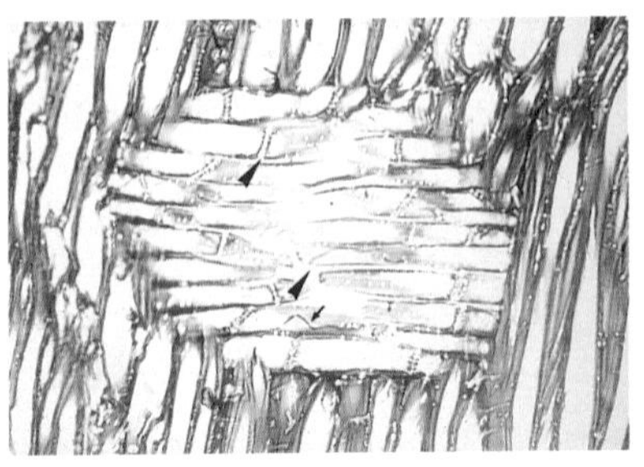

Plate 75 Inonotus hispidus *in wood of* Fraxinus excelsior *(radial section); the xylem rays are degraded at an early stage of colonisation, in contrast to those of* Platanus

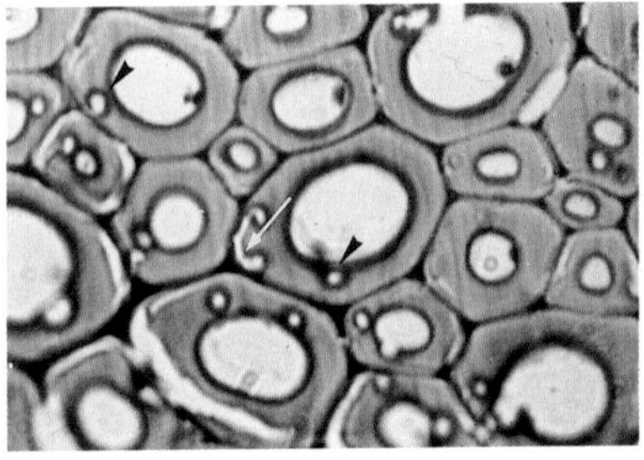

Plate 76 Inonotus hispidus *in* Fraxinus excelsior*; soft rot cavities are visible in the cell walls of the fibres. The tunnel-like cavities run parallel to the cellulose microfibrils, so that those in the S_1 layer (white arrow) are cut obliquely in this transverse section of the wood, while those in the S_2 layer (black arrowheads) have a circular appearance*

Inonotus hispidus, syn. *Polyporus hispidus* (Plates 71–76)

• *Hosts*

Inonotus hispidus is the most frequent decay fungus in *Fraxinus excelsior* and *Platanus* x *hispanica* in Britain and is also found on other broadleaved hosts, including *Malus*, *Juglans*, *Ulmus* and *Acer pseudoplatanus*.

• *Fruit bodies*

The fleshy bracket measures **6 – 35 cm** across and **2 – 10 cm** deep. The slightly domed upper surface is initially **orange-rust** in colour and covered with short, densely matted hairs, but soon darkens to become **black and rather bristly**. The more-or-less flat pore-bearing under-surface, together with the flesh and the tubes, is similarly coloured. The fruit bodies develop on the trunk or major branches, sometimes emerging from wounds, but are more often associated with depressed strips of tissue, where the fungus has caused a canker as well as decaying the wood. They are sometimes found exuding drops of liquid, which is thought to be a possible mechanism of drying the underlying wood to a moisture content that favours fungal development. Although the fruit bodies are not perennial, they can appear from May to February and sometimes persist for some months in a black desiccated or putrescent state after death.

• *Decay*

This fungus can destroy both lignin and cellulose at roughly equal rates and has therefore been classed as a cause of a simultaneous white-rot. This type of rot results in a fairly brittle fracture, owing to the loss of both tensile and compressive strength. However, in common with certain other white-rot fungi, it can degrade cellulose preferentially in the early stages of its invasion of fibres and tracheids [151], in a soft-rot pattern which results mainly in the loss of tensile strength. By contrast, in its white-rot mode, it can cause a certain amount of selective delignification in the compound middle lamellae between cells, thus causing the cells to separate.

The effects of decay by *I. hispidus* vary greatly according to the nature of the wood that is being invaded, so that the incidence of mechanical failure varies between host species. The fungus has a relatively poor ability to utilise heavily lignified cells, and these are degraded only at a late stage of decay. This effect is seen particularly in the xylem rays of *P.* x *hispanica*, which are mechanically very strong and probably provide the high resistance to axial splitting that is typical of timber of this tree [107]. In the wood of *F. excelsior*, the rays are much less heavily lignified and are rapidly weakened in a way which allows their cells to pull apart easily [146]. In any case, the wood of this species has only about half the ray content of the wood of *P.* x *hispanica*, and therefore has relatively poor radial strength even when decay by *I. hispidus* is not very advanced. This allows splitting to occur, as observed in infected timber that has been allowed to dry [30, 121].

Failure in standing trees of *F. excelsior* seems to result from the combined effects of splitting, and the kinking of the early-wood fibres, which are affected by a simultaneous white-rot at an early stage of invasion, and therefore lose both tensile and compressive strength. Mechanical failure in trunks and branches of *P.* x *hispanica* invaded by *I. hispidus* is rare except when decay has become advanced to the point of very extensive cavity formation. Failure at this stage is thought to involve shell-buckling of the hollow cross-section [106].

This fungus appears to be relatively successful at breaching the active defences of the host tree. In *P.* x *hispanica* it can, at least for a while, be confined within a reaction zone which forms in the sapwood. This zone contains gummy deposits which block the lumina of vessels and fibres, thus deterring the development of fungal hyphae whose enzymes could otherwise degrade the cell walls. The fungus can, however, grow across reaction zones by switching to its soft-rot mode, in which its hyphae grow within the cell walls [151]. This probably happens during host dormancy when defences are not very active. Also, the ability of *I. hispidus* to cause a canker as well as decay allows it to invade wood formed after the initiation of infection. This means that the barrier zone (see Section 3.4.3) is not totally effective in preventing the outward spread of decay, although this zone tends to be breached only in the immediate vicinity of the canker.

• *Significance*

Since *I. hispidus* weakens the wood of *F. excelsior* at a early stage of decay, its presence on this species, and perhaps also on walnut, often indicates that breakage of the affected branch or trunk could be imminent. In Britain, the fungus is commonly found in hedgerow and on roadside trees of *F. excelsior*. Also, products made from infected timber of *F. excelsior*, such as the handles of tools and sports equipment are liable to fracture. The presence of the fungus in timber may not be obvious in the early stages of decay. In *P.* x *hispanica*, the early stages of decay do not seriously weaken branches or trunks. Even when decay has advanced to the stage of cavity formation, the strength of the surrounding sound wood is usually sufficient to provide adequate safety, although its extent should nevertheless be assessed.

Inonotus obliquus, syn. *Poria obliqua*

• *Hosts*

This fungus occurs on *Betula* in north-east Scotland, but is rare elsewhere in Britain.

• *Fruit bodies*

There are two kinds of fruit body; sterile and fertile. The sterile fruit body is a **tumour-like, perennating black mass** which forms on the trunk or a main branch. It is deeply cracked, and can reach up to **400 mm** across. It plays a part in preventing the host tree from forming occlusion tissues over the wound where infection was initiated. The fertile fruit body, which develops when the tree dies, forms a pore-bearing layer under the bark. Both types of fruit body can be found throughout the year.

• *Decay*

The decay does not appear to have been studied in detail, but it is known to cause a brittle fracture.

• *Significance*

Inonotus obliquus is a canker-rot fungus owing to its ability to prevent new wood and bark from forming around the infection site. This means that its decay near this point is fairly unrestricted and therefore likely to cause stem breakage.

Plate 77 Laetiporus sulphureus; *fresh fruit body on* Quercus robur

Plate 78 Laetiporus sulphureus, *old, bleached fruit body on* Robinia pseudoacacia

Plate 79 Laetiporus sulphureus, *decay in* Quercus robur

***Laetiporus sulphureus*; chicken-of-the-woods** or **sulphur polypore** (Plates 77–79)

• *Hosts*

Laetiporus sulphureus occurs on a range of both broadleaved and coniferous trees, but is particularly common on *Quercus*, *Castanea* and *Taxus*. In the last named species it is by far the commonest decay fungus. Another quite frequent host is *Robinia pseudoacacia*.

• *Fruit bodies*

The fruit bodies consist of **brackets or fronds** with wavy margins, which occur either singly or in overlapping groups ranging from **10 – 30 cm** across. The young fronds sometimes exude a pale yellowish juice from their upper surfaces. When fresh, the fronds are bright **yellow**, or occasionally orange, and are somewhat darker above than below. They soon fade with age to a **dull cream or whitish** colour. Occasionally, old fronds may develop a brownish discoloration. The **tubes** are very short, opening at small rounded pores which become torn with age. The flesh in young yellow fronds is soft and cheesy in texture, but becomes dry and fragile in old, bleached specimens. The fruit bodies are not perennial, but often persist into the winter as dry, faded remains following their development during May to November.

• *Decay*

The earliest stages of fungal development may be inconspicuous, since the entry of hyphae of *L. sulphureus* into wood cells can be followed by the formation of resting spores; one spore per cell [146], with no further cell wall degradation until the moisture regime on the wood becomes suitable for active fungal growth. In the early stages of decay a yellow or red discoloration develops in the wood, and this changes to a rich red-brown as the decay advances. In advanced decay, the wood develops cubical cracking and is very brittle. A **yellowish or whitish leathery sheet** of fungal mycelium often fills the cracks. Decay is usually confined to the heartwood, which it enters via pruning wounds or broken branches. In some cases, it is found in the stem base and in major roots. The fungus develops slowly and may persist for many years in old stumps.

• *Significance*

Eventually, a large proportion of the wood in the main stem or in the roots tends to be decayed by this fungus, leading to snapping or windthrow. In trunks, the undecayed sapwood can provide a sound outer shell, but this is often too narrow to provide adequate support, especially in the case of *R. pseudoacacia*, in which the sapwood band is particularly narrow. The fungus can therefore cause a serious hazard, although trees may remain relatively safe for many years until decay becomes extensive. It can also cause problems in structural timbers, probably because its resting spores can survive the dry conditions that occur when the timber is seasoned.

Lenzites betulina

• *Hosts*

This fungus grows on dead parts of a wide range of trees, most frequently on *Betula*.

• *Fruit bodies*

These are brackets which reach up to **200 mm** across. Their uppersides are a pale grey, and bear **short woolly hairs**. Underneath, there are gill-like plates rather than pores, but there are cross-connections which can sometimes produce a maze-like effect, as in *Daedalea quercina*.

• *Decay*

The decay is a white-rot, particularly affecting the xylem rays [31].

• *Significance*

This fungus is found mainly on fallen wood or stumps and, although commonly found, is of little significance for tree safety.

Plate 80 Meripilus giganteus *at base of* Fagus sylvatica

Plate 81 Meripilus giganteus *at base of* Fagus sylvatica, *showing a growth form different to that in Plate 80. (The fungus fruiting on the left is possibly a* Ganoderma *sp.)*

***Meripilus giganteus*; giant polypore** (Plates 80–81)

• *Hosts*

Meripilus giganteus is found mainly on *Fagus*, but also occurs rarely on other broadleaved trees such as *Quercus* and *Platanus* x *hispanica*, and on conifers such as *Araucaria araucana*.

• *Fruit bodies*

The fruit bodies consist of a mass of **overlapping fronds**, each **10 – 20 cm** wide, which may collectively measure **60 cm or more** across. They are found mainly at the bases of trees or on stumps, usually developing from below ground-level, and often appearing on the ground above decayed roots at some distance from the stem base. When fresh, the upper surfaces are **brownish-yellow** to **chestnut-brown** with a paler margin. The surface texture is scurfy and granular. The undersides are **whitish, bruising black**, a colour change which distinguishes this fungus from the rather similar *Grifola frondosa*, and bear numerous very small angular or irregular pores, at which the tubes, also whitish at first but later darkening, emerge. The consistency of the flesh is soft, becoming somewhat leathery in maturity. A strong, unpleasant smell develops on drying. The fruit bodies, which form from July to January, are not perennial and are killed by severe frost, becoming black and slimy, although they can persist for some time in sheltered locations.

• *Decay*

This is one of several white-rot fungi which have been shown to colonise the woody cell walls in a soft-rot mode under certain conditions or in the early stages of decay. This form of degradation, in which the wood attains a brownish colour, produces a fairly brittle consistency due to the selective destruction of cellulose, but the fungus also has a strong ability to degrade pectin. Since pectin helps to 'glue' the wood cells together, its degradation renders the wood liable to split apart. There can also be fracture across the grain from cellulose degradation in the soft-rot mode. Progression of the decay is marked by the appearance of pockets of white-rot, followed by cavity formation due to the total destruction of wood.

• *Significance*

By the time that large fruit bodies of *M. giganteus* appear, especially on *F. sylvatica*, it is likely that a high chance of windthrow exists. Crown symptoms may be present by this stage, but by no means always. Indeed, the upper roots may be largely sound, even though the deeper ones are extensively decayed. Due to this pattern of symptom development, and to the severe weakening of the partially decayed wood, *M. giganteus* is one of the most dangerous decay fungi to be found on *F. sylvatica*. The mechanical effects of its decay on other hosts are not documented.

Plate 82 Oudemansiella mucida *on* Fagus sylvatica

***Oudemansiella mucida*; the beech tuft or porcelain fungus** (Plate 82)

• *Hosts*

This fungus occurs on *Fagus sylvatica*, perhaps more in woodlands than amongst urban plantings.

• *Fruit bodies*

The fruit body is a **toadstool**, **3 – 9 cm** across, which grows on stems or branches and not on the ground. The cap is borne on a central stalk which can be up to 100 cm long and bears a large pendulous **ring**. The entire fruit body has a glistening white appearance, although the stalk may have a greyish tinge. The top of the cap is coated with a **slimy mucilage**. The underside consists of broad, widely spaced, white gills. The flesh is thin and mucilaginous. The fruit bodies, which are edible, often form high on a tree. Although the toadstools are not persistent, they have been observed at various times of year.

• *Decay*

In the early stages of decay, this fungus has been shown to develop in a soft-rot mode, at least in artificially inoculated wood blocks [37]. Advanced decay seems to occur only slowly, and is a yellow-tinged white-rot in which cellulose and lignin are both degraded. The decaying wood contains **orange** zone-lines, which are composed of aggregated hyphae in a gummy matrix. The decay appears to affect branch wood more than wood in large stems.

• *Significance*

There is little evidence of major tree failure associated with decay by *O. mucida*, perhaps reflecting a tendency for the fungus to colonise only a small volume of wood. Nevertheless, the presence of the fruit bodies on a major branch or trunk indicates the need for detailed inspection.

Plate 83 Perenniporia fraxinea

Perenniporia fraxinea, syn. *Fomitopsis cytisina* (Plate 83)

• *Hosts*

This fungus is rather rare in Great Britain, but occurs on a wide range of broadleaved hosts, including *Fraxinus*, *Robinia*, *Laburnum*, *Ulmus*, *Platanus* x *hispanica*, *Populus* and *Fagus*.

• *Fruit bodies*

The fruit body is a **hard, woody bracket** which most commonly forms on the stem base of the host. It is whitish when young but becomes dark brown or blackish in maturity, when it reaches as much as 400 mm across. The tubes and flesh are both **pale fawn or yellowish**, and this similarity of colour distinguishes the fungus from the otherwise similar *Rigidoporus ulmarius* (Plate 95). The bracket is perennial.

• *Decay*

This fungus causes an intense white-rot in the advanced stages, culminating in cavity formation. The partially decayed wood has a rather brittle fracture.

• *Significance*

The zone of advanced decay can become large enough to cause stem breakage.

Plate 84 Phaeolus schweinitzii

Plate 85 Phaeolus schweinitzii *decay, longitudinal section*

Phaeolus schweinitzii (Plates 84–85)

• *Hosts*

This fungus occurs on various conifers, especially *Pinus*, *Pseudotsuga menziesii*, *Picea sitchensis*, *Larix* and *Cedrus*. *Taxus baccata* is an occasional host in Great Britain.

• *Fruit bodies*

The fruit body can occur as a **more or less circular pileus** when growing on top of a stump or on the ground near a decayed root. When growing laterally from the stem base of tree, it can appear as a short-stalked or stalkless **bracket**. Individual fruit bodies reach **100 – 30 cm** across, and can sometimes overlap and unite. The **upper surface** is mainly dark brown with a reddish felty covering and, in young specimens, the **margin is golden yellow**. The tubes and pores of the under-surface are **greenish-yellow** and turn **dark brown when bruised**. The pores are rounded at first, and become oblong-labyrinthine. The flesh is a deep rusty brown and is soft and spongy, although hardening when old and dry. The fruit bodies form during May to October and persist only as dead, blackened remains at other times of year.

• *Decay*

The decay begins in the roots, where a primary infection by honey fungus (*Armillaria* sp.) appears to pave the way for colonisation [8]. A brown-rot develops in the heartwood and this can extend as much as 6 – 8 m up the stem in *P. menziesii*, but usually far less in *Pinus* spp. The decayed wood has the typical cubical cracking of a brown-rot and also has a smell of turpentine. The shrinkage cracks in the wood are lined with a chalky or fluffy coating of yellowish or creamy-white fungal material.

• *Significance*

The brown-rot in the decayed wood leads to brittle fracture of the stem or to root-plate failure due to the severe loss of tensile strength. In hazard assessments, the decayed zone should be regarded as having a weakening effect similar to a cavity of the same extent. The fungus is not very common in amenity trees, although it is a common cause of butt and stem rot in conifer plantations established on sites previously occupied by broadleaved species.

Plate 86 Phellinus igniarius

Phellinus igniarius (Plate 86)

• *Hosts*

The main host of this fungus in Great Britain, where it is rather rare, is *Salix* but it also occurs on other broadleaved genera.

• *Fruit bodies*

The fruit body is a **very hard, woody hoof-shaped bracket** with a greyish black upper surface. It has a fawn coloured edge when growing, and measures up to **200 mm** across. The bracket, which is perennial, is sometimes confused with that of *Fomes fomentarius*.

• *Decay*

The decay is a soft-textured white-rot, surrounded by a zone of yellowish-green or dark discoloration, and contains dark zone-lines.

• *Significance*

The decay usually occurs in the main stem, and can lead to fracture if it becomes very extensive.

Plate 87 Phellinus tuberculosus *on* Prunus *sp.*

Phellinus tuberculosus, syn. *Phellinus pomaceus, Fomes pomaceus* (Plate 87)

• *Hosts*

This fungus occurs on various rosaceous trees, and has not been reported from trees in other families. It is quite common on some types of *Prunus*, including *P. domestica* and *P. cerasifera*.

• *Fruit bodies*

The fruit body is **hard**, **woody**, and can be a hoof-shaped **bracket** with a thick base, or **resupinate**, i.e., forming a laycr appressed to the bark of the host stem. An intermediate form is also common. When a distinct bracket forms, it grows to about **50 mm** across, whereas the resupinate form is about **10 mm** thick. The upper surface, when present, is an ashy grey when young, becoming brownish-grey later. The surface on which the **minute pores** are borne is also ashy at first, but becomes a **dark cinnamon-brown** in maturity. The bracket is perennial.

• *Decay*

There is some evidence that the fungus develops in a soft-rot mode during the early stages of colonisation [150], perhaps within the zone of incipient decay, which forms a dark purplish-brown border, 10 – 20 mm wide, around the zone of advanced decay in the centre of an affected branch or stem. The dark material appears to be a gummy deposit formed by an active response of the sapwood, and is later degraded by the fungus as the decay extends. The heartwood is also degraded, despite the presence of pre-formed defensive materials (extractives). The advanced decay is a crumbly white-rot.

• *Significance*

This fungus is a common cause of decay in rosaceous trees, especially in orchard crops which have received large pruning wounds or which have suffered branch breakages. The decay often leads to breakage, since much of the stem cross-section can be severely weakened.

Plate 88 Pholiota squarrosa *on* Tilia *sp.*

Pholiota squarrosa; the shaggy pholiota (Plate 88)

- *Hosts*

This fungus is found on various broadleaved trees, especially *Sorbus aucuparia.*

- *Fruit bodies*

These are **fleshy toadstools**, which form in **clusters** at the stem base of the host. The caps, which reach **50 – 120 mm**, are **pale ochre** to **yellowish-rusty** in colour and carry conspicuous, dark brown, recurved **scales**, which are most dense at the centre. The stems are similarly coloured and are also conspicuously scaly. Each stem bears a tattered ring just below the cap, but no volva. The gills are yellowish at first, becoming rust-coloured at maturity as the brown spores form. The toadstools form mainly in the autumn and are soft and non-persistent.

• *Decay*

The decay occurs mostly near the base of the tree; it does not appear to have been described in detail.

• *Significance*

This fungus has been found to cause a serious butt rot of *Populus* in North America, but its significance in Britain is uncertain. Some observations indicate that it can grow and form toadstools on the bark of *Fraxinus excelsior* without doing any harm to the wood. However, its presence warrants a close examination of the tree for other indications of decay or root killing.

Plate 89 Piptoporus betulinus

Plate 90 Piptoporus betulinus*; brittle snap of decayed stem*

Piptoporus betulinus, syn. *Polyporus betulinus*; **razor-strop fungus** or **birch polypore** (Plates 89–90)

• *Hosts*

This fungus is almost entirely confined to *Betula*, on which it is the main decay fungus in southern Britain. In the north, it is partly 'replaced' in this rôle by *Fomes fomentarius*. It has also been reported from *Fagus sylvatica*.

• *Fruit bodies*

The fruit bodies are **soft, smooth**, kidney- or hoof-shaped **brackets**, **75 – 200 mm** across and **15 – 35 mm** thick, which normally occur singly on the main stem or larger branches, although several are often present at various points on the tree. When young, the bracket is a knob-like structure with a smooth, bare upper surface consisting of a thin, skin-like covering. As the bracket expands, it sometimes develops a short stalk, and its covering layer becomes leathery and often somewhat cracked, while darkening to a **pale shade of grey or brown** with a slight silvery sheen. The upperside curves downward to form a lateral margin which projects below the tube-bearing underside. The tubes and their **small, round pores** are whitish, becoming darker in maturity. The flesh is soft at first, becoming corky with a firm, uniform consistency which makes it suitable for cutting into sheets which are used for pin-mounting small insects in museum collections. It has in the past also been used for sharpening knives (hence the common name) and as tinder and as a styptic and antiseptic. The brackets are not perennial, but persist for several months following their formation in May to January.

• *Decay*

A brown-rot is caused in the sapwood, which first shows a reddish brown discoloration, progressing to a cubical rot and eventually to a friable disintegration of the wood. Invasion is often associated with broken branches or pruning wounds, but it also seems possible that the fungus may develop after primary infection by *Chondrostereum purpureum*, the silver-leaf fungus [110].

• *Significance*

By the time that a tree bears fruit bodies of this fungus, it is usually in a state of irreversible decline, invariably due to other causes such as drought stress, fire damage or infection by a primary pathogen such as *Chondrostereum purpureum*. Either before or soon after death, brittle fracture occurs due to the severe brown-rot occupying much of the stem cross-section. Prompt felling of affected trees is necessary in all sites where mechanical failure would be a hazard.

Plate 91 Pleurotus ostreatus *on dead stem of* Fagus sylvatica

***Pleurotus ostreatus*; oyster mushroom** (Plate 91)

• *Hosts*

This fungus is common on a wide range of broadleaved hosts, including *Fagus*, *Aesculus* and *Populus*.

• *Fruit bodies*

The fruit body, is a **soft, fleshy, fan-** or **shell-shaped pileus**, up to **150 mm** across and up to **25 mm** thick. It is sometimes borne laterally on a stem, 2 – 4 cm long. When developing, the upper surface of the cap is a very dark bluish grey, maturing to a pale greyish-brown or fawn colour, sometimes with the formation of cracks in the cuticle. With age, a yellowish colour develops. The underside consists of **white gills**, which run down to the base, where they tend to join together. (Despite the presence of gills, rather than pores, this fungus belongs taxonomically among the pore-bearing basidiomycetes.) The flesh, which is edible, is white and soft in the young fruit body and becomes firm on drying. The fruit bodies are non-persistent and are formed mainly in **late autumn and winter**, but also at other times throughout the year.

• *Decay*

In the early stages, delignification occurs preferentially in the spring wood, with relatively little effect on the middle lamellae between the fibres and in the xylem rays [93]. In *Populus*, a marked cracking across the grain develops at a stage when the wood remains generally firm, perhaps because the rays are easily degraded in this genus. In the advanced stages of decay, an intense white-rot with a flaky consistency is produced throughout. A dark brown discoloration is observed at the boundary between decayed wood and living sapwood.

• *Significance*

Severely decayed wood has relatively little strength, owing to the rapid degradation of both lignin and cellulose, with the corresponding loss of both compressive and tensile strength. The nature of strength loss in the earlier stages of decay has not been documented. If extensive areas of a branch or trunk become decayed, breakage is likely. However, as in the case of *Polyporus squamosus*, the decay seems sometimes to be localised within the part of the trunk or branch cross-section which was damaged by the initial event (e.g. branch breakage, vehicular impacts or lopping) which allowed the decay to develop.

Plate 92 Polyporus squamosus *on* Ulmus *sp.*

Plate 93 Polyporus squamosus*; decay in stem of* Ulmus

***Polyporus squamosus*; dryad's saddle, scaly polypore** (Plates 92–93)

• *Hosts*

This fungus occurs on several genera of broadleaved trees, including *Acer* (especially *A. pseudoplatanus*), *Fagus*, *Ulmus*, *Fraxinus* and *Tilia*.

• *Fruit bodies*

The fruit body is a **soft, fleshy**, fan-shaped or semi-circular **bracket, 100 – 400 mm** across, with a short, stout, **laterally attached stem**. The upper surface of the cap is characterised by a covering of **dark brown scales** on an ochre-yellow or straw-coloured background. The density of the scales is greatest at the centre. The **pores** on the under-surface are large and angular and are whitish or cream-coloured and extend on to the apex of the stem. At this point, the stem is pale in colour, but is **black** towards the base. Fruiting, which often takes place annually at the same site on the tree or stump, occurs mainly in late summer, after which the brackets soon decompose.

• *Decay*

In the early stages of colonisation, the fungus causes very little structural alteration of the wood, and probably establishes itself by utilising soluble nutrients from the sapwood cells [146]. The decay is an intense white-rot of the sapwood or ripewood, progressing eventually to cavity formation. The cavities are characteristically lined with a brown, felt-like mass of mycelium. The decayed wood contains dark 'zone lines' (pseudosclerotial plates). The decayed zone usually seems not to extend beyond the region of dysfunction that was associated with the injury or zone of dieback that initiated the development of the fungus. Thus, although it can occupy the entire cross-section of a trunk that has been topped, or of a felling stump, it often occupies a distinct cone of decay associated with an individual pruning wound.

• *Significance*

Wood in an advanced stage of decay by this fungus has very little tensile or compressive strength, and can therefore fail if the affected stem has less than one third of its radius occupied by sound or incipiently decayed wood. Such extensive decay is, however, mainly confined to trees which have been topped or damaged by excessively large or numerous pruning wounds or storm breakage. In many cases, fruit bodies of the fungus develop from zones of decay which are too restricted to pose a serious hazard.

Plate 94 Pseudotrametes gibbosa

Pseudotrametes gibbosa (Plate 94)

• *Hosts*

This fungus occurs on a wide range of hosts, but more often on dead stumps and timber than on living trees. *Fagus sylvatica* is one of most frequently colonised species.

• *Fruit bodies*

These are **firm, corky** brackets, up to **180 mm** in diameter, and are whitish when young, becoming a pale grey or buff when mature, and often characteristically bear bright green patches of algae. The base of the bracket is domed and its margin is usually rounded in profile, though sometimes forming a thin horizontal extension to the fruiting tissue. Underneath, the **regular**, radially elongated, **whitish pores** are **straight** and of equal length. The fruit bodies are found throughout the year.

• *Decay*

This is known to be a white rot, but does not appear to have been described in detail.

• *Significance*

Perhaps due to a limited ability to invade living trees, *P. gibbosa* is not documented as a cause of structural failure.

Plate 95 Rigidoporus ulmarius *on stump of* Ulmus *sp.*

Rigidoporus ulmarius (Plate 95)

• *Hosts*

The main host in Great Britain used to be *Ulmus*, on which the fungus was quite common. Due to the loss of most large elms in the Dutch elm disease epidemic, it has become fairly rare but occurs occasionally on other hosts, including *Acer*, *Quercus* and *Populus*.

• *Fruit bodies*

The fruit body, which usually develops near the stem base, is a **thick, woody bracket**, reaching up to **300 mm** across, with a whitish or cream-coloured upper surface which is usually discoloured green by algal growth in old specimens. The tubes are **cinnamon-coloured**, in contrast to the **pale flesh** and this contrast of colour distinguishes the fungus from the similar *Perenniporia fraxinea* (Plate 83). The bracket is perennial.

• *Decay*

The decay caused by *R. ulmarius* is a friable brown-rot, with cubical cracking. This is usually confined to the central region of the buttress zone of the tree.

• *Significance*

The loss of tensile strength due to the brown-rot can lead to windthrow if the rot is extensive.

Plate 96 Schizophyllum commune

***Schizophyllum commune*; the 'split gill'** (Plate 96)

• *Hosts*

This fungus has a wide host range, but occurs mainly on dead trees and stumps. When it colonises living trees they are often thin-barked species, such as *Fagus sylvatica*, which have been damaged by sun-scorch or fire. It sometimes occurs together with *Coriolus hirsuta*.

• *Fruit bodies*

These are **thin, frond-like** structures which usually occur in dense clusters on bark or wood. They each measure **20 – 50 mm** across and are mussel- or fan-shaped, stalkless and often have scalloped margins. Their upper surfaces are pale grey and felty-woolly and they are tough in texture. Underneath they bear gill-like plates, arranged like a fan and split lengthwise along their edges. They can be found all year round.

• *Decay*

The fungus can cause a white-rot within dysfunctional zones of sapwood in standing trees.

• *Significance*

As the decay caused by *S. commune* in standing trees is usually localised, it is not regarded as a cause of structural failure. However, the affected trees are often in a state of decline for other reasons and can fail due to decay by other fungi or embrittlement of wood due to desiccation.

Plate 97 Sparassis crispa *at base of* Pinus sylvestris

Plate 98 Sparassis crispa *brittle snap of decayed* Picea sitchensis

***Sparassis crispa*; cauliflower fungus** (Plates 97–98)

• *Hosts*

This fungus occurs on various conifers, fruiting most commonly on *Pinus* and quite often on *Pseudotsuga*, *Abies*, *Picea* and *Larix*.

• *Fruit bodies*

The fruit bodies are essentially of a frondose type, but have an unusually **cauliflower-like** or open sponge-like appearance owing to the finely branched structure of the tape-like, sinuously lobed fronds. The mass of fronds forms a roundish **white to ochre** structure which can exceed **30 cm across and 20 cm high**. These fruit bodies develop at the base of living trees or on the cut surfaces of freshly felled stems, arising from thick fleshy stalks which emerge from below ground level. The spore-bearing surface is borne directly on the fronds, without the formation of any pores or gills. As the fruit bodies are highly perishable, they can be found only during or soon after their formation in August to November. When young, they are edible.

• *Decay*

The fungus develops mainly within the root system, but sometimes extends as much as 3 metres up the stem. It causes a brown-rot, which is confined largely to the heartwood. In the earlier stages of decay, the wood shows a yellow to dark reddish brown discoloration, and later darkens almost to black, while developing cubical cracking.

• *Significance*

The decayed wood has virtually no tensile strength, and extensively affected trees are liable to brittle fracture. This can result in root-plate failure or breakage of the stem near its base.

Plate 99 Stereum gausapatum *on* Quercus robur

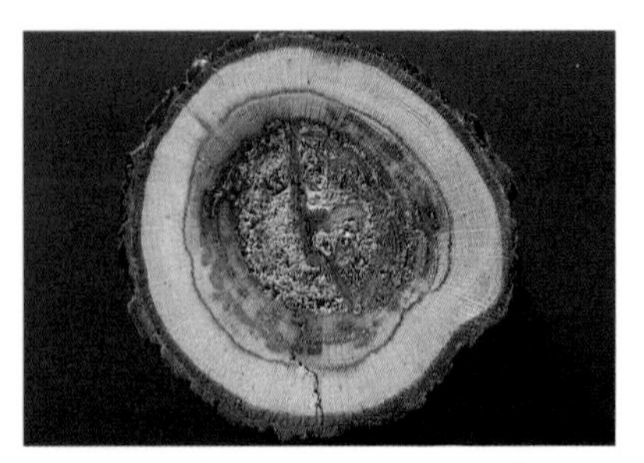

Plate 100 Stereum gausapatum*; decay in stem of* Quercus robur

Stereum gausapatum, syn. *S. spadiceum* (Plates 99–100)

• *Hosts*

This fungus is common on the fallen twigs and branches of a wide range of broadleaved tree species but its rôle as a decay fungus of standing trees appears to be confined to *Quercus*.

• *Fruit bodies*

The fruit body is a **thin skin-like layer** which is often entirely resupinate, i.e. lying flat on the surface of the bark, but it forms lobes which are often reflexed, i.e. projecting outwards. A number of fruiting layers may form together, overlapping or joining together. Most of the exposed area of the fruit body is the spore-forming layer, which has **no pores or gills**, but bears the spores directly. This has a rich brown colour, becoming darker with age, and appearing to '**bleed**' (i.e. turning red) if cut or bruised when fresh. In places where the fruit body projects from the bark, the reverse surface is hairy and greyish or brownish with a whitish margin. The fruit bodies are not perennial, but can be found throughout the year, often in a dried-out state.

• *Decay*

The decay commonly affects the branches of *Quercus* spp., in which the sapwood shows a white-rot with a soft consistency and yellowish-white colour. The affected branches tend to die back rapidly before the decay develops, perhaps due to shading or other environmental stress. This pattern of branch decay is also associated with other fungi such as *Vuilleminia comedens* [15]. The decay can also extend to the central part of trunks and large branches, causing a 'pipe-rot' (i.e., a long, narrow decay column), although it is not clear whether this is initiated before or after heartwood formation. In this central region, the fungus seems to spread first along the early-wood vessels, causing a streaky dark brown discoloration and initially a 'ring-rot' (i.e. a cylinder of decay surrounding undecayed wood). The discoloured areas later become pale, as an intense white-rot results in the almost total degradation of the wood, and the decay later spreads to the intervening areas.

• *Significance*

Small branches that are completely decayed by this fungus may snap off, although they may persist for many years if they have an undecayed heartwood core. If the centre of a trunk or major branch is affected by pipe-rot, there might be an increased chance of fracture, but this is unlikely since there is in many cases a sufficient outer shell of sound wood to provide support. If this fungus, or similar resupinate fungi, are found on dead branches of standing trees in high-risk locations, it is advisable to cut off the affected branches just beyond the dead-live junction. If the resulting wound exposes a zone of central decay, the extent of this will help to indicate whether there is a significant safety hazard in the parent stem [106].

Plate 101 Stereum hirsutum

Plate 103 Stereum sanguinolentum

Plate 102 Stereum rugosum

Other *Stereum* species: fungi with thin, skin-like fruit bodies without gills or pores (see also *Amylostereum* and *Chondrostereum*)

Stereum gausapatum has many relatives, which are rapid invaders of sapwood in a wide range of trees and shrubs, but which are mainly of limited importance with regard to structural safety.

Stereum hirsutum deserves some mention, because it is very common on a wide range of woody species, notably *Quercus* spp., both on standing trees and on fallen material. As with *S. rugosum*, the fruit body (Plate 101) is a thin layer but it is not usually appressed to the stem surface, instead forming numerous overlapping or tiered, flexible **bracket-like fronds**, each up to **40 mm** across. The spore-producing under-surface is a **bright yellow-brown** or sometimes **orange-brown**, while the upper side is very **hairy** and is a dull yellowish-grey. The fruit bodies are not perennial, but form throughout the year. The fungus is not associated with any major safety hazards, but is one of many species that decay dead branches and cause them to snap off.

Stereum rugosum, which grows on many broadleaved tree and shrub species, resembles *S. gausapatum* in the form of its fruit bodies (Plate 102), but the spore-bearing surface is **yellowish-buff**, while the reverse side, where exposed at the upturned margins of the fruit body, is brown and wrinkled. As with *S. gausapatum*, the spore-bearing surface **bleeds** red if cut or bruised when fresh. The decay is usually too restricted to pose a safety hazard, except in *Q. rubra*, where the fungus can cause a **canker-rot** at the stem base [172]. This is revealed by the presence of the fruit bodies of the fungus on the face of the canker. In such cases, a detailed safety inspection may be needed to help decide whether remedial action is advisable.

Stereum sanguinolentum occurs on various conifers, especially spruce (*Picea* spp.). Its fruit bodies (Plate 103) resemble those of several other *Stereum* species, in forming a thin and skin-like layer on the surface of the host. They can occur on standing trees, around wounds where the fungus has entered the sapwood, but are much more common on the end-grain of felled timber, on which they often form very thin bracket-like projections which overlap like roof tiles. The spore-bearing surface is **greyish-ochre** in colour. As the name *sanguinolentum* implies, the tendency for the fruiting surface to 'bleed' a **red juice** if wounded is pronounced in this species. The fungus can cause an extensive discoloration and then a white-rot in spruce trees that have been wounded, but it is not clear whether this becomes severe enough to cause structural failure.

Plate 104 Ustulina deusta, *perfect stage of fruiting on stump of* Fagus sylvatica

Plate 105 Ustulina deusta *imperfect stage of fruiting*

Plate 106 Ustulina deusta; *fracture surface of decayed wood, with brittle texture and narrow dark zone lines*

Ustulina deusta, syn. *U. vulgaris, Hypoxylon deustum* (Plates 104–106)

• *Hosts*

This fungus has a very wide host range amongst broadleaved genera of trees, but is particularly common on *Fagus* and *Tilia*. Species of *Acer* and *Quercus* are quite often invaded.

• *Fruit bodies*

Like *Daldinia concentrica*, *U. deusta* is an ascomycete and similarly has **black, charcoal-like** fruit bodies which bear spores in small chambers just below their upper surfaces. They are individually quite small, often being about **2 – 3 cm** across, but they form part of a sometimes extensive black crust-like structure (a stroma) which can reach up to **50 cm** across. The fruit bodies are, however, much less conspicuous than those of *D. concentrica* because they usually form only at the stem base of an infected host and are often concealed by vegetation or leaf litter. Typically, they occur in clefts between the buttresses or on the surface of exposed dead wood. Before the mature fruit bodies form, asexual fruiting structures, consisting of flat, very thin disc-like structures, up to 5 cm in diameter, can be found, often together with fruit bodies that have matured previously. These are at first **bluish-grey** with a whitish margin, and later become yellowish-grey and powdery. The mature fruit bodies can persist for several years.

• *Decay*

This fungus can cause a white-rot in the more advanced stages of decay, but recent research has shown that it can persist in a soft-rot mode within much of the decayed zone. By preferentially destroying cellulose, while failing to degrade the most heavily lignified parts of the wood cell walls until a very late stage, *U. deusta* induces a brittle ceramic-like fracture [146]. This can occur in main stems and root systems, since the fungus is exceptional amongst ascomycetes in being able to grow in the central wood of very large trees. Fracture often occurs before an advanced white-rot has developed, so that the fracture surface can be quite hard. The decayed areas have a pale straw or greyish colour, and usually contain irregular fine, black 'zone lines'. As with other fungi that form 'zone lines', the lines are really sheets in three dimensions, and these sheets can be found lining the cavities which form in very advanced regions of decay. A wider irregular reaction zone, unlike the fine internal zone-lines, often marks the boundary between the decayed and sound wood.

The seat of the decay within the tree is usually at the stem base, where in some cases the fungus appears to have entered through a wound. In such cases, it can extend 4 m or more up the stem, as well as into the roots. It can also enter via the roots, eventually causing windthrow.

• *Significance*

This is a particularly dangerous decay fungus, partly because its fruit bodies are often overlooked, also because of its very common occurrence and wide host range, and finally because of the type of decay that it causes. The brittle fracture associated with this decay often occurs with no warning of incipient failure, and without the compensatory thickening of the stem that can occur with fungi which cause selective delignification (e.g. *Ganoderma* spp.). Except in very advanced cases, this decay cannot be detected with a stress-wave timer and may also escape detection by certain kinds of mechanical probe [153].

Chapter 5 Tree inspection procedures and reporting

5.1 A strategy for assessing hazards and risks

Site occupiers or managers need to be aware of their legal liability for damage or personal injury caused by trees under their control. The risk of such damage or injury occurring as a result of tree failure is dependent on the nature and intensity of site usage. To take an obvious example, a tree failure next to a busy highway is much more likely to cause injury than a similar event in a woodland, far away from any roads or paths [e.g. 183, 186]. It is necessary to try to quantify the risk by considering the factors which relate to the potential severity of harm and the probability of its occurrence, as outlined in Chapter 1. (For convenience, people and property at risk are called 'targets' although, strictly speaking, a target is something at which deliberate aim is taken.)

The damage caused to a target in the event of failure in a tree can be total or partial, depending both on the nature of the target and the size and height of the tree or part of tree concerned. On this basis, the potential severity of harm can be predicted within broad categories and must be considered when the overall hazard potential of the tree is assessed. Small twigs are very unlikely to cause harm, whereas an entire tree or a large branch could maim or kill a person or crush a car. Nevertheless, a larger target such as a house would probably sustain only partial damage even from a major impact. Indeed, if a tree falls on to a house it is quite likely to penetrate the roof while causing little if any damage to the walls. The example shown in Plate 126 represents an unusually severe impact.

The probability that a target will be struck as a result of mechanical failure can range from almost nil to very high, depending on the length of time that the target is present within falling range. Stationary targets, such as buildings or parked vehicles, are generally more likely to be struck than moving ones, unless the density of traffic is very great. The quantification of risk is still a matter of some debate, and it is necessary to keep abreast of current thinking. Recent contributions to the debate have been made by Helliwell [71, 72] and Ellison [49].

Unless the risk to targets is negligible, there is a need to identify any tree defects or site conditions that could contribute to major failures. This means that trees must be inspected regularly by persons who are competent in the recognition and evaluation of defects and can identify trees that require specialised assessment, perhaps using diagnostic devices. The frequency of the inspections is a matter for local decision, according to the characteristics of the tree population and its surroundings. The size, age, past treatment and species of the trees can all affect the time interval over which serious hazards are likely to develop. A high density of people or other 'high-value targets' on a site may also be a factor in deciding to carry out relatively frequent inspections. When there are large old trees on such a site, it is usually considered advisable to inspect them annually and as soon as possible after very severe storms [97].

Some defects can be evaluated on the basis of a visual inspection, whereas others sometimes need more detailed assessment. A reasonable principle is that trees do not generally need to be subjected to detailed assessment unless they are found to require it during the course of visual inspection. Provision for identifying such trees should be stated within the written terms of the visual inspection (see Section 5.4). Another principle which is worth adopting is that a proper assessment of trees and of any associated risks is the correct basis for deciding whether to carry out remedial action. Such action should not be carried out as a substitute for proper assessment.

It should be noted that all the procedures and techniques outlined in this chapter are relevant not only to risk assessment but also to investigations following injury or damage caused by tree failure. In such cases, additional information – for example, evidence of the cause of any fracture of the wood – is likely also to be needed. All parts of the tree and surrounding objects which might provide relevant evidence should be retained until they can be recorded or preserved for future examination, even when a fallen tree has to be cleared away from a highway.

Evidence recorded 'after the event' can also be extremely useful in building up a library of information about the causes of failure in trees. Such information has often been lost or poorly recorded in the past, and there is a need for a systematic approach. Such an approach was adopted in 1987 in California under the California Tree Failure Report Program, and could provide a model for similar schemes elsewhere.

5.1.1 Visual inspection

Most types of hazard can be detected by regular inspection of the tree population for external signs of decay, physical damage, growth-related defects and adverse site conditions. This approach provides a mainstay for hazard management, as it has proven to be a cost-effective means of placing trees into categories for further action. Three main categories can be recognised: (a) trees that currently appear to present no significant hazard, (b) trees showing immediately diagnosable hazards which may require remedial action and (c) trees with suspected defects which require more detailed assessment.

General inspections for visual signs of hazard can be carried out by persons with a general grounding in arboriculture and basic training in hazard recognition. Trees that they identify as requiring more detailed investigation may require the services of a specialist practitioner. In some cases, however, it is not appropriate to distinguish between general inspection and detailed assessment as separate operations. For example, a specialist practitioner is sometimes called in to look at a specific defect that is suspected by a site owner, and which requires investigation to whatever degree of detail may be appropriate. Equally, the owner or manager might decide to delegate all aspects of a hazard evaluation to the practitioner, rather than to conduct a general inspection beforehand.

Some defects, especially certain forms of decay, do not give rise to external signs and therefore tend to escape detection in a purely visual survey. Basal cavities sometimes escape attention for this reason, and also because of materials piled around the foot of the tree but they can sometimes be detected by means of a sounding mallet during the primary visual inspection. This might be advisable in cases where such cavities have previously been found within a tree population. If there is no such reason for suspecting a hidden defect to occur within a particular part of the tree, there is no reasonable basis for carrying out a detailed internal assessment. Although in theory, an unsuspected defect might be detectable by the use of specialised diagnostic devices, this would be impracticable in the absence of some external sign to indicate the place which should be probed. Also, internal examination without good reason is undesirable, as it usually causes injury to the tree and is unreasonably time-consuming and costly.

Although most types of hazard can in theory be detected through visual inspection from the ground, reasonable care should be taken to examine parts of the tree that may be hard to see due to their height or to obscuring features such as a covering of ivy. Despite the possibility of overlooking defects that cannot be seen from the ground, it is usually considered sufficient to examine high parts of the tree with binoculars, rather to inspect them by climbing or from a hoist. Such measures can generally be justified only if defects requiring close examination are first observed from the ground.

Signs of defect are distinguishable only with reference to the normal appearance of the types of tree concerned, and mistakes may be made by persons who are unfamiliar with those trees. For example, some species such as Douglas fir *(Pseudotsuga menziesii)* develop thick plates of bark in maturity which could be mistaken for signs of bark loosening due to the deformation of the stem. Also, a particular type of defect may be of much less consequence in some species than in others, and it is therefore valuable to be aware of all available information on the 'track record' of failure for the type of tree concerned, including any experience which is relevant to local climate or soil conditions.

Unfortunately, information on the incidence of different modes of failure among various types of tree has not been well documented, and has not yet been shared widely enough. As a preliminary step towards remedying this situation, Appendix 2 of this book contains a summary of experiences that a small sample of arboriculturists have gained with a range of tree genera.

5.1.2 Detailed assessments

A routine visual inspection is often sufficient for the evaluation of hazards, but it may identify some trees with suspected defects which can be properly evaluated only by means of a more detailed assessment. Such assessments usually involve the use of diagnostic tools and need to be done by persons who have special knowledge and experience. The specialist assessor needs to be familiar not only with all the external signs of defect, but also to have some understanding of the underlying biology and biomechanics. Another important requirement is adequate **professional indemnity insurance**.

A detailed assessment is a **focused** and **stepwise** procedure which helps to avoid the use of lengthy or invasive tests unless they are necessary. As in the primary visual inspection, the assessor may occasionally need to climb the tree or to use a hoist; the latter may be needed if cumbersome devices have to be used. Also as in the primary inspection, a checklist of possible defects and of other factors contributing to potential hazards helps to ensure that nothing of importance will be missed. Such a list can be incorporated into a recording form of the type designed by Matheny and Clark [101], and reproduced here in Appendix 3. Such a form could be adapted for use on a portable data-logger for computer input. The completed form can help to demonstrate subsequently that the assessment has been carried out systematically, but is not a substitute for more detailed notes that may be needed for the recording of specific defects.

The overall stepwise approach to hazard tree assessment is shown in Fig. 5.1 and the specific procedure for detecting and mapping decay is shown as a more detailed flow-chart in Fig. 5.2.

5.1.3 Systems for quantifying hazard and risk

The setting of arboricultural management priorities can be simplified by using a numerical system to help quantify hazards and the associated risks to persons and property. Quantified risk assessment is a valuable approach, but the use of numerical scores should not be allowed to lend an exaggerated air of objectivity to a procedure that is inherently subjective in many respects. The assessment form mentioned above [101] makes provision for assigning scores to the following factors:

- the severity of each defect (incorporating site factors such as wind exposure)
- the size of the part of the tree that might fail due to the defect
- the nature and intensity of site occupancy by persons or property.

By adding these scores, an overall hazard rating is calculated for each tree. In effect, this rating includes both the hazard presented by the tree and the degree of risk, represented by the probability of damage to one or more 'targets'. A computer-based version of this system (Tree Risk Assessment and Management System) has been developed and is currently being evaluated in Britain. Also, a modification of this approach, for more accurate assessments under British conditions and incorporating a 'ready reckoner' for on-site calculation, has been proposed by Ellison (in press; see Appendix 3).

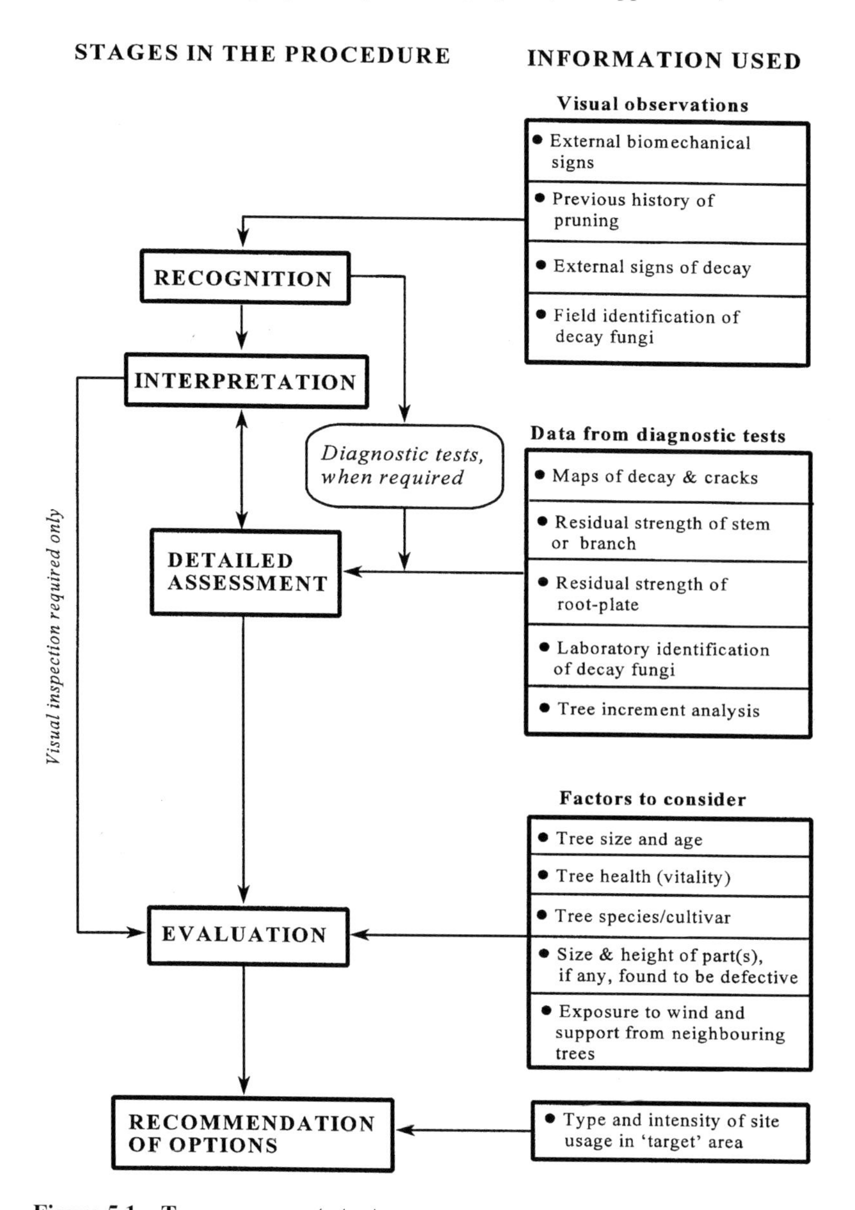

Figure 5.1 Tree assessment strategy

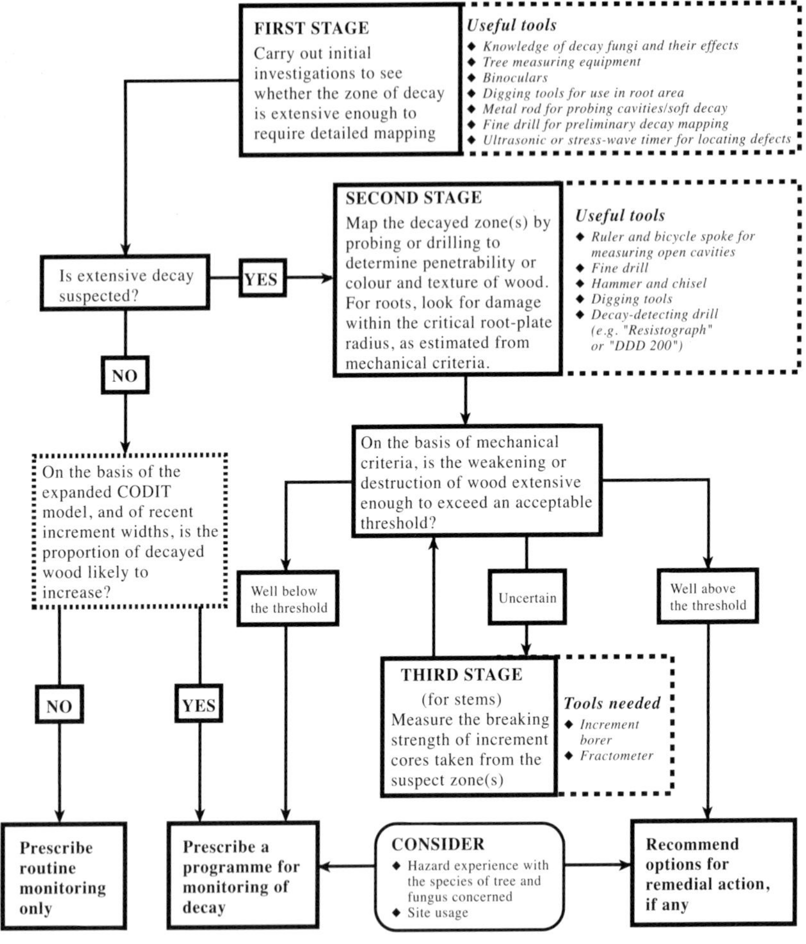

Figure 5.2 Strategy for detailed assessment of decay

5.2 Recognition of specific defects

The main features which need to be looked for in a general inspection are listed below, with brief descriptions of particular signs that may indicate defects or other potential causes of hazard. Some signs, such as the presence of exposed disintegrating wood or of particular kinds of fungal fruit body, indicate the presence of decay. Information about the nature and extent of the decay can subsequently be obtained through a detailed assessment using diagnostic devices. The need for such an assessment can often be judged from externally visible features, such as the identity of fungal fruit bodies and the type and size of the apparent point(s) of infection. As explained in Chapters 3 and 4, fungal species differ in their ability to cause loss of strength in a particular tree species.

All external signs of decay and of growth-related defects above ground can, at least in theory, be recorded quite quickly and easily from ground level, using binoculars where necessary. Signs such as the presence of fungal fruit bodies or of forks with included bark have long been familiar to tree inspectors, together with more subtle indications of the mechanical condition of trees. Mechanical signs have become better understood in recent years under the general heading of 'body language', with the recognition and interpretation of mechanical and other external signs, as expounded by Mattheck and Breloer [106] under the name **Visual Tree Assessment (VTA)**. The application of this approach to the assessment of specific signs is outlined in Section 5.2.1.

It is usually convenient to assess the condition of each main part of a tree in turn: overall crown condition, mechanical balance of the crown, root stability, strength of the main stem, strength of major branches. The scoring system developed by Matheny and Clark [101] and modified by Ellison (in press) is operated on this basis. Major defects in the main stem or root-plate contribute very significantly to the numerical scoring system that is included in this form, and particular attention should be paid to any stem defects that occur between one metre above ground and the base of the crown; the so-called hot-spot [2], at which a high percentage of failures are reputed to occur.

The question as to whether an apparent defect has significance for the safety of the particular tree should always be considered in relation to the overall condition of the tree and of the site. For example, a fork or branch union with included bark might be regarded as defective, but it may well be safely stabilised within the crown structure (see Section 2.1.2.3). Similarly, the bark of a branch may show signs of progressive downward bending, but the rate of bending may be insufficient to cause cracking of the wood or the creation of a gap in the crown structure (see Section 2.3.2.1). In this context, it should be noted that gaps in the crown structure can be the result of storm damage or previous arboricultural work.

The following headings are arranged partly on the assumption that the tree will probably be inspected in structural sections. However, as some defects are inter-related, important information is cross-referenced between the headings. For convenience, the hazard implications of each type of defect are mentioned briefly, in addition to the fuller information provided in Chapter 2.

5.2.1 Defects found within various parts of the tree

5.2.1.1 Cankers or wounds as mechanically weak points

FEATURES TO OBSERVE

- Circular cankers, especially target cankers (Plate 11)
- Deep or extensive wounds

SIGNIFICANCE AND HINTS FOR ASSESSMENT

Major cankers and wounds, quite apart from being sites where decay may have originated, sometimes act as stress notches, where breakage is more likely than elsewhere.

5.2.1.2 Included bark

FEATURES TO OBSERVE

- Areas of obvious bark-to-bark contact
- Branch bark ridges with a lip-like or gaping structure (Plates 4–6)
- Signs of rainwater overflow from cup-like crotches or seepage from between two stems in contact

SIGNIFICANCE AND HINTS FOR ASSESSMENT

Bark inclusions act like cracks in having no resistance to tensile (pulling) stress and little resistance to shear (sliding) stress. They can lead to the tearing apart of forks and branch crotches (one of the commonest types of failure in some species and cultivars), or to the propagation of cracks when they occur in the buttress zone.

Any branch junction or fork which contains included bark can in theory be diagnosed as a weak union, but the probability of failure is greatly influenced by factors such as crown structure and the amount of bending stress on the members of the union (see Section 2.1.2.3). Also, different tree species and cultivars seem to vary quite a lot in their frequency of failure at weak unions (see Appendix 1). This is a separate matter from the tendency to form such unions in the first place, which also varies between types of tree. A visual examination by an experienced person can help to decide whether the area of bark-to-bark contact is great enough to pose a hazard. Forks or branches which have been braced because of suspected weakness (see Section 6.5) should be regularly inspected.

Once a zone of included bark has begun to form, it may be externally obvious (Plates 1 & 127), while in other cases its existence must be deduced by the abnormal development of the branch bark ridge, like a pair of parted lips as shown in Plates 4 to 6. If, however, the 'lips' gape in a wide 'V' shape for part of their length (Plate 4), this is a sign that the two members have united in this region to form a shell of wood around the bark inclusion (Plate 6).

5.2.1.3 *Cracking of wood* (see also Section 5.2.1.7)

FEATURES TO OBSERVE

- Open cracks
- Longitudinal ribs of occluding tissues

SIGNIFICANCE AND HINTS FOR ASSESSMENT

Care is needed to distinguish cracks in the wood from those that only involve bark (Plate 13). The latter can be caused by a rapid expansion of the woody cylinder, and are usually occluded without harm to the tree. Cracks are often self-evident at the surface, except perhaps when they have formed in association with included bark (i.e. a bark-to-bark contact; Plate 1), and are thus rather difficult to distinguish from the bark inclusion itself.

Cracks in the wood are sites of partial failure, which in some cases could be followed by major failure. The location and nature of a crack help to indicate whether it represents a significant hazard. In some cases further failure is easily predictable, for example when a crack below a fork is gaping widely. Generally, however, there is a need for detailed assessment by a practitioner with appropriate understanding and experience. Cracks can be a sign of **other types of defect** that are not associated with structural development, especially **decay**, which need to be investigated in their own right. If decay is so extensive that cracks have formed, the tree has probably been seriously weakened. Albers and Hayes [2] suggest that the incidence of serious failure is especially high in conifers which have both cracks and central cavities.

Although, like decay, cracks can be mapped internally using diagnostic devices, this is not usually necessary for hazard assessment. A specialist practitioner can often make an evaluation by interpreting mainly visual observations in the light of biomechanical knowledge [106]. Background information on the mechanics of cracks is summarised in Chapter 2 of this book and may be helpful in conjunction with the following notes.

- New wood and bark usually develop along each side of a crack. The absence of such growth usually indicates either that the crack is very recent, or that the vigour of the tree is very poor. Occasionally, the new tissues are separated from the crack by an area of dead bark.

- It is a relatively good sign if new bark and wood forming on both sides of a crack have joined together to form a single rib with a blunt profile (Fig. 5.3a). If there is still a bark-to-bark contact between the two sides, the absence of fusion may be due to continuing movement within the crack, and is sometimes a bad sign. The same applies if the rib has a sharp profile (Fig. 5.3b), as it probably owes its shape to repeated phases of becoming occluded and breaking open again. A rib which occurs near the stem base, with no sign of 'welding' between two united halves, may be an upward extension of a buttress, rather than a sign of a crack.

- Cracks on opposite sides of a stem or major branch ('**diamétral cracks**', Plate 20) are often major shearing planes which pass right through the cross-section. The structure could split in two by a sliding movement along the crack.

- Cracks that run between axially aligned flush-cut **pruning wounds**, **cankers** or other substantial injuries (Plate 12) sometimes trigger major failure, but this is less likely if they have been fully occluded by round-profiled ribs.

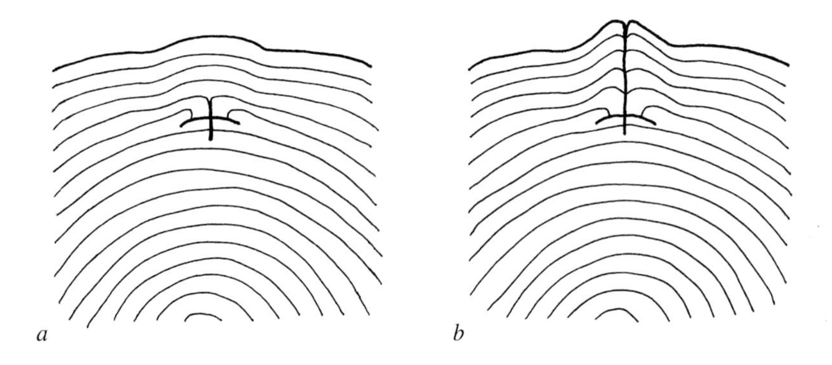

Figure 5.3 Diagrammatic cross-sections through (a) an occluded and (b) an unoccluded rib associated with cracking in wood

- Open cracks can allow the development of decay, in which case any associated loose bark can be detected by means of a sounding mallet. If there is any evidence of decay, a detailed assessment may be necessary.

- Cracks that develop below **unions with included bark** (Plate 1) are produced by the pulling apart of the members of the union. Such cracks are often very likely to fail seriously without remedial action.

- If cracks have developed above **ingrown flutes between buttresses** they can act as radial shearing planes ('fault-lines') for major failure of the stem (**VTA**). This may be unlikely if they have been fully occluded by round-profiled ribs.

- A crack that forms between **the base of a major root** and the rest of the buttress zone represents a form of hazard beam failure. This can lead to snapping of the stem (**VTA**).

- If cracks are found on the lower sides of **curving stems and branches** (Plate 19) this may indicate a process of splitting such as occurs in the skin of a banana when it is bent straight (**VTA**). Progressive downward bending of the structure is revealed by the failure of any associated ribs to close fully. In such cases, snapping could eventually follow (see also bark distortion below).

- Cracks of the 'hazard beam' variety, which form in a small proportion of **curving stems and branches** (**VTA**), pass through the cross-section from side to side. Fracture across the grain could eventually occur if extensive decay sets in.

- **Helical cracks**, which may follow the grain of a tree, occasionally open up sufficiently to allow major failure if the tree is strongly twisted by the wind and if extensive decay is also present. Such cracks are quite common on old specimens of Sweet chestnut, *Castanea sativa*, in which they may be concealed by thick plates of bark.

5.2.1.4 Deformation or cracking of bark

FEATURES TO OBSERVE

- Crumpling (congestion) of bark plates on the underside of a leaning stem or heavy branch, perhaps with signs of stretching on the upperside (Plates 17–18)
- Tension cracks in cavity fillings or in wound sealants
- Axial cracks in bark (not in underlying wood)

SIGNIFICANCE AND HINTS FOR ASSESSMENT

Progressive bending of a trunk or branch is often revealed by distortion or cracking of its bark, if the bark contains corky plates. This may happen before the wood itself shows any outward sign of buckling or cracking, and is therefore thought to be an early warning sign of possible failure from further bending (**VTA**). Similarly, brittle materials used for cavity fillings or wound dressings may give a warning by cracking on the tensioned side of the structure; their use is, however, becoming increasingly rare.

The above warning signs are not necessarily an indication of hazard, and should normally be used in conjunction with other criteria. In particular, it should be noted that the strength of progressively bending branches is often maintained by the adequate formation of new wood. Excessively rapid bending tends to cause a gap to open within the crown structure (see Section 2.3.2.1). Also, axial cracks that involve bark and not wood are usually harmless, as they are caused by a spurt in growth that cannot be accommodated by the normal process of expansion of the bark.

5.2.1.5 *Poor balance or lack of sturdy taper in stems or branches*

FEATURES TO OBSERVE

- Lopsided crown, resulting from storm damage or uneven pruning, or removal of neighbouring trees or other shelter
- Individual branches with poor balance
- End-loading of the twig structure of individual branches (lion-tailing), e.g. produced by unsuitable thinning
- Relative lack of stem-taper in a tree exposed to strong winds

SIGNIFICANCE AND HINTS FOR ASSESSMENT

These features usually indicate an increased chance of breakage in high winds. They occur mainly as a result of events such as unsuitable arboricultural work or storm damage, since the growth pattern of a tree otherwise tends towards mechanical optimisation under the prevailing conditions. For this reason, the hazard may lessen with time.

5.2.1.6 *Decay: positive external signs* (see also Section 5.2.2.1)

FEATURES TO OBSERVE

- Fungal fruit bodies or their remains, including bark discoloration
- Exudation of fluid from bark
- Insect holes or nests
- Exposed decaying wood or cavities

SIGNIFICANCE AND HINTS FOR ASSESSMENT

These signs all indicate the need for closer inspection to determine whether a specialist assessment is appropriate. This can include the examination of cavities and the probing of exposed wood with a narrow chisel or steel rod. Most open cavities are readily evident, but some may become partly or wholly hidden by occluding tissues around their margins.

In many trees, decay is restricted to within a few millimetres of the areas of injury and dieback where the protective covering of live bark has inevitably been lost. Even if a fungal fruit body has been found, the zone of decay might be quite localised and of no significance for safety. If decay is clearly more extensive or is at a critical position, as evidenced by an open cavity or the results of probing with hand tools, a more detailed assessment may be needed (see Section 5.3.1). In some cases, however, it may be immediately apparent that decay is extensive enough to warrant a management decision on this basis alone.

The identity of fruit bodies may shed light on the likely implications for loss of wood strength, but identification is sometimes a job for a specialist laboratory. For fungi that normally produce long-lived perennial brackets, death of such fruit bodies may indicate that decay is inactive, at least locally. Most fungal fruit bodies that grow on the ground under trees are those of harmless or beneficial species, and some knowledge of fungi is required to distinguish between the harmless species and those that decay roots. Where there is any doubt about the soundness of roots, inspection by digging, as described below, is advisable.

Generally, the fruit bodies of the principal fungi that cause decay are large enough to be seen easily when looked for, but some (e.g. *Ustulina deusta*) have small inconspicuous fruit bodies that are not likely to be seen except at close quarters, especially when concealed beneath leaf litter, moss or even tarmac between the buttresses. Some fruit bodies, such as those of *Ganoderma pfeifferi*, are perennial, persisting on the tree for many years, but most are short-lived and are best looked for in early autumn when many species are most likely to form them. Otherwise, it is often possible to find the decomposing or mummified remains of fruit bodies or traces of their attachment to the bark, sometimes after they have fallen to the ground. In some cases, information can be supplied by site owners or local residents who may have observed fruiting previously.

It is necessary to look for fruit bodies both in the aerial parts of a tree, where they are usually associated with decay developing from wounds or branches that have died back, and near the base of the tree. Fruit bodies at tree bases (e.g. Plate 81) usually indicate decay in the adjacent roots and in the butt. However, in the case of a few fungi such as *Meripilus giganteus*, the fruit body may be superficially attached to the base at soil level, but connected by strands of fungal tissue through the soil or along root surfaces to decaying roots that are some distance away. Thus a fruit body of *M. giganteus* arising from decayed beech roots has been found attached to the base of a perfectly sound London plane (*Platanus* x *hispanica*). Usually, however, such a fruit body at a tree base indicates decay in some or all of the deeper roots of that particular tree. For some species, such as *Inonotus dryadeus*, the decay does not often extend much above ground level, so that attempts to detect it in the stem base close to a fruit body might indicate that the tree is in a safer condition than it really is.

The size of fruit bodies is not usually a good indication of the extent of decay, although very large ones can only develop if the volume of affected wood is substantial. Indeed, as just explained, fruit bodies may be absent at the time of inspection or might not have yet formed despite the presence of extensive decay.

5.2.1.7 Decay: points of likely occurrence
(see also Sections 5.2.2.3, 5.2.2.4 and 5.2.3)

FEATURES TO OBSERVE

- Old pruning wounds or pollarding cuts, which may have hard, crust-like or painted surfaces concealing advanced decay (Plates 32–33)
- Places where the wood shows signs of cracking
- Areas of dead bark (which can be detected by tapping with a mallet)
- Areas where bark is missing (e.g. due to vehicle impact or fire damage: Plate 34)
- Cankers or excrescences
- Crotches or buttress flutes with included bark

SIGNIFICANCE AND HINTS FOR ASSESSMENT

Extensive decay is by no means invariably present in association with these features, but they should be examined closely and if necessary probed as described under the previous heading.

A tree's history of pruning is a major consideration in hazard assessment. In particular, excessively large or numerous wounds (see Chapter 3) can pave the way for the extensive development of decay, especially if they have been made too close to the parent stem. The pattern of wood formation after severe pruning can also lead to the development of cracks (see below).

Dead bark may conceal decay and sometimes remains intact for years, though perhaps differing in colour or texture from the surrounding live bark. Visual recognition of dead bark is particularly difficult when a tree is growing too slowly in girth for the early development of an appreciable raised edge around the dead area. Cankers and excrescences are easily seen, the latter being particularly common on Red horse chestnut (*Aesculus x carnea*), although rarely associated with breakage in this hybrid.

Decay sometimes starts in crotches which contain included bark, where the bark may be under pressure or subjected to persistently anaerobic conditions, and also in the cracks in the wood which sometimes form below such crotches (Plate 1). Decay associated with pinched bark may also be present within flutes at the stem base. Perhaps less often, decay occurs in crotches of the cup-shaped type (Plate 2), in which water collects and creates persistently anaerobic conditions. Although such a formation may be difficult to recognise from below, its presence is often betrayed by signs of water overflow, irrespective of whether decay is present.

The investigation of suspected root decay should extend below ground, perhaps with the aid of a decay-detecting drill. This is important since some decay fungi tend to colonise the undersides of the major roots, without extending very much above ground except perhaps in the fluting between roots.

5.2.2 Defects confined mainly to stems and major branches

5.2.2.1 Deformation of the cross-section

FEATURES TO OBSERVE

- Bulging which extends beyond the smooth line of stem-taper, often known as 'bottle-butt' in the basal part of the stem (**VTA**)
- Indentations

SIGNIFICANCE AND HINTS FOR ASSESSMENT

If decay or internal cracking increases the flexure of a structure, the cambium tends to respond by laying down wider annual increments. This increased growth (which does not usually occur with brittle decay) often compensates for any loss of strength. Detailed assessment may be required to map the relative extent of sound and defective wood.

An indentation could be a sign of the caving-in of the cross-section, usually with associated cracking (**VTA**). If so, an extensive zone of advanced decay or a cavity is likely to be present (detectable with a sounding mallet) and total collapse could be imminent. If sounding gives no evidence of decay, the indentation may be a sign of a foreign body that was formerly affecting growth and has now been removed or enclosed within the growth of the tree. If a supporting structure (e.g. a wall) has recently been removed, the possibility of failure through loss of stress optimisation must be considered (**VTA**).

5.2.2.2 Stem fluting

SIGN TO OBSERVE

- Deep fluting in species that do not normally show it, especially in the buttress zone or above or below wounds or dead branches

SIGNIFICANCE AND HINTS FOR ASSESSMENT

The underlying bark and cambium may be dead, with associated decay (see above). It is important to be familiar with species, such as yew, in which fluting is often a normal feature of growth. In some cases, the bark and cambium are alive, but the flute represents a region of reduced sap flow associated with a dead branch or root.

5.2.2.3 *Decay and weakness following loss or removal of a leading shoot*

SIGN TO OBSERVE

- Abrupt bends in branches or sharply kinked main stems (Plate 27)

SIGNIFICANCE AND HINTS FOR ASSESSMENT

Such formations often develop after a branch has been broken or cut back, leaving a wound which can become the seat of decay. Occlusion tissues can usually be found marking such a position. Even in the absence of decay, the upward curve where the new growth has formed might perhaps be prone to 'hazard beam' failure.

5.2.2.4 *Graft incompatibility*

FEATURES TO OBSERVE (Plates 7–8)

- Marked bulging both above and below a graft line
- Zone of included bark at a graft line
- Transverse cracking at a graft line

SIGNIFICANCE AND HINTS FOR ASSESSMENT

A graft with poor compatibility may be liable to snap, especially if decay has set in.

5.2.3 Defects in the rooting area

5.2.3.1 *Direct signs of root instability* (see also Section 5.2.1.6)

FEATURES TO OBSERVE

- Leaning tree, with mounding of soil on one side and/or a depression on the other (Plates 24–25)
- Cracks in soil around root-plate
- Visible movement of the root-plate in a breeze

SIGNIFICANCE AND HINTS FOR ASSESSMENT

Leaning and mounding of recent origin may be accompanied by cracking in the soil or disturbance of vegetation. Loose soil may, however, quite soon fall or wash back into the cracks, so obscuring them. If the cracks radiate from the tree, rather than encircling the root-plate, this may be a sign of flexing of roots under tension without loss of anchorage. In some cases, individual holes, rather than extensive cracks, appear in the soil; these could be mistaken for the burrows of animals. Movement that can be seen or felt beneath one's feet is further proof of current instability. If movement has begun some months or years earlier, stability may have been partly or wholly restored by new root growth. Follow-up studies (see below) can be carried out to see whether a lean is stable.

Quite a high proportion of trees undergo some movement of their root systems early in life, so that they develop a lean. In most such cases, root stability is restored and the stem grows back towards the vertical. This can lead to a curvature in the lower part of the stem (basal 'sweep'). If, as occasionally happens, a lean later becomes more pronounced due to continued movement of the root system, there may be signs of recent adjustment of the angle of leading shoots in the crown. This can be determined during an initial inspection, but a simple monitoring procedure can additionally be carried out as shown in Fig. 5.4.

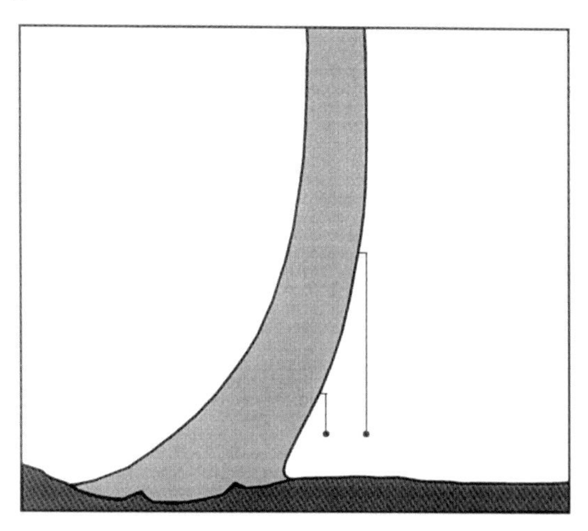

Figure 5.4 Method for monitoring the lean of a tree: an increased lean will widen the distance between two plumb-lines attached at fixed points (Adapted from a suggestion by H. Girling [59])

5.2.3.2 *Root defects betrayed by crown condition*

Crowns of trees can be in poor condition due to a wide variety of causes, not all of which have much significance for hazard assessment. Diagnostic skills and the availability of good sources of information [e.g. 173] may therefore be important in such cases. Examination of the crown, with binoculars if necessary, can often indicate whether the problem is localised within the crown (e.g. cankers on individual twigs) or more general.

FEATURES TO OBSERVE

- Generally low crown density for the type of tree, allowing for age, locality and other relevant factors
- Pale colour or premature autumn coloration of leaves
- Undersized leaves
- Sparse leaves or twigs, ranging to obvious crown dieback
- A marked reduction in shoot growth in the upper crown (growth may of course be very slow in old trees anyway)

SIGNIFICANCE AND HINTS FOR ASSESSMENT

If not explained by local disease in the crown, these signs usually indicate impaired uptake of water or mineral nutrients. Poor shoot growth often occurs when the damage is not severe enough to cause crown thinness. All the above symptoms can result from drought, in which case stability is unlikely to be affected, provided that more adequate rainfall eventually returns. Otherwise, a poor crown condition may indicate serious or long-term damage to the root system, and hence the need for further investigation to assess the stability of the tree. Such damage can be caused by physical injury or decay or by the impairment of soil conditions (e.g., through compaction, contamination or alteration of the water regime).

Although a poor crown condition does not necessarily indicate the presence of root decay, it quite often does so in middle-aged and old trees. As trees get older, they show an increasing incidence of root death and decay, caused by fungi such as *Armillaria* spp. (Plates 42–45), *Meripilus giganteus* (Plates 80–81) or *Heterobasidion annosum* (Plates 67–68).

5.2.3.3 Defects betrayed by features of the site

FEATURES TO OBSERVE

- Evidence of soil excavation (trenching, ditching, dredging etc.)
- Evidence of compaction or dumping
- Lack of above-ground root flare as evidence of soil infill
- New buildings, new hard surfaces or signs of demolition on site (see Section 5.3.4)
- Evidence that other trees have been removed

SIGNIFICANCE AND HINTS FOR ASSESSMENT

Excavation may have caused severance of roots, perhaps leading immediately to instability or initiating decay. Other activities may have damaged roots mechanically, chemically or indirectly through oxygen deprivation or an altered soil moisture regime. Changes affecting physical support or shelter may have exposed trees to increased wind pressure. A study by Bakken [5] in Northern California showed that harmful failures of forest trees were not adequately prevented by a programme of assessment and management which failed to take proper account of the effects of shelter from wind.

5.3 Methods for detailed assessment

On sites with a 'high target value', a detailed examination with diagnostic devices is generally needed for trees showing suspected defects that cannot be fully evaluated from a visual inspection. In the case of root-plates which are suspected to be unstable, but show no obvious signs of movement, the only way of gaining further information may be to carry out exploratory hand excavation of areas around the tree where the presence of sound roots is judged to be important. This should be done with care so as to minimise further damage to the roots. The development of accurate, non-destructive methods for locating roots, (e.g. based on radar technology), is a possibility for the future.

5.3.1 Assessment of decay

The purpose of assessing decay in detail is to find whether it represents a significant hazard by virtue of its position and extent within the tree concerned. If it occupies either a very small or a very large proportion of the woody cross-section, the question of hazard evaluation can easily be decided one way or the other. In such cases, an experienced person may be able to gain sufficient information from a visual inspection, perhaps together with the use of simple tools such as a mallet and steel rod. The need for more detailed assessment arises mainly when the extent of the decay is less certain. A possible exception may arise when a number of neighbouring trees of the same species and age have a case-history of extensive decay; it is then possible to argue that detailed assessment is justified even if a hazard is not apparent from the visual inspection.

It might be imagined that a decayed tree would have to be probed at a great many points in order to assess the extent of the decay, but this is unnecessary, provided that the assessor is familiar with the ways in which decay columns originate and develop. On the basis of this background knowledge, it is usually quite easy to 'home in' on the parts of the tree that need a detailed assessment of the cross-sectional extent of decayed wood or cavities. Essentially, these are the points where the greatest proportion of the woody cylinder is decayed, and where decay is present together with mechanical defects or regions of unusual mechanical loading. Particular attention should be paid to parts of the structure that bear particularly high static loads, such as the roots on the uphill side of trees on steep slopes, or the upper and lower sides of heavy branches and leaning stems. If, in such cases, decay is present at the surface so that the bark and cambium are dead or missing, the consequent inability of the tree to form new annual increments at such points may considerably increase the probability of failure.

The type of decay concerned, as well as its extent and position, is an important consideration in the assessment of its mechanical effects in partially decayed wood. Background information on this is given in Chapter 3, in which the main types of decay; brown-rot, simultaneous white-rot, selectively delignifying white-rot and soft-rot are described. The more brittle kinds of decay, especially brown-rot, are generally the most likely to cause failure, owing to the almost total loss of tensile strength, especially so in areas of high tensile loading, some examples of which are mentioned in the previous paragraph. The more flexible types of decay are most significant in regions of high compressive loading.

When assessing the weakening effects of decay, it is essential to take into account other factors which may increase or reduce the hazard. The height and the sail area of the crown are of particular importance in this respect, as is the degree of exposure to the wind. The case history for the tree species, especially in the locality, must also be taken into account. It is with these considerations in mind, that the best use can be made of mechanical criteria for hazard assessment, as outlined below and explained in detail by Mattheck and Breloer [106].

Although there are now various aids to diagnosis, including specialised devices, they are never a substitute for experience, together with knowledge of relevant principles and a healthy measure of common sense. By observing the stepwise approach outlined in Fig. 5.2, and thus minimising the use of invasive techniques as far as possible, costs can be kept down and trees can be protected from unnecessary injuries. In some cases, economic considerations may decide how detailed the investigation needs to be. For example, a woodland tree near a path might warrant less expenditure than a specimen tree in an urban park.

The flow-chart in Fig. 5.2 shows a suggested sequence of investigations, but this is merely a guide. Only some of the items of equipment shown in the chart will usually be available, and it may therefore be necessary to adapt this scheme accordingly. Some devices can to some extent be regarded as either complementary or interchangeable, as explained in Section 5.3.1.2.

5.3.1.1 Criteria for 'allowable' amounts of decay in stems

A detailed consideration of the mechanical effects of decay columns of various sizes and positions is provided in a companion volume within this series [106], and this should be consulted for further details. The most important of the assessment criteria relate to the proportion of the stem cross-section which can be reduced in strength or destroyed before the tree's safety factor is substantially eroded. For a stem containing a central cavity, Mattheck and Breloer [106] have estimated that the safety factor is reduced only to 3.2, compared with their estimate of 4.5 for a solid stem, provided that the thickness of the sound outer wall is at least 0.30 to 0.35 of the stem radius (Fig. 5.5).

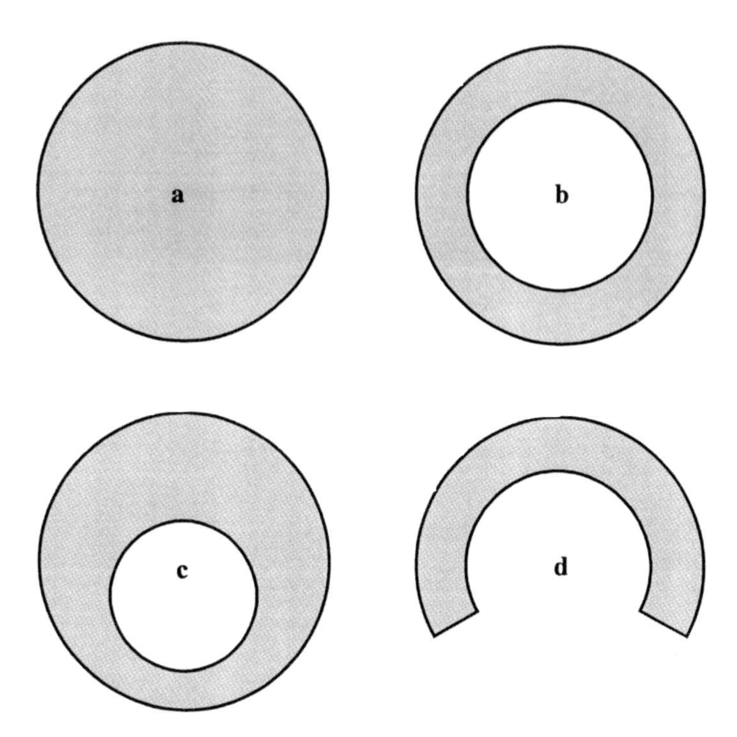

Figure 5.5 Criteria for strength assessment of hollow stems, adapted from Mattheck & Breloer (1995):

a) normal safety factor of solid stem

b) safety factor reduced by only 29% due to central cavity occupying ⅔ of stem diameter

c) stem with safety factor estimated as similar to (b), having an eccentric cavity occupying ½ of stem diameter and minimum wall thickness ⅓ of depth to centre of cavity

d) cavity as in (b), but with no safety factor remaining, due to an opening occupying ⅓ of stem circumference

The minimum advisable wall thickness ratio of 0.30 to 0.35 can be applied with greatest confidence when the cavity is central and has no external opening, but Mattheck and Breloer also provide a certain amount of information on open and eccentric cavities. A small opening does not seriously reduce the safety factor of a tree which has a wall thickness ratio not less than approximately 0.35 but if the opening occupies a third or more of the stem circumference, the safety factor is completely eroded (i.e., the maximum load equals the working load). Mattheck *et al*. [104] have also carried out studies on eucalypts in Australia, which indicate that cavities with more than one opening are unlikely to collapse as long as the width of the openings in total does not exceed half the girth of the stem where they occur.

The advice given by Mattheck & Breloer [106] concerning eccentric cavities (Fig. 5.5) applies if the cavity occupies more than half the stem diameter. If so, the wall thickness ratio should be calculated by measuring the sound wall at its thinnest point and then dividing this value by the shortest distance from the centre of the cavity to the outside (not by the stem radius). If the resulting ratio exceeds the usual value of 0.30 to 0.35, failure by collapse of the cavity is said to be very unlikely, as in the case of a central cavity with an average ratio of the same value. If the wall of an eccentric cavity is breached by an opening it will have zero thickness in this region, so that the ratio would also be zero. In such a case, it seems appropriate instead to assess the cavity as an open one, using the criteria mentioned above.

Partially decayed wood, which is found more often than extensive cavities, at least in British conditions, may have significant resistance to cross-sectional flattening despite its reduced strength. This has not yet been investigated experimentally, and for the present it may generally be advisable to err on the side of caution by assuming that partially decayed wood has no strength, as in the case of a cavity. A more lenient approach is, however, sometimes supported by case histories, as with *Inonotus hispidus* in London plane (*Platanus* x *hispanica*) and *Fistulina hepatica* in oak (*Quercus* spp.).

Although the use of mechanical criteria has made tree safety assessment more objective, it is extremely important that it should not be mis-applied, nor used in isolation. For example, a tree with a hollow stem might be judged relatively safe on the basis of its residual wall-thickness, and yet might have a high probability of failing due to some other defect or change in its environment that had been overlooked. Conversely, a tree with a theoretically inadequate wall-thickness but with a reduced load, as in the case of an old pollard with a small crown, could be retained with very little risk.

5.3.1.2 Techniques for measuring and mapping decayed zones

The first stage in the assessment of decay is to determine whether a rapid decision can be reached without detailed mapping. This is often the case if the decay is either so limited in extent that a hazard is not in question, or so extensive that the hazard is obvious. Such judgements should be made only by persons with adequate knowledge of the range of spatial patterns of decay which occur in living trees; examples are shown in Fig. 5.6 and Plates 35–37 and 143–144. Only a brief inspection is required at this stage, aided by very simple devices such as a mallet for making a sounding test, or a steel rod for probing soft decay.

Various specialised instruments have become available for the assessment of internal defects. Some of them, such as stress-wave timers and ultrasonic timers, are best suited for the overall assessment of the presence and extent of decay or cracking. In cases where a more detailed map of the defects is required, it may be necessary to use other devices, such as the various types of decay-detecting drill. These can be used both for preliminary investigation and for detailed mapping. When using any diagnostic device, it is very important to

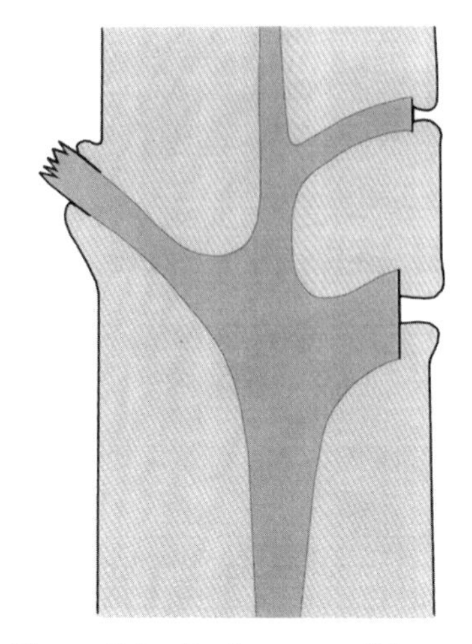

Figure 5.6 Coalescence of decay columns originating from a number of wounds or dead branches

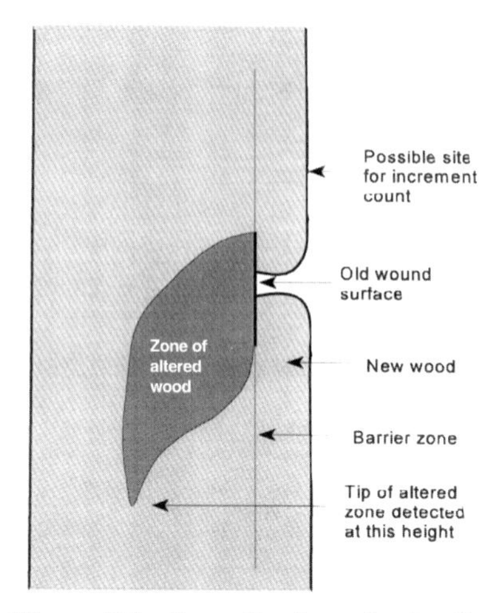

Figure 5.7 Investigation of rate of decay extension and of recent growth history in the host tree

place the probes in an appropriate position and to be aware of features such as included bark, which could give misleading readings.

In the measurement of sound wood surrounding cavities or decay columns, it is clearly important that the devices employed should be suitable for the size of tree concerned. Drilling devices are limited to the length of the drill-bit or probe (often 200 – 300 mm), while ultrasonic timers will provide data only if the cross-section is small enough to allow a measurable signal to pass across it (approx. 1 m in the case of the "Arborsonic Decay Detector", a device which is mentioned below). It is, however possible to assess the outer wood of quite large trees using a drilling device, since an acceptable safety factor depends on as little as the outermost 30% of the cross-section being completely sound. On this basis, a 300 mm drill could be used in a stem of up to 1.8 m across. A stress-wave timer can occasionally be of help in making an initial assessment of trees too large in diameter to be assessed with other devices.

The following notes and the accompanying summary in Table 5.1 explain the mode of operation of several devices and the uses to which they can be put. The table includes the best information available at the time of writing. The field is, however, rapidly expanding, and practitioners will need to keep abreast of new developments.

The damage caused to the tree by diagnostic devices is another factor which must be considered. The main concern is that holes bored into existing decay columns will allow the decay to extend into the previously sound shell of outer wood that formed after it was initiated. If this happens, the future safe retention time for the tree might be seriously reduced. There is very little reliable information to indicate to what extent such concern is justified, but it is in any case a wise precaution to keep the number of drill holes to the minimum required for mapping the decay.

Of the devices named in the flow-chart in Fig. 5.2, the most damaging is probably the increment borer for reasons that are discussed later. There has therefore been increasing concern over the traditional practice of extracting increment cores for the routine determination of the presence and extent of decay. There are, however, situations in which cores are needed for the measurement of strength or of incremental growth in wood. The relevant procedures are outlined below.

• *Stress-wave timer* (Plate 107)

Plate 107 A stress-wave timer ("Metriguard")

This is an acoustic device which measures the time taken for a stress or 'shock' wave to pass between a 'start probe' and a 'stop probe' inserted at a measured distance elsewhere on the test object. The stress wave is initiated by a hammer blow which is delivered to the start probe. If the speed is very different from that obtained in healthy wood of the species concerned, a defect should be suspected. The approximate size and location of the defect can be deduced using a series of readings taken across different diameters of the stem.

Among devices of this type, the "Metriguard" stress wave-timer has been evaluated on trees, rather than only on timber [102], and has sensitively detected decay caused by a number of fungal species [148], as well as internal cracks. A similar device, the "Sound Impulse Hammer" also provides such information [10]. Unlike ultrasonic devices (see below), stress-wave timers can be used on exceptionally large trees. They can also be used with relative ease at the stem-base, where it is important to be able to detect decay that may have originated in the root system.

A small disadvantage with stress-wave timers is that the probes are mounted on steel screws which must be inserted into the outermost wood of the tree, causing some injury. A potentially more serious disadvantage is that these devices seem unable to detect certain kinds of decay at an early stage. This is because decay alters the velocity of sound in wood in a number of ways, which vary according to the nature of the decay. Thus, a reduction in density will increase the velocity, while a reduction in the modulus of elasticity will decrease it. Also, it is believed that the presence of very small breaks in the wood structure can reduce the velocity considerably. The nett effect of these changes is an alteration (usually a slowing-down) of the stress-wave in most kinds of decay, but this does not happen for example in the case of partial decay caused by the ascomycete fungus *Ustulina deusta* [148]. In view of this limitation in the use of acoustic techniques, it may be advisable for them to be used only on types of decay for which their value has been experimentally proven. Research is proceeding in this area.

• *Ultrasonic devices* (Plate 108)

The development of medical ultrasound scanners raised hopes that similar devices could be used for imaging decay or cracks in trees. However, when such devices were first tested for this purpose, the resulting images were too poor to be interpreted with any accuracy. Less ambitiously, it has been known since the work of Waid and Woodman [176] that ultrasonic devices, like stress-wave timers, can provide a general indication of the presence, location and extent of any serious defects. In recent years, devices employing ultrasound have been used on trees, and one has been especially developed for this purpose; the "Arborsonic Decay Detector", which is marketed by Fujikura Europe Ltd. It measures the transit time of an ultrasound pulse between a transmitting and a receiving probe, which are attached to the tree using a gel or other medium to allow good transmission of the pulse.

Ultrasonic detectors have the advantage that they can be used without drilling or inserting screws into the wood. However, their probes are flat-ended and must be brought into good acoustic contact with the tree in order to allow passage of the impulse, thus usually necessitating the removal of bark. In the case of the "Arborsonic Decay Detector", the standard procedure is to remove bark discs of approx 40 mm diameter. The manufacturers advise that these discs should be subsequently replaced, in which case the occlusion of the wound is sometimes hastened by the formation of patches of callus and subsequently new bark on the protected face of the wound. More often, however, occlusion begins from around the edge of the wound, and this eventually tends to dislodge the disc (Plate 109). The gel or petroleum jelly applied during the test assists the growth of new tissues by preventing the wound from drying out.

As in the case of stress-wave timers, certain studies have indicated that the test readings obtained with ultrasonic timers generally need to be evaluated by reference to readings from sound wood of the species concerned [e.g. 118]. However, the manufacturers of the "Arborsonic" detector state that this requirement has been overridden by their having selected a single frequency of ultrasound (78 kHz) which is transmitted at 2000 metres per second through all types of sound wood.

Another problem that ultrasonic devices might be expected to share with stress-wave timers is the inability to detect certain kinds of decay, in particular that caused by *Ustulina deusta*, which can render the wood brittle at a stage of

Plate 108 An ultrasonic device ("Arborsonic Decay Detector")

Plate 109 Hole in bark of Platanus x hispanica, *created for probing with the Arborsonic Decay Detector (the bark plug was replaced but has now fallen out due to growth of occluding tissues)*

decay when the cell walls remain sufficiently intact to transmit stress waves with little or no reduction in velocity [153]. It has been stated by the manufacturer that there are no such limitations as far as the "Arborsonic" detector is concerned. However, there remains a need to evaluate all available sonic timers for their accuracy in a wide range of combinations of tree species and types of decay. For this reason, readings obtained with these devices should be interpreted with caution.

Unlike stress-wave timers, currently available ultrasonic devices cannot be used on very large trees, as the signals that they emit are quite rapidly attenuated in wood. In the case of the "Arborsonic Decay Detector", the maximum path length is about one metre, although it is possible to take non-radial readings (quadrant readings) which allow assessments to be made on trees up to 1.4 m in diameter. The resulting readings need to be adjusted, as the velocity of sound in wood is less in the tangential than in the radial direction.

• *The increment borer*

The increment borer is a hollow auger which is used for the extraction of a radial core of wood. Its original purpose was to allow the counting and measurement of wood increments. In a tree with decay or other defects the record of recent increments helps in the assessment of the tree's ability to lay down a shell of new wood around the defective zone. Increment measurements from sound wood near the defective zone give specific information about any local growth response to concentrations of mechanical stress, while others from completely sound parts of the main stem give a general idea of the rate of wood formation.

In the assessment of decay, increment cores provide a direct visual means of examining zones of discoloured or decayed wood. These zones can thus be mapped accurately within the cross-section. However, the increment borer creates a wide hole, up to 10 mm in diameter, and a yet wider zone of compression damage. It therefore seems likely that the concerns that exist about the extension of decay along holes created by diagnostic devices may be well founded in the case of this particular device. Decay fungi that were already established in sampled trees have been observed to grow out along auger holes, thus gaining access to wood that was formerly protected by the natural barriers within the tree. The extent to which they are likely to grow into wood beyond the immediate vicinity of the hole is, however, uncertain.

It is possible to reduce the damage done to natural barriers if the cores are taken by boring into exposed decayed wood and stopping as soon as sound wood is reached on the far boundary of the decayed zone. Nevertheless, it seems advisable to use the increment borer only when it cannot be replaced by less damaging devices. One such situation is the measurement of increments in sound wood, as mentioned above. The other special use of increment cores is the direct measurement of wood strength, using a special device, the "Fractometer" (see below).

• *Simple drills*

Detailed mapping of decay can be achieved using various drilling techniques. The simplest technique is to use an ordinary low-speed portable drill equipped with a narrow drill-bit (2–3 mm diameter). By examining the colour, texture and odour of drill shavings at frequent intervals, the practitioner can map discoloration, decay and cavities with reasonable accuracy. It is also possible to locate any zones which have a greatly reduced resistance to penetration of the drill.

A major advantage of a simple drill over a less invasive device is that the drill shavings can provide direct evidence of the presence and location of decay. Detailed mapping of decay in this way may be rather time-consuming, but is not always necessary, since the first few drill holes sometimes provide enough evidence to aid a management decision. Thus, drilling can be used initially for rapid assessment, as an alternative to acoustic methods.

The main disadvantage of the simple drill is that it provides little or no indication of the strength of the wood. It can also be argued that, like the holes created by increment borers, drill holes might open up new pathways for the extension of existing decay. The very small diameter of the holes made by a narrow drill bit, together with the virtual absence of compression of the surrounding wood, makes this relatively unlikely.

• *Endoscopes*

An endoscope allows the inside of a hole or cavity to be viewed via a flexible fibre-optic probe. Endoscopes are used widely in industry and in medical diagnosis, and have been used to some extent in the detection of defects in wood. The fibre-optic probe is inserted into a pre-drilled hole in the wood and provides a view of the walls of the hole, thus allowing zones of decay, cavities or cracks to be mapped. The first endoscopes that were marketed for use in living trees used relatively wide probes which had to be inserted into holes cut by increment borers or other augers. It is, however, now possible to obtain very narrow probes that can be inserted into drill holes of about 3 mm diameter. It remains doubtful whether such instruments are very useful for revealing the subtle changes in colour or texture that can result from decay, but they are perhaps more useful than other devices for the detection of cracks.

• *Electrical resistance meters*

If a narrow drill bit has been used for the examination of wood shavings or for endoscopy, the resulting hole can additionally be probed at intervals along its length with a device such as the 'Shigometer' [111], which measures the resistance of the walls of the drill hole to a pulsed direct electric current or alternating current. Altered wood and normal wood usually differ in electrical conductivity (altered wood is usually more conductive due to a higher concentration of mobile potassium and other ions), and so the demarcations between them can be mapped. An alteration in electrical conductivity does not, however, necessarily indicate that the wood has been weakened, as it may be merely discoloured. Discoloured wood may become decayed in time, but there are situations, partly depending on the species of tree and fungus, where such wood may remain sound. It can therefore be misleading to assume that a zone of wood with low values of electrical resistance is weakened throughout, or even that it will become so in time. Conversely, a zone of advanced decay may show a normal or perhaps an elevated electrical resistance if it has dried out to the point where moisture content is limiting the passage of the current. This problem can be solved by artificially re-wetting the wood with de-ionised water before taking the readings, but a zone of advanced decay may even then show a normal or high resistance if ions have been leached away from it.

• *The "Portable Compression Strength Meter"* (Plate 110)

After the use of a drill to examine the colour and texture of wood shavings, the wood surrounding the drill hole can be tested for its resistance to compression by forcing a specially constructed metal probe into the hole. This is the principle of a device marketed in Britain as the "Portable Compression Strength Meter", or "PCM" [9]. The "PCM" probe is a rod whose head is slightly wider than its shaft. It is inserted into the drill hole using an engineer's

Plate 110 The Barret/Seaby "Portable Compression Strength Meter"

punch which delivers a series of thrusts of equal force. The 'compression strength' is measured by the number of thrusts required to insert the probe along any chosen length of the hole. The probe carries a screw thread on the expanded head, and this allows it to be extracted by rotation in a drill after use.

This system has the advantage of providing visual information from the drill shavings, as well as mechanical data. Thus, to some extent at least, it is possible to distinguish between decayed wood and other wood of low drilling resistance. The equipment is also relatively cheap. A major disadvantage of the "PCM" is that it is very slow in operation, especially on species with dense wood. Also, the drill hole created for the "PCM" is wider (4–4.5 mm), than would be necessary for a visual examination of drill shavings alone, and it is also wider than the penetration tracks that are produced by the decay-detecting drills.

• *Decay-detecting drills* (Plate 111)

Resistance to drilling is not a complete measure of wood strength, but it is usually reduced in wood weakened by decay, compared with sound wood. For this reason, devices that measure drilling resistance along a radial penetration track (Plate 112) can give a somewhat more direct indication of wood quality than can be judged by looking at the shavings from a simple drill. Two devices of this type have been tested on wood decayed by a number of fungal species [148], the "DDD 200" and various models of the "Resistograph". In wood decayed by the brown-rot fungi *Fomitopsis pinicola* (which is not native to Britain) and *Laetiporus sulphureus*, both devices showed a very marked reduction in drilling resistance, even when the loss in dry weight was fairly small. Decay caused by white-rot fungi was also detected by these devices, but such decay reduced the drilling resistance less than the brown-rots, relative to weight loss. Decay caused by some white-rot fungi, such as *Polyporus squamosus*, could not be detected at a dry weight loss of less than 5%, but such an early stage of degradation might equally escape detection by other techniques.

Devices which measure drilling resistance can be used to construct accurate maps of wood quality. They also cause no more damage, perhaps less, than a fine drill-bit, as they leave behind only a narrow penetration track without removing wood. A disadvantage is that sound wood may contain zones of differing resistance, sometimes prompting a false suspicion of decay. To some extent, such zones can be explained by the predicted presence of reaction wood, sapwood and heartwood. Conversely, zones of decay are occasionally associated with column boundary layers which show greater resistance than sound wood, even when they have been breached and partially degraded by the decay fungus. Such layers are, however, narrow and occur adjacent to regions in which the resistance is markedly reduced by decay. Certain other factors that might affect drilling resistance, such as the presence of resin and variations in moisture content have not yet been studied in detail. Complexities such as these serve to emphasise the need for informed interpretation of the results obtained with diagnostic devices. Such devices are worse than useless in the hands of people who know nothing about the structure of trees and patterns of decay.

Plate 111 Decay-detecting drills: "DDD200" and "Resistograph"

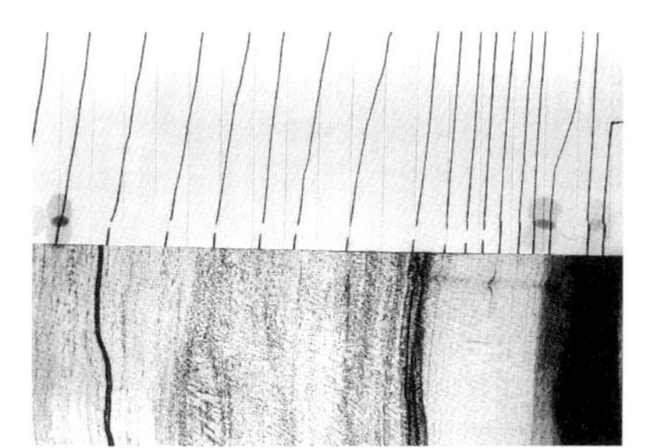

Plate 112 Pen tracing from "DDD200", placed alongside the corresponding wood sample

5.3.1.3 Measurement of wood strength in trees with decay

In many instances, the detection or mapping of decay or other defects shows them either to be minor or very extensive, so that the safety of the tree can be assessed without further tests. However, in cases where the extent of apparently sound wood is only just sufficient to meet accepted criteria for safety [106], it is necessary to test the strength of this wood.

• *Use of the "Fractometer" with sample increment cores* (Plate 113)

Plate 113 The "Fractometer"

In timber technology there are several different kinds of strength test that can be applied to wood, but they require the use of sawn samples. This is not feasible in the case of standing trees, but it is possible to measure the bending strength of an increment core using the "Fractometer". The core is broken at a number of points along its length, as explained in the operating instructions and in the companion volume in this series by Mattheck and Breloer [106]. The resulting measurements of breaking strength allow zones of weakened wood to be mapped within the stem cross-section. Also, by measuring the bending angle, the assessor can determine whether the wood is liable to undergo brittle or non-brittle fracture. The values obtained are a measure of the resistance of the wood fibres to longitudinal separation (delamination), which is an important component of the bending strength of the stem. Experimental data have shown that the "Fractometer" is sensitive in measuring strength loss from decay caused by a range of different fungi [148].

One of the difficulties experienced by users of the "Fractometer" is in knowing the breaking strength values that should be expected for sound wood. A provisional table of ranges for some common tree species has been provided [106], but these values should not be regarded as 'standards', since breaking strength differs not only between tree species, but also between individuals and between the 'upper' and 'lower' sides of leaning stems. Also, climate and local growing conditions affect the development of wood and may therefore influence its breaking strength; the published values refer to trees in Germany.

The completely sound wood of the tree being tested with the "Fractometer" should in theory be the best guide as to the value that should be expected, at least if it is sampled from a point close to the decayed area. It is, however, necessary to avoid basing this value on wood that, although undecayed, might have been weakened by incipient failure such as could have occurred due to the progressive bending of a branch or stem base. Similarly, any wood sampled from the vicinity of pruning wounds or other injuries may contain a barrier zone, and a sample core will very easily break at this point when placed

Table 5.1 A comparison of some devices that give measurements related to the mechanical properties of wood

Device	Property measured	Type of data	Some advantages	Some disadvantages
Decay detecting drill ("DDD 200")	Speed of drill entry	Pen tracing or computer-generated plot of penetration speed	• Little damage to tree • Allows rapid mapping of wood with reduced penetration resistance • Probe is designed with a blunt tip	• Values obtained are not necessarily related to breaking strength • Some tendency for the probe to deviate from a radial track • Length of device may limit accessibility to tree
"Resistograph" (various models)	Electrical power needed to drill along the entry hole	Computer-generated tracing of drilling resistance along the entry hole	• Little damage to tree • Allows rapid mapping of wood with reduced penetration resistance	• Values obtained are not necessarily related to breaking strength • Slight tendency for the probe to deviate from a radial track • Blunting of probe tip affects performance
"Metriguard" stress-wave timer (impulse hammer)	Speed at which sound travels through the tree	Sound transit velocities shown on a meter	• Damage confined to outer wood • Fairly modest cost • Data closely represent density and modulus of elasticity • Useful for detecting butt-rot, especially in large trees	• Requires insertion of screws into wood • Reliability of detection is affected by type of decay, since readings depend on both stiffness and density • Values obtained are not necessarily related to breaking strength • Effects of various properties of sound wood on stress wave velocities are not thoroughly known
"Arborsonic Decay Detector"	Speed at which ultrasound travels through the tree	Ultrasound transit times shown on a meter	• Damage confined to bark • Fairly modest cost • Data closely represent density and modulus of elasticity • Relatively simple evaluation of results	• Uncertain whether reliability of detection is affected by type of decay • Values obtained are not necessarily related to breaking strength • Effects of various properties of sound wood on ultrasound velocities are not thoroughly known
"Fractometer"	Bending strength of an increment core and angle of bending at breaking point	Visual meter readings of bending angle and breaking force at successive points along the core sample	• Fairly modest cost • Directly measures stiffness and strength, even at early stages of decay, thus providing an accurate map of strong and weak zones • Differentiates between different kinds of loss in strength and stiffness	• The necessary increment boring damages sound wood, perhaps allowing extension of decay

in the machine. A diagrammatic example, showing how the "Fractometer" can be used to aid a final decision, is shown in Fig. 5.4.

5.3.1.4 The value of identifying decay fungi

The identification of decay fungi, which sometimes requires the services of a specialist laboratory, can play an important part in the diagnosis and prognosis of hazards. This is, however, only true if something is known about the potential for hazard associated with the fungus concerned. The more important considerations include the ability of the fungus to spread within the tree, the rate at which it degrades the wood that it has colonised, and the strength properties of the partially degraded wood. Our knowledge in such matters is unfortunately very patchy at present, and is more often based on observation than on the findings of scientific research.

Many of the species described in this book (Chapter 4) are common, but are rarely associated with major mechanical failures. Some of these fungi appear to have only a limited ability to colonise large volumes of wood, or to overcome unfavourable conditions in living trees. Conversely there are other species that are of major concern in hazard assessment. One of the most important of these is *Ustulina deusta* which, perhaps regardless of the host species, causes a brittle form of decay which tends eventually to cause a sudden snapping at the base of the tree. In beech (*Fagus sylvatica*), *Meripilus giganteus* is perhaps the fungus most frequently associated with root failure. It occurs in other host species, but too rarely to judge its effects on their stability. In ash (*Fraxinus excelsior*), severe weakening is caused by *Inonotus hispidus*, whereas the same fungus rarely causes failure in London plane (*Platanus* x *hispanica*). In oak (*Quercus robur* and *Q. petraea*), the beefsteak fungus *Fistulina hepatica* causes very little loss of strength except at a very advanced stage of decay. More information on these and many other species can be found in Chapter 4.

As far as general principles are concerned, it is helpful to be aware that the more brittle the type of decay, the more likely it is to cause failure if and when it becomes extensive. Brown rots in general thus tend to be potentially rather dangerous, although relatively few are encountered amongst amenity trees in Britain. A common example is that caused by *Laetiporus sulphureus*, although this fungus appears to develop rather slowly and may therefore take many years to weaken trees seriously. The brown rot of birch (*Betula*) caused by *Piptoporus betulinus* may cause stem fracture by the time that large fruit bodies of the fungus appear, but the tree is usually dead or dying by this stage in any case. In conifers, particular attention should be paid to *Sparassis crispa* and *Phaeolus schweinitzii*.

Although embrittlement is typical of brown-rots, it can also occur in the advanced stages of most other kinds of decay. Even at a relatively early stage, simultaneous white-rots can lead to a brittle fracture, as in the examples of *Fomes fomentarius* and *Bjerkandera adusta*. Some fungi with the ability to cause white-rots also cause embrittlement when they switch to a soft-rot mode of cell wall degradation (see Section 3.2.2.3). Such embrittlement is especially severe in the case of *Ustulina deusta* [152].

5.3.2 Prognosis of future decay development

For many trees, perhaps the majority of those that are assessed in detail for the extent of decay, remedial action is not immediately essential but could become so later. It is usually hard to predict how soon this might be, but any further development of decay can be assessed through a programme of monitoring. The interval of monitoring should, as far as possible, be prescribed on the basis of objective evidence for the likely rate of decay and the effectiveness of defence mechanisms in the tree. In the least serious cases, where the zones of decay are unlikely to become more extensive, the justification for monitoring may be purely precautionary. If, on the other hand, there is evidence that decay will probably extend beyond acceptably safe limits, the purpose of monitoring may be to help decide how soon remedial action will be necessary. For many trees, the prognosis may lie somewhere in between these extremes.

5.3.2.1 'Compartmentalisation' of decay: implications for prognosis

The concept of compartmentalisation [159], is of key importance in assessing the potential of existing decay to extend further (see Chapter 3). It is particularly important to be aware that xylem dysfunction, and therefore decay, usually remains confined within the annual increments that were present at the time of the initiating trauma. If such a trauma occurs when the tree is young, the pre-existing wood may eventually occupy only a narrow core surrounded by a wide 'shell' of new wood. The situation is obviously different in a mature tree, in which the pre-existing wood may continue to make up most of the total tree's volume, so that serious weakening would result if it were to become wholly decayed. Fortunately, however, there are many cases in which only part of this older wood becomes decayed, as there are barriers within it which help to restrict the spread of decay fungi. The difficulty is in determining whether the decay has been arrested in this way; in other words, whether its current boundaries represent barriers.

Perhaps the most reliable indication of a stable boundary (i.e. a barrier) is the presence of sound wood immediately adjacent to a zone of advanced decay. If the zone of decay were actively progressing, it would probably have a margin of partially and incipiently decayed wood. Even if there is such a margin, a very dense dark line between the sound wood and the partially decayed wood is a reasonably good sign of a stable boundary. A diffuse band of discoloration at the edge of the affected zone is more likely to be an advancing boundary.

Unfortunately, the need to avoid damage to trees makes it very difficult, if not impossible, to make an adequate inspection of boundaries except in the 'post-mortem' situation when a tree is dissected with a chainsaw. Small portions of a boundary can be inspected by taking cores with an increment borer, but often only at the risk of breaching the very barriers that are of value. A small-diameter endoscope could perhaps provide a less damaging means of looking at boundaries, as revealed on the wall of a narrow drill hole. Even if such costly equipment is not available, a narrow drill-bit used on its own can provide useful information from the colour, texture and odour of the wood shavings at various depths within the tree. Mechanical devices such as the portable compression strength meter, the "DDD 200" or the "Resistograph" can also reveal sharp boundaries by virtue of a sudden change in the resistance to penetration, but they provide no direct visual information.

The past rate of extension of a decay column is often a useful clue as to its potential for spread, provided that its boundaries have not been breached by later wounding. The average rate of extension of a column of known length can be calculated by determining its time of initiation, provided that the site of initiation can be reliably located. This necessitates the extraction of an increment core from somewhere near this point, although preferably not passing through the decayed zone itself. If a suitable sample can be obtained, the age of the wound or other trauma can then be determined by counting the annual increments that have been laid down outside the barrier zone that represents the signature of the initiating trauma (Fig. 5.7). A very slow average rate of spread is a good sign for the future, but this does not preclude the possibility that the decay column might be re-activated by fresh wounding or by changes in the overall health of the tree.

Although there is a need for caution when making prognoses about barriers that have formed within pre-existing wood, certain patterns of decay are not usually much cause for concern. For example, discoloration or decay is often restricted to a discrete zone in the vicinity of a pruning wound (Plate 143). If there are no similar zones developing from nearby wounds (Fig. 5.6, Plates 36–37), there is often a very good chance that the cone will not extend very far, or that its extension might be very slow. In such cases, the identity of the decay fungus and the host tree will also have some bearing on the potential for decay to spread, since there is a wide range of variation in both the ability of different fungal species to overcome host defences and the defensive capacity of their host trees. There are some fungi that have a 'track record' of not being very invasive, such as *Pleurotus ostreatus*, which tends to remain strongly compartmentalised even in beech (*Fagus sylvatica*), whose defences are at best moderately effective. The same is sometimes true of *Polyporus squamosus*, as long as the pruning wounds are not very large or close together, whereas *Fomes fomentarius* usually tends to form extensive decay columns in most of its host species.

Decay in roots can be compartmentalised [174], but some root decay fungi can nevertheless spread very extensively through the root system. For species which have a serious case-history for causing failure, the prognosis for the acceptable retention time of trees affected by them is usually very poor. One of the best known examples is *Meripilus giganteus*, which is a frequent cause of root-plate failure in *F. sylvatica*.

5.3.2.2 *Prognosis in relation to the growth potential of the tree*

Although decay above ground-level rarely extends into wood laid down after the initiating event, it must be appreciated that later injuries may initiate decay in this new wood. In some cases, such injuries (including perhaps those created by the use of an increment borer during a previous assessment) may have opened the way for a decay fungus to cross a barrier zone. Also, as mentioned in Section 3.4.3, decay in root systems often spreads into new wood, particularly if bark-killing fungi are involved.

Provided that the barrier zone between old and new wood is not breached, the continued formation of an outer shell of sound wood can often maintain or enhance the strength of a decayed region of the tree [106]. This is clearly the case when a decay column has already occupied the entire cross-section of the old wood, and cannot therefore weaken it any further. More commonly the old wood is partly sound, so that there is still room for expansion of the decay column. In this situation, the new wood will similarly add strength to the tree, but the question is whether it will form rapidly enough at least to keep pace with any extension of decay within the older wood. The age of the tree is clearly important in this context (Fig. 8.1).

Another interesting aspect of new growth has already been mentioned; this is the ability of the tree to lay down wood increments of extra width in regions where there is a local concentration of mechanical stress due to decay involving selective delignification [106]. Provided that the tree has sufficient potential for diameter growth, this adaptive growth can restore an adequate safety margin. If the ability to form substantial annual increments is in doubt, its recent growth history can be assessed by the examination of a shallow increment core, extending only into sound wood (Fig. 5.7).

5.3.3 Internal investigation of cracks

Most cracks can be assessed visually as described above, but some may be concealed or completely internal. If other evidence or experience suggests that such cracks may be present, they can sometimes be detected with the aid of the same diagnostic devices that are used for the assessment of decay. Stress-wave timers and ultrasonic timers can detect cracks because a wide crack prevents the transmission of a detectable signal. On this basis, the presence or absence of readings at various orientations around a stem can be used to map the position and extent of cracks. Drilling devices such as the “DDD 200” and the “Resistograph” can detect severe cracks as local points on the print-out where the resistance to drilling abruptly decreases. However, if the expanded tip of the probe is longer than the crack is wide, no such change in resistance is likely to be registered. The smaller size of the “DDD 200” probe tip, compared with that of the "Resistograph", may be an advantage in this respect. Increment borings reveal cracks as breaks in the extracted wood cores, but breakage may also occur during extraction if there is a barrier zone, rather than a crack, present.

5.3.4 Assessment of root-plate stability

In many cases a general inspection reveals no sign of movement of a tree's root-plate, and yet the site history or the condition of the crown indicates that it might have been damaged, for example by trenching or by decay. If decay is present in the major roots that radiate from the buttress zone, it can be detected with one of the drilling devices described above. Detection of decay or other damage is more difficult further away from the tree, where the roots are entirely below ground level, and it may be necessary to dig carefully along the course of the main lateral roots to expose any such damage. This may not be practicable if a paved surface is present, but the recent laying of paving materials is in itself an indication that digging or compaction and therefore root damage may have occurred.

Unlike most forms of physical damage, which are generally evident near the surface, decay sometimes occurs only in deep roots, leaving the upper ones unaffected. In practice, this possibility is rarely investigated, although this can sometimes be attempted by digging several small pits going down at least 450 mm. This is, however, very laborious and some damage to smaller roots is unavoidable even with care.

In cases where roots are found to be decayed or otherwise damaged, the question is whether the remaining sound parts of the root system can provide acceptably safe anchorage. On the basis of the mechanical criteria proposed by Mattheck and Breloer [106], all the roots need to be sound within a radius that is dependent on the stem diameter and can be read from a reference graph that these authors have provided. Graphs which have been plotted for a range of individual genera are similar [104]. The radius derived from the graph corresponds to the size of root-plate that is estimated to provide a safety factor of about 4.5. If this approach is adopted, the calculation of the 'safe' radius helps to decide where to dig any exploratory pits.

If major roots are decayed or damaged within the 'safe' radius, further exploration is needed nearer to the stem base. If only 60% of the theoretical root-plate diameter is occupied by sound roots, the safety factor has been reduced to 1.0, according to the above criterion. In such a state, the tree would be able to withstand only average wind pressures unless it could be subjected to quite severe cutting so as to reduce the lever arm and sail area.

The criteria for root-plate stability are perhaps less certain than those that are now widely accepted for assessing the strength of hollow stems. In any case, they only apply to the lateral roots of trees with symmetrical root systems. For the present, considerable subjectivity is involved in the assessment of stability of trees with eccentric root systems, or with decay present only in the centre of the root-plate. In such cases, casebook experience of the tree species and of the relevant decay fungus may be valuable.

5.3.5 Possibilities for whole-tree testing

It has been suggested by Sinn and Wessolly [162] that the bending strength of a stem can be measured by means of a strain gauge when a modest bending load is applied by pulling the stem. They have also suggested that instability of the root-plate can be detected by a similar pulling test, in which a device near the base of the tree measures any tilt during application of the load.

As far as the detection of decay is concerned, an abnormally high strain in the stem is detectable during the pulling test if there is a loss of stiffness due to decay. This alteration occurs with some types of white-rot in which lignin (the stiffening component of the wood) is removed preferentially, leaving behind the cellulose (the component of the wood that provides tensile strength: see Section 3.2.1). On the other hand there are brittle forms of decay which do not reduce the stiffness of the stem, and it seems unlikely that they could be detected by this means. Even when stiffness is reduced, the safety of the tree cannot be judged properly from a strain gauge reading unless the location and extent of the decay are known.

As weakness in stems is not caused exclusively by decay, it is worth considering whether other potential defects could be assessed by means of a pulling test. For example, trees sometimes undergo incipient failure in severe winds. This may be detectable in the form of reduced stiffness of the stem or looseness of the root-plate, but it seems doubtful whether there is a basis for distinguishing between 'safe' and 'unsafe' values, as measured with a strain gauge. If however, a visual assessment reveals an incipient failure point by the presence of distortion in bark or wood, a pulling test might perhaps provide supplementary information about some of the associated mechanical effects.

The detection of excessive mobility in a root-plate may appear to be a potentially valid use for a pulling test. A certain amount of movement might, however, be detectable in a sound root-plate, especially if it is of the wide-spreading and shallow type. The presence of cracks in the soil round the edge of the root-plate may be a visual sign of excessive movement, which could be further investigated with a pulling test. It should, however, be noted that cracks sometimes develop radially from the base of a tree without necessarily indicating any hazard. Such cracks may be caused by flexing of the rope-like roots of shallow-rooted trees.

5.4 Recording and reporting

For all investigations, it is essential to prepare a statement of the objectives and to record the results, together with the date and the name(s) of the persons involved. For general inspections, it may be appropriate to keep an archive of completed survey forms, electronic data files or perhaps just a written note that all the trees in a defined area were inspected at a particular time. For assessments involving particular trees, a written report is usually required. In a report, the objectives should be stated in the form of a specific **brief** which must indicate whether a full hazard assessment has been commissioned, as opposed to an investigation of a specified defect that was suspected on the basis of a preliminary inspection. In some cases, the tree owner may be unable to formulate the brief precisely, but this can be determined by prior discussion. Additionally, unexpected defects may come to light during the assessment. If any such findings indicate the need for further investigation, the owner should be notified accordingly.

It is generally necessary for a report to include a statement indicating whether the tree or trees concerned pose a significant risk to persons or property. The hazard may relate to a specific defect defined in the brief, or to all aspects of the tree's condition. To this end, it may sometimes be helpful to allocate a numerical rating, as outlined in Section 5.1.3 [49, 101]. Experience indicates that the scores derived in this way vary considerably between assessors, so that a statement of the actual score in the report could be misleading to the site owner. A scoring system can, however, help an individual assessor to compare the tree in question with similar specimens in the locality. Such a comparison can help to put the matter in perspective for the site owner.

Finally, the evaluated options for remedial action (see Chapter 6) or for future inspection should be stated in the report, taking into account the overall requirements for managing the site. Recommendations for monitoring or remedial work should take account of whichever aspects of a tree's condition are most likely to give rise to hazards in the foreseeable future. It would be wrong to recommend expensive work in the crown of a tree that was showing signs of imminent root-plate failure. This approach follows on from the stepwise assessment of decay, whereby it would be inappropriate to assess a tree in great detail if a short, inexpensive inspection had already shown it either to be very hazardous or to be passed as acceptably safe (Fig. 5.1). In between these extremes are trees for which it is not easy to predict how rapidly decay will extend, and for which personal judgement must be exercised in prescribing an interval for further assessments. Anything between six months and five years might be reasonable in the first instance, but such a prescription may have to be modified when the results of later assessments are obtained.

If work by a contractor is specified, it should be emphasised that a reputable company should be chosen, perhaps by reference to a system of approval, as operated in Great Britain by the Arboricultural Association.

Since different situations demand different requirements for reporting, it could be misleading to provide a 'model report' as a guide until perhaps there can be an accepted set of guidelines for recording and reporting for various purposes. It is, however, possible to summarise the main elements of a report on a detailed assessment as follows:-

- Date
- Weather conditions
- Specification of which tree or trees were assessed
- Statement of the brief
- General description of site, including site usage, soil conditions, slope and wind exposure
- Statement of risk factors associated with site (presence and occupancy of 'targets'), including the potential for personal injury or damage to property
- General description of the tree(s), including: species; cultivar (if appropriate); stem diameter; angle and direction of lean or basal sweep (if any); description of architecture of scaffold limbs (if any); height; crown spread in compass directions of minimum and maximum dimensions; previous arboricultural work; specification of any buildings, roadways etc. that are overhung
- General report on defects identified in various parts of the tree(s) main stem; scaffold limbs (if any), branch base conformation (e.g. tendency to produce bark inclusions); crown (including presence of deadwood)
- Detailed assessment of specific defects which may have been cited as the main cause of concern
- Risk appraisal
- Conclusions and, where required, recommendations (including specification of advised date for future inspection).

Chapter 6 Remedial action

The purpose of remedial action for tree-related hazards is to remove or mitigate them, so that there will no longer be an unacceptable risk of damage or personal injury. Although, by definition, remedial action is concerned with hazards that already exist, it should also be part of a programme of continuing management which allows for the possible recurrence of hazards or the development of new ones. In this context, there is a need to monitor the condition of trees which have been subjected to remedial work and to take further action if necessary. In particular, if a tree is cut so as to reduce its height or wind resistance, the new shoots that develop subsequently may need to be cut periodically. It will also be necessary to monitor the possible development of decay near the cuts.

Another consideration for management after the immediate hazard has been dealt with is whether the site might be used differently or more intensively in the future. If so, the risk of damage or injury to 'targets' could change, in which case the best option for remedial action might not be apparent from a consideration of the current site usage alone.

The details of the planned work should be made known to all parties responsible for management of the site and neighbouring sites that could be affected. A written schedule of the agreed operations should be supplied to the site owner and, if appropriate, there should be communication with any relevant authorities, such as those responsible for the regulation of tree work or traffic safety. Under UK law, it must be ascertained whether the site or the individual tree is subject to a Tree Preservation Order [195] or lies within a Conservation Area [196] or a site designated for scientific or heritage value [210, 211]. Also, it may be necessary to apply to the Forestry Commission for a Felling Licence [191] if the work is to be done other than in a garden and would involve the felling of a number of trees or a substantial volume of timber. There must be compliance with the relevant procedures and restrictions except in cases where the trees concerned are exempt [200, 191].

Once the decision to carry out remedial action has been made, the work should be done within an appropriate period by suitably trained and insured operators and in accordance with all relevant safety guidelines, including the erection of warning signs and barriers to access if necessary. Proper training, equipment and insurance are important because most aspects of tree work are potentially dangerous to operators and to persons or property in the vicinity. Unsuitable or poorly executed work can also be very damaging to the trees themselves.

Information on good practice and safety under UK regulations can be found in a series of guides published by the Forestry and Arboriculture Safety and Training Council (FASTCo). Currently available guides in this series with especial relevance to remedial tree work [199] are listed in Appendix 1. It is also important that the credentials of contractors should be checked before they are employed. Professional bodies such as the Arboricultural Association and the International Society of Arboriculture have lists or certification schemes which indicate whether a particular contractor has achieved a certain level of expertise. An advisory leaflet on the employment of contractors has been published by the London Tree Officers' Association [206]. For operations involving the felling of trees in substantial numbers or within woodlands, it may be appropriate to seek the services of a contractor with experience in forestry, especially if any timber is to be marketed.

6.1 A rationale for remedial action

The main question in assessing the need for remedial action is whether failure to carry out such action would leave an unacceptable risk to persons or property (targets). There may be a desire to 'play safe' by felling or topping every tree that conspicuously shows anything that might possibly be a defect. Such an approach is, however, inconsistent with the concept that risk should be assessed and kept within a limit of acceptability, rather than eliminated entirely. This concept is established in industry and in activities involving public safety (for example, transport), and is gaining acceptance on the part of tree owners and managers. If risk is quantified as far as can be achieved with available methods (see Chapter 5), appropriate decisions about remedial action can be taken.

As with the assessment of hazards and risks, the decision whether or not to take remedial action must be made in the knowledge that there can never be an absolute guarantee of safety for trees or for any other structures exposed to extremes of weather. The appropriate question is whether the tree concerned shows the potential to fail under the range of conditions that can reasonably be expected to occur before the next hazard inspection is due. Even those trees that show such a potential may pose a very low risk to targets if they are on sites far from roads, paths, buildings or recreational areas. At such sites, it is often inappropriate even to carry out potentially expensive detailed hazard assessments in the first place, let alone to plan remedial action. Although a site owner could still be held legally liable for tree-related injury, negligence could be proved only on the basis of evidence to show that the risk was both foreseeable and unacceptably high.

It must be remembered that new risks may be created by a change in site usage following a tree inspection, especially if people or property come into closer proximity to the trees concerned. Similarly, trees may have been damaged by the development of the site. In such situations, tree inspection and risk assessment should be repeated.

The potential of a major failure involving a tree's root-plate, stem or major branch is an especially important consideration if the site concerned is built up or much frequented by people or traffic, as there could be serious consequences for persons or property. If either of these types of failure appears imminent on the basis of a tree hazard assessment at such a site, remedial action may be urgently needed. The most urgent situation arises when a major hazard has resulted from a particular event, such as partial root-plate failure in a recent storm [97] or the severance of major roots from trenching.

There is some cause for concern over the possibility that to take remedial action (e.g. the bracing of a weak fork) is to admit in the eyes of the law that a hazard was known to exist. In the event of litigation following injury or damage caused by the tree in question, such an admission could be exploited by the plaintiff. The fear of this must, however, be set against the fact that the case will usually rest on the question as to whether the failure of the tree and the resulting damage or injury was foreseeable under all but the most exceptional conditions. If the tree had not been inspected for hazardous features, all that could be said would be that the potential for failure was not known; not that it was unforeseeable. If, however, remedial action had been taken and was demonstrably unsuitable or inadequate, the plaintiff might have a valid case.

In the particular case of woodland trees, defective specimens are often removed for reasons of commercial management. There may also be significant risks to targets if the trees concerned are near rides, car parks or recreational areas. If, however, trees do not need to be removed for any of these reasons, they might as well be left to stand or fall naturally. They can then provide much needed habitats for the many forms of wildlife that depend on old or decaying trees. For invertebrates with poor powers of dispersal, items of deadwood habitat need to be in close proximity and to be available continuously.

Most forms of remedial action are directed toward defects in trees, although the problem may sometimes lie more with the site (e.g. unstable soil conditions) than with the trees themselves. Roadside trees are, however, something of an exception since even a very small stem or branch, incapable of causing serious injury directly, could cause a road traffic accident if it were suddenly encountered as an obstruction on the carriageway. For this reason, the risk even from fairly minor defects is sometimes considerable on stretches of road with restricted visibility. It is also necessary to take into account the speed of the traffic, since this determines not only the stopping distance needed to avoid an obstruction, but also the force of impact of an airborne broken branch or leading shoot. The brittle tops of motorway-verge sycamores that have been girdled by squirrels are a particular hazard in this respect [59].

6.1.1 Choosing between options for remedial action

The choice of remedial action must be determined primarily by the need to remove or mitigate a hazard, but in many cases there is more than one course of action that can satisfy this need. It is then important to take account of the likely effects of different remedies on all aspects of the value of the tree concerned, such as wildlife conservation and amenity. One remedy may be to fell the tree, but its loss represents a price to pay in addition to the cost of felling, not to mention any new hazards or problems that may thereby be created. Indeed, felling a tree in a built-up area can cost more money than a more conservative treatment for achieving acceptable safety.

If the choice is to retain the tree, the next decision is whether the tree itself requires remedial action, or whether the risk to potential targets can be mitigated by moving or diverting them away from the zone of hazard. If the tree requires treatment, the type and severity of treatment required can usually be determined by the nature of the defect and its estimated influence on the safety factor of tree or the affected part of the tree. Guidance on assessing hazards is given in Chapter 5, and a detailed mechanical explanation is provided by Mattheck and Breloer [106]. Also, a guide to the choice of remedial action is shown as a flow chart in Fig. 6.5. In summary, the main factors to consider are as follows:

- The part of the tree that is defective (if any)
- The size and height above ground of the defective part or of parts which it supports
- Any constraints on possible action, resulting from previous management
- The type and age of the tree
- Site usage, current and predicted, with regard to buildings, vehicles, people and other targets
- The growing conditions, including soil type and depth and exposure to wind.

6.2 Moving the 'target'

The idea of moving the target, rather than removing or cutting the tree, may involve a shift of viewpoint and so may not always be obvious. Some targets can be moved at a cost comparable to that of felling the tree, or indeed more cheaply. Examples include park benches and light buildings such as kiosks or cycle sheds. Also, the boundaries of high-usage areas such as car parks or picnic sites or the routes of relatively short lengths of footpath or driveway can sometimes be re-designed. On low-usage public highways, a single-file traffic regulation has also recently been applied in at least one local authority area as a means of keeping vehicles away from projecting branches (Plate 114).

Plate 114 Traffic warning sign indicating single file traffic around tree crown: moving the target instead of cutting the tree

If necessary, access to a potential danger zone could be actively discouraged by the installation of fencing or the planting of woody ground cover plants or thorny shrubs. Such measures may not, however, always be ecologically appropriate on sites such as nature reserves, in which case access may have to be restricted or discouraged by means of warnings. Even if moving the target is more expensive than other options, it may confer a nett benefit if the value of the standing tree is taken fully into account.

If trees are defective or likely to become so, but are not currently placing targets at risk, one of the conditions for retaining them is that targets are not brought more into their proximity in the future. All other implications of retaining them should also be fully considered. This strategy is perhaps more preventive than remedial, but it is a response to the need for action when defects in trees are detected at sites on which new access routes, buildings or other facilities might be constructed. In this context, particular attention should be paid to trees that might become hazardous in the foreseeable future. These could include large old trees of any species, as well as younger ones of species that are more likely than most to become hazardous (e.g. many types of poplar). Proper collaboration with developers and planning officers in these situations could be very cost-effective, especially when the option of re-locating targets in the future would be too difficult or expensive.

6.3 Removal of defective trees or parts of trees

The option of removing a defective stem or branch entirely is different to that of lightening the load on the defective part (see Section 6.4), but the two options involve a similar range of cutting techniques. In practice, both options are often used together, perhaps in combination with other forms of remedial action. Cutting treatments collectively represent the main choice for remedial tree work in present-day practice.

6.3.1 Felling the tree

If a hazardous tree is felled, the immediate cause of the hazard is removed but there are many situations where an individual tree is too valuable for its loss to be treated lightly. In such situations, other options should be considered if they would allow the tree to be retained with an acceptable margin of safety.

After felling, trees are often removed or destroyed, but there is a growing awareness that they would provide deadwood habitats for wildlife if at least some of the wood could be retained. Many invertebrates, fungi and other organisms are completely dependent on such habitats and some of them are endangered because of excessive tidiness (see Chapter 8). It is therefore important to leave the felled material on-site wherever this can be agreed, preferably keeping long sections of uncut stem, and placing them in a shady spot. As standing deadwood habitats are particularly scarce and threatened, it may be of value in a site such as a large garden or a nature reserve to retain a tall stump up to four metres high. Such a stump may, however, eventually fall with considerable force, and its condition must therefore be monitored.

In most cases, the retention of fallen deadwood does not expose any remaining trees to increased attack by pests and pathogens. The main exceptions are in conifer plantations, where recently felled material may provide a habitat for damagingly high bark beetle populations, and in sites where the felled trees carry a pre-existing infection by an aggressive pathogen such as *Chondrostereum purpureum* or *Erwinia amylovora*.

6.3.1.1 Situations where felling is appropriate

Some trees have such major defects that felling may be the only safe option, apart from severe and generally undesirable treatments such as topping. Harsh cutting may in any case lead to future hazards by encouraging the development of weakly attached branches or of extensive decay columns. At the very least, these possibilities impose a need for monitoring and probably for further remedial action. Felling can often solve the problem without the need for such commitments, and it leaves space for a potential replacement tree which in time may acquire more amenity value than an older one that has been mutilated.

For valuable specimen trees, felling should be chosen as a remedy only if it is justified on the basis of an adequate evaluation of risk. Detailed assessments are, however, sometimes economically difficult to justify for trees deemed to be of low value as individual specimens. This applies particularly to trees which are unexceptional members of a large woodland population. General inspections of woodland trees near roads, recreation sites or built-up areas sometimes reveal features such as fungal fruit bodies that would require a detailed assessment to see whether they indicate significant hazards. However, the mere presence of such features often leads to the affected trees being felled as a precaution and in the knowledge that they are surrounded by similar individuals or by younger trees which may serve as replacements. Another consideration is that a gap in a dense stand favours many woodland plants and invertebrates that need direct sunlight.

It must be emphasised that the need to save money is not an excuse for felling valuable specimens that deserve to be fully assessed and, if necessary, sensitively treated. Conversely, resources may be wasted if devoted to detailed work on trees in woodlands and within groups which could be better managed on a silvicultural basis. For example, trees that have been severely suppressed by their neighbours often carry dead branches which could be expensive to remove. From a silvicultural point of view, it can be recognised that such trees usually have a short life expectancy and that they should perhaps be felled so as to make more space for other trees to grow well. The same often applies to trees that are declining due to serious disease or decay of their roots. Diseased plantation trees or municipal parkland trees should, however, not be confused with valuable 'veteran' trees that may also show signs of decline.

A silvicultural approach to the management of tree stands, with felling as its main *modus operandi*, is a cost-effective basis for managing hazards and for preventing the development of new ones. Detailed assessments and work on the crown should nevertheless be considered in cases where felling might harm wildlife habitats or amenity value, but the cost of such measures could often be usefully diverted towards the more sensitive management of other trees that are arguably more worthy of retention.

6.3.1.2 Situations where felling may be inappropriate

Although, on balance, felling may be the best remedy for a proportion of hazardous trees, the loss of trees is often detrimental to landscape, wildlife, historical interest and sentimental value. The last of these attributes can all too easily be dismissed, but it can be paramount in the minds of people who have come to regard a particular tree as part of their local environment. Sometimes, however, they may need to understand that all trees eventually die, even though some can live for many human generations.

The various values that can be attached to trees are not a reason for allowing a hazardous situation to continue, but they create a need to ensure within reason that trees are not felled unnecessarily. For specimens of particular visual, historic or ecological value, this means that any hazards should be assessed in detail, and that remedial action should not be carried out merely because there are signs that give cause for suspicion. It also means that alternatives to felling should be considered for such trees.

The ecological value of trees is an especially important consideration, as even a single tree may be supporting rare or endangered plants, animals or fungi. In some cases, legally protected species of wildlife may be present, or the site may be covered by legal restrictions on certain practices, perhaps including tree work. In the UK such restrictions may apply, for example, at national nature reserves and at 'sites of special scientific interest'.

Although felling totally removes a particular hazard, it may create a new one by increasing the exposure of neighbouring trees to the wind (see Chapter 2). This problem may persist if the trees are mature and unable to improve their anchorage very much through root growth. Younger trees, with a good potential for root growth, can eventually gain a better anchorage than they had before their neighbours were felled. Felling can sometimes also lead to damage to nearby buildings as a result of soil heave due to the re-hydration of a shrinkable clay soil previously kept dry by the tree's root system. This is a less common problem than subsidence, but must be considered, especially if the tree was well established before the building was erected.

Finally, it should be understood that it is a mark of poor management to fell trees simply in order to 'play safe', rather than to place trust in a more suitable form of remedial action, or indeed to spend some money on a detailed hazard assessment.

6.3.2 Removal or cutting back of hazardous branches

In a situation where the risk of injury or damage is especially high, for example by a busy road or in a school playground, dead or damaged branches are often hazardous. Even a branch as small as 50 mm in diameter might be considered a serious hazard, especially if it had a long clear route of fall. If a branch has snapped or cracked across the grain, any hanging or dead attached portion which could place people or property at risk should be removed. In situations where dead branches do not represent a significant risk, there is seldom any valid reason why they should be removed.

If a hazardous branch is completely dead or partly broken near its base, it should be cut back to its junction with the parent stem using the 'natural-target pruning' method [157]. Even this method is not necessarily a guarantee against the development of decay behind the wound. The extent of decay, if any, depends partly on several factors, including the type of tree concerned and the size of the wound. Wounds of more than about one third of the parent stem diameter are quite likely to encourage the development of extensive decay. Also, if a number of adjacent branches are removed, any resulting zones of decay may then coalesce into an extensive column within the main stem (Plates 36–37). Wounds in vertical alignment may also become a source of future defects, as cracks may develop between them. The need to minimise the size and number of wounds on the main stem is discussed in more detail in Chapter 7, especially in relation to the desirability of formative pruning.

A partial breakage or dead portion on a branch can often be dealt with by cutting it just distal to a substantial healthy side-branch rather than removing it entirely (Fig. 6.1). This may help to keep xylem dysfunction away from the main stem, and also to avoid creating a gap in the crown. This practice of removing only the hazardous part of the branch is similar to the shortening (or 'tipping') of a branch which is healthy but overloaded (see Section 6.4.1.3). In both situations there is a need to assess the visual effect and the likelihood of subsequent dieback in the retained portion of the branch due to shading from the crown above.

It is not clear whether it is better to risk the shading out and dieback of low branches by shortening them, rather than to remove them entirely in the first instance. The removal of a large branch may create an excessively large wound on the parent stem, with the potential for serious decay to endanger the entire tree. If, however, a large dead stub is left, it could become a foodbase for a decay fungus, as mentioned at the end of this chapter. In most cases, however, a branch dies back in a series of successive portions, each bounded by a union with a lateral. It can be argued that this staged process probably gives the tree more of a chance to lay down effective barriers than the early removal of the entire branch. There is, however, a need to carry out periodic cutting back of dead portions if they present a hazard. When only a completely dead stub is left, it too can be removed so that occlusion is allowed to occur at its base.

At sites where conservation of the deadwood fauna and flora is an important consideration, and where people or property are not much at risk, there is merit in leaving a ragged or splintered snag for colonisation by insects and fungi.

If a branch is dead or carries dead side-branches, the cause of death should be ascertained as far as possible, as this might determine the appropriate course of action. Branches die from internal suppression within healthy crowns, but very large numbers of dead branches sometimes indicate that the whole tree is suppressed and should perhaps be felled.

The death of individual branches may be due to attack by various aggressive pathogens, which kill or block the tissues within the wood or bark which convey water and nutrients to the shoots. Some of these, like the silver-leaf fungus (*Chondrostereum purpureum*), or the fire-blight bacterium (*Erwinia amylovora*) invade the tissues extensively, while canker fungi such as *Nectria* spp. confine their attack mainly to the bark, causing death of the branch distally if the canker completely girdles it. These infections can sometimes be eradicated by cutting the diseased branches beyond the visible limit of damage, as advised in books dealing with diseases [e.g. 173]. Tools used on certain types of infected material may need to be sterilised [193: Section 9].

Branches may die due to diseases elsewhere in the tree which reduce the supply of water or mineral nutrients locally or generally within the crown. The main categories are root rots and diseases of the xylem (e.g. Verticillium wilt) in the main stem. Branches in the upper crown are especially likely to die back if a root disease is present. If the roots are extensively decayed, the main hazard may be instability of the entire tree, rather than the brittleness of the dead branches.

If a tree with dead branches has been shown to have a sound root-plate and main stem, removal of the branches themselves may be all that is required for safety in a site that is much frequented by people. It is, however, sometimes suggested that a reduction of the live crown may be beneficial if the tree is of poor vitality. This suggestion is based on the idea that a reduced crown size will place smaller demands on the tree's ability to supply its tissues with water, mineral nutrients and photosynthetic products. A reduced water demand will often allow the growth of vigorous shoots, perhaps forming a denser but lower crown than had previously existed (see also Section 6.6.1, regarding trees with severed roots). There is, however, room for debate on this issue, especially regarding the effect of removing photosynthetic capacity as a result of crown reduction.

A rather special situation arises with dead or partly dead branches on ancient ('veteran') trees. The protection of such trees against excessive injury and the unnecessary removal of deadwood wildlife habitats is important, and the question of achieving this safely is discussed in Chapter 8. The need to conserve wildlife, while not compromising safety requirements, applies to trees in general; not just those singled out as veterans. If, therefore, deadwood is neither a hazard nor a threat to the health of a tree, it is advisable not to remove it. This view contrasts with certain statements in the current version of the British Standard on tree care [193: Section 12], but these will be reviewed for the next edition.

Perhaps the most intractable hazard involving large branches arises with those that are alive and unbroken, but nevertheless show signs of progressive downward bending or basal splitting (see Chapter 2). As such a branch is likely to be large, its removal can result in the development of extensive decay in the main stem. Thus, as mentioned below in relation to the mechanical stress placed on defective parts of the tree, a lightening of the load should be considered if there appears to be a good chance that the remaining portion could survive the effects of a reduction in photosynthetic area.

6.4 Cutting in order to lighten the load on a defective part

Most types of hazard involve the potential failure of a tree or part of a tree under its own weight or as a result of movement in the wind. In many such cases, the likelihood of failure can be lessened by cutting back twigs or branches so that the load placed on the defective zone by weight or wind pressure is reduced. The several practices which involve the cutting of twigs and branches are described by various terms, some of which vary somewhat in their meaning. They include the following: pruning, lopping, drop-crotching, topping, crown reduction, crown thinning and crown lifting. Their usages for the purposes of this book are described where appropriate in the text, and the glossary also includes some relevant definitions.

Wind-induced stresses can be reduced very effectively by shortening the 'lever arm' of the structure [106]. This is done by reducing the height of the tree or the length of an individual hazardous branch, and by repeating such treatment if subsequent growth re-creates the hazard. The simplest assumption is that the amount of height or length reduction required is in proportion to the severity of the defect. In practice, however, a less severe treatment is usually sufficient, since reduction not only shortens the lever arm, but also removes some of the 'sail area' in the form of twigs and foliage. Thus, a fairly modest shortening, perhaps two or three metres for a 20-metre-high tree, can often significantly lessen the mechanical stresses. A further useful effect of shortening a hazardous tree or a branch is that it reduces the potential zone of fall.

Another way of reducing the sail area is to thin the crown, and this practice is sometimes combined with crown reduction and perhaps other measures. This combination of treatments produces smaller wounds than by reduction alone, and fewer than by thinning alone. Treatments that create numerous large wounds may lead to such severe dysfunction, decay or disease that the tree dies or eventually has to be felled anyway, and are not carried out by reputable contractors except in special cases (e.g. for deadwood habitat production). Some trees are less tolerant than others to harsh wounding, especially those that are already affected by diseases. In particular, pathogenic fungi in the genus *Armillaria* thrive in trees which have severely depleted carbohydrate reserves and dysfunctional wood. In the absence of existing disease or decay, the type of tree is an important factor in determining its tolerance to cutting (see Appendix 2). Other factors, such as the age of the tree, the time of year and the weather conditions at the time of cutting are discussed in Section 7.7.2.

Although severe wounding can be condemned, it must be borne in mind that even a modest form of cutting results in a certain amount of dysfunction and perhaps decay within the wood of a tree. A cutting treatment may be a remedy for a hazard in human terms, but it is a form of wounding as far as the tree is concerned. Generally, wounds that are numerous or large in relation to the parent stem or branch (perhaps, over one third of its diameter), are more injurious than those that are small and relatively few in number. Consideration of all relevant factors can help decide the advisability of a possible treatment, as well as the timing of the operation. There are, however, only a few guidelines that can be given for trees in general (see the discussion of pruning in Chapter 7), and the practitioner therefore needs to exercise judgement in the light of knowledge and experience of the species concerned.

One important difference between species is that they vary considerably in the decay resistance of their older wood when it is exposed by cutting (see Chapter 2). In some species, such as English and Sessile oaks (*Quercus robur, Q. petraea*), Sweet chestnut (*Castanea sativa*) and yew (*Taxus baccata*), the living sapwood is naturally converted to a durable and largely dead heartwood when it reaches a certain age; often in the range five to fifteen years. If exposed, this wood has considerable resistance to decay fungi apart from a few heartwood specialists such as *Laetiporus sulphureus*. There is generally much poorer decay resistance in the exposed older wood of trees such as birches (*Betula* spp.), beech (*Fagus sylvatica*), poplars (*Populus* spp.) and Horse-chestnut (*Aesculus hippocastanum*), whose sapwood is either converted into a non-durable heartwood or gradually ages without a distinct change.

The younger portion of the sapwood in all species can respond actively to injury, so as to restrict dysfunction and decay, and this is often very effective in the relatively small wounds that are created by the pruning of young branches. However, even this mechanism is weak in some types of tree. This is particularly true of *Betula* species, in which wounds often trigger fatal disease and decay and should not be created if possible, or at least kept to a maximum of about 75 mm in diameter.

Another cause of decay or dieback following pruning or lopping is the susceptibility of some species to aggressive pathogens. In particular, rosaceous trees, eucalypts, *Betula* spp. and some of the maples (*Acer* spp.) are very susceptible to attack by the fungus *Chondrostereum purpureum*, which causes both dieback and decay. There is a related fungus, *Amylostereum laevigatum*, which occasionally causes a severe canker-rot in harshly cut stems of Lawson cypress (*Chamaecyparis lawsoniana*) and thuya (*Thuja* spp.) [173]. Some rosaceous trees, especially *Prunus* spp., are also liable to severe bacterial infections following wounding, leading to dieback or canker formation. Other pathogens such as *Nectria cinnabarina* (the coral spot fungus) can also cause severe dieback or cankering in some species, especially if the cutting is done during a period of moisture stress [173].

6.4.1 The shortening of weak or defective structures

For trees with major defects, an overall reduction of their height (usually together with a proportionate reduction of crown spread) can often reduce a hazard to within acceptable limits. The tree's value is preserved in at least some respects; its wildlife value may in some cases be undiminished, and its mere presence may partly satisfy the needs of local people who look upon it as part of their familiar surroundings, even in an arguably disfigured state. On the other hand, if the defect is so severe as to require harsh cutting, with its attendant potential problems of dieback and decay, felling might be a better option. Even when the value of a tree is such that a major height reduction is regarded as preferable to felling, there is a need to be aware of how it will look after the reduction, and to establish an adequate programme of aftercare.

As with other treatments involving cutting, it is possible to lessen the potentially harmful effects of wounding. In particular, carbohydrate reserves can to some extent be protected within the tissues where they are most needed by positioning the cuts immediately distal to unions with substantial branches (Fig. 6.1). These are storage regions at least in some species [18]. This practice will avoid the retention of leafless 'snags' which tend to die back, as well as helping to preserve something of the existing twig structure. It is also generally advisable to avoid cutting when reserves have been depleted by spring flushing or flowering and have not yet been restored. For this and other reasons mentioned in Chapter 7 in connection with formative pruning, late winter is probably a relatively good time for cutting a wide range of species.

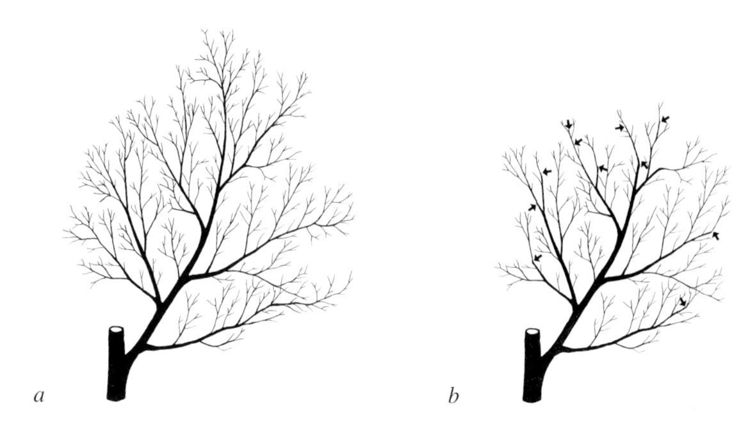

Figure 6.1 Positions of cutting (arrowed) for reduction and thinning of a branch: (a) before, (b) afterwards

The shortening of a tree should normally allow its natural crown shape to be preserved. This involves an overall reduction of both the height and spread of a crown which, in the UK, is described as **crown reduction** [193: Section 13]. This is distinct from the more severe form of height reduction known as **topping**. Topping is usually understood to involve the removal of all or most of the crown, leaving only the bases of the scaffold limbs or perhaps just the main stem. It is, furthermore, a term that is usually applied to mature trees, in contrast to **pollarding** which involves a similar pattern of cutting but is carried out on an immature tree so as to create a particular growth form. The pollard form is characterised by numerous branches, arising from approximately the same height; these are cut after one or more years, and the cutting cycle is repeated thereafter (see Chapter 8).

In the particular case of a weak fork, cutting treatments to lighten the load can be combined with artificial restraint such as bracing (see below), or restraint alone may be sufficient.

6.4.1.1 Crown reduction

Crown reduction, in the sense outlined above, involves only the outer part of the crown, and therefore provides only a modest reduction in overall height (i.e. the lever arm of the tree). This, combined with the accompanying decrease in sail area, is often sufficient to mitigate all but the most severe types of hazard. The resulting wounds are usually quite near the tips of the branches and are therefore comparatively small.

Crown reduction usually allows a high proportion of the foliage-bearing structure to be retained. A maximum of 30%, variously interpreted (Fig. 6.2), is sometimes advised for the allowable reduction in crown volume [193: Section 13], with a view to retaining enough photosynthetic area for healthy growth and the maintenance of defences against dysfunction and decay in the

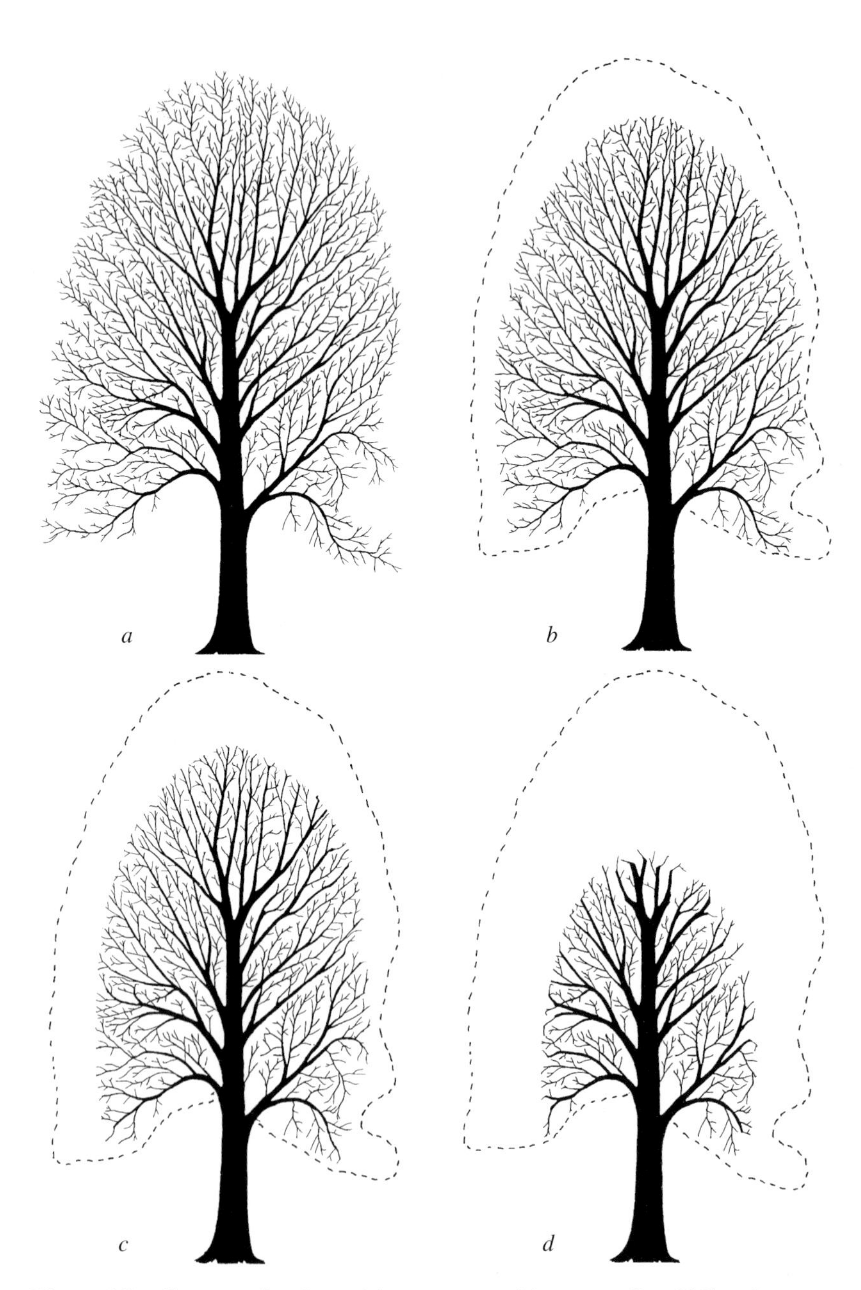

Figure 6.2 Crown reduction: a) intact crown; b) crown after 30% volume reduction; c) removal of outermost 30% of branch and twig length; d) 30% tree height reduction, with proportional crown width reduction

wood. The 30% limit is, however, a very arbitrary value, because of the great variability amongst tree species in their capacity to tolerate various cutting treatments.

Reduction, if done skilfully, often allows the natural shape of the crown to be retained initially (Fig. 6.2), but the habit of the subsequent new growth is often rather atypical of the species. The deviation from normal growth habit is greater in some species than in others, and the likely response of a given species or cultivar must be taken into account if its aesthetic appearance is a consideration in deciding which sort of remedy to apply. The range of responses amongst various combinations of species and age of tree cannot be catalogued here, but it should be noted that an atypical growth habit after crown reduction is especially pronounced in species with an excurrent growth habit (including many conifers). The single, dominant main stems of such trees extend virtually to the tops of their crowns and therefore have to be cut if the treatment involves a significant shortening of the lever arm. Some information on the growth responses of different tree species to lopping and pruning is given in Section 8.3.7.

Although the ability of a given type and age of tree to produce healthy, attractive new growth after crown reduction is an important consideration in choosing this remedy, vigorous growth often becomes a problem in itself. This is because it may rapidly restore the height and sail area of the crown so that the hazard of a weak stem or root system is re-established quite soon. The sail effect is sometimes compounded by the high density of the shoots or by the production of unusually large leaves. Also, individual new branches may tear away from their attachments or snap if they become heavy or crowded. These problems usually need to be forestalled through a programme of cyclic cutting of the new growth, at intervals determined by the experience with the type of tree concerned (see 'shoot renewal pruning', below). Cyclic cutting should be relatively easy to plan for familiar street trees, such as London plane (*Platanus x hispanica*) and common lime (*Tilia x vulgaris*), but the intervals may otherwise have to be decided on the basis of monitoring.

Although some increase in height after crown reduction is usually inevitable (with the possible exception of trees with a weeping habit), an effort should be made to encourage the growth of shoots that are pointing outwards or downwards rather than than upwards. This can be done by careful selection of the laterals that are to be retained. Some species are much more likely to 'co-operate' than others; particularly *A. hippocastanum* (Plate 115), in the opinion of many practitioners.

6.4.1.2 Topping

Topping (Plate 116) is highly disfiguring for most kinds of tree (especially when seen in winter) and is also more likely than crown reduction to cause severe xylem dysfunction and decay in major structural parts of the wood. It is now generally regarded as an undesirable practice, and should not be undertaken except in special circumstances. For example, if a tree of exceptional value could not otherwise be retained in reasonable safety, topping might be accepted as an alternative to felling. Such a situation can arise when

Plate 115 Aesculus hippocastanum *following crown reduction*

Plate 116 Topped specimen of Populus *sp.*

a defect is so severe that the tree can withstand no more than average wind pressure; i.e. its safety factor is about 1.0 instead of the notional 4.5. The height of the tree (i.e. the 'lever arm') might then need to be reduced considerably, although probably by a factor of considerably less than 4.5, as the sail area is also lessened by crown reduction.

Topping is usually a drastic treatment as far as xylem dysfunction, carbohydrate depletion and the loss of dormant buds are concerned, quite apart from any aesthetic considerations. If a mature tree survives topping, it will form an outer shell of new wood around a dysfunctional core, as in an ancient pollard (see Chapter 8), and will therefore require careful management as the new branches increase in girth and weight. Even though some types of tree are known to have a good chance of surviving such treatment, not all of them have much ability to 'wall off' decay in the injured xylem so that, for example, *Populus* spp. and willows (*Salix* spp.) require especially good aftercare to ensure the mechanical safety of the new branches that they form after cutting. These considerations underline the fact that topping is rarely an acceptable treatment for trees that are to be retained in the long term and that it could be regarded as an act of vandalism if done without special reason.

Another undesirable effect of topping, as with felling, is that it reduces shelter for adjacent trees, so that increased windspeed might render them hazardous unless they are subjected to crown reduction.

6.4.1.3 The shortening of hazardous branches

For branches that appear to be in danger of failing, for example if they show marked signs of progressive downward bending, the load can be lightened by cutting back the distal portion (branch tip reduction). This can be combined with the thinning of twigs and side-branches if the weight and wind resistance still seem excessive. The shortening of apical growth should be done using the technique known as drop-crotching (Fig. 6.1), so that a well developed lateral branch is retained at each cut and is itself shortened to a desired length if necessary. A general requirement in all work that involves the removal or shortening of branches is to ensure that the crown as a whole is not thereby put seriously out of balance. In some cases, it may be necessary to carry out further pruning to restore a balanced shape.

The exact pattern of cutting must be chosen to suit the form of each particular branch. A branch might not bear any substantial side-branches except near its base, and could not therefore be lightened without shortening it considerably or leaving a leafless snag. The main problem that can occur with a shortened branch is that it could die back due to excessive shading of its remaining foliage (see Section 6.3.2). Dieback is also quite likely to occur if the side branch retained at the point of cutting is too small in relation to the parent branch. It is therefore advisable to choose a side-branch that has at least one third of the parent branch diameter when considering this option. Also, in the interests of maintaining a good photosynthetic area for the branch, the trimming of other side branches and twigs should be kept to the minimum required for the relief of excessive loading.

The growth of new side-branches from a shortened parent branch can also bring problems, as they might eventually break away from a decayed point of attachment. The same may happen if the retained side-branch eventually grows large. Such cases may become a matter for hazard assessment and remedial action in their own right. They can often be recognised by an abrupt change of direction at the position of cutting, giving rise to a 'dog-legged' or 'elbowed' formation. If a weak attachment of new growth is detected, the branch may have to be cut back further or removed. Even this may, however, be preferable to the removal of the entire branch in the first place if this would have created a wound with more than one third of the parent stem diameter.

In all cases where hazardous branches have been shortened, future monitoring is necessary, as with other forms of remedial cutting. For branches that have previously shown signs of progressive downward bending, the monitoring should reveal whether this is continuing at an excessive rate and is thus creating a gap within the crown structure (Plate 16). Branches that show continued incipient failure, or that die back as a result of being shortened, may need treatment so as to mitigate a continuing hazard.

6.4.1.4 Lateral reduction of poorly balanced crowns

Slight asymmetry is normal in tree crowns, and is not a hazard in itself. Indeed, trees on very windy sites sometimes show strong asymmetry but have good stability. The strong asymmetry that develops in the crowns of trees at the edge of a group is also no cause for concern, except in cases where one or more other trees in the group have fallen or have been removed. Such crowns can then become poorly balanced and exposed to unaccustomed loading from the wind. Altered wind loading, which can also result from the demolition or erection of buildings or from major earth-moving activities, is of course a more general problem, which also affects trees with relatively symmetrical crowns.

Another problem of poor balance can occur when crowns lose branches due to storm damage [97] or unsuitable lopping. In order to restore a more balanced distribution of weight and of wind loading [106], lateral reduction of the crown on the excessively weighted side of such trees is advisable. Lateral reduction should never be carried out on trees whose asymmetry has developed in harmony with their environment; they could immediately become very unstable as a result. As with other forms of crown reduction, the creation of large decay-prone cuts should be avoided as far as possible by cutting only minor branches if possible.

6.4.2 Reducing the sail area to lighten the load

It is reasonable to assume that a reduction in the area of twigs and foliage exposed to the wind (a tree's 'sail area') will lessen the maximum stress placed on weak or defective parts. This effect can be achieved to a considerable extent by crown reduction, and also by crown thinning. The sail area is also reduced by the procedure known as 'crown lifting' [193: Section 13] which involves removing the lower part of the crown. This is commonly done to give clearance over highways, to reduce unwanted shade, and also to prevent the development of low branches which might otherwise become excessively heavy or attract unauthorised climbing. Although crown lifting can prevent vehicle impacts, accidents to unauthorised climbers and the breakage of low dead branches, it can also bring about problems of end-loading and multiple wounding of the stem and should not generally be regarded as a form of remedial action for hazards.

6.4.2.1 Crown thinning

Crown thinning can reduce the sail area, while not necessarily having much effect on the overall shape and size of the crown or the tracery of the outer twigs. Its value in mitigating a hazard is, however, more difficult to determine than the effect of shortening the lever arm by crown reduction. The aerodynamic properties of the crown are determined by many factors which vary not only with the characteristics of the tree species concerned, but also with the windspeed. It nevertheless seems reasonable to assume that thinning can reduce the sail area so as to place less stress on the main stem and root-plate in windy conditions. Most of the evidence for such an effect is probably observational, but an experiment by the author involving light crown thinning of *F. sylvatica* in a forest stand showed that the crown-thinned trees resisted windthrow far better than their unthinned neighbours.

In view of the uncertainty over the benefits of thinning for hazard management, it is probably better to combine this treatment with some degree of crown reduction, rather than to use it in isolation. Crown reduction will in any case bring about a diminution of the sail area, as it involves the removal of foliage, but thinning will not, conversely, reduce the lever arm to any significant extent.

Thinning, like reduction, can have undesirable effects if carried out badly or to excess. Excessive opening up of the crown structure may expose individual branches to increased increased wind penetration and turbulence, so increasing the chance of their breakage. This is a particular problem when the inner and lower parts of the crown are heavily thinned, while the outer and higher parts are left densely foliated. This unsuitable practice also produces a problem of end-loading ('lion's tailing'), as some of the branches are largely denuded of their laterals while retaining dense apical foliage. This problem can largely be avoided by a more even and selective removal of laterals, and additionally by a modest crown reduction, using the method known as drop-crotching (Section 6.4.1.3). This is another reason for combining reduction with thinning.

Like crown reduction, thinning results in some dysfunction within the xylem due to wounding, but the wounds consist of lateral, rather than terminal, cuts and are usually smaller in size; preferably no more than one third of the parent branch diameter. It is, however, possible to remove an excessive amount of foliage (i.e. photosynthetic area) even by making small cuts if they are numerous, and it is therefore advisable to set an upper limit of, perhaps, 30% of the total leaf area for removal [193: Section 13]. Even then, there is some reason to believe that the depletion of photosynthetic area through thinning may be more stressful to the tree than a similar loss through crown reduction. The basis for this idea is that thinning may retain a greater proportion of the tree's woody tissue, with a correspondingly higher requirement for photosynthetic products for tissue maintenance and radial growth.

New growth following thinning may soon increase the load once more by restoring the crown density, and this may happen more rapidly in a thinned crown than in one reduced in height. In either situation, however, there may sometimes be an accompanying 'repair' of the defect, as in the case of a newly stabilised root system that was previously wind-rocked. Future inspection and, if necessary, further remedial action are in any case essential.

6.4.3 Crown maintenance by staged cutting treatments

6.4.3.1 The thinning of new growth following crown reduction

Following the crown reduction of a specimen tree, it will usually be necessary to cut back the new growth at intervals to keep any hazard within acceptable limits. Repeated cutting of all new growth will, however, usually perpetuate a rather unnatural appearance and will also create dysfunction in the new wood. Cyclic cutting is an accepted practice for trees which have always been managed as urban pollards, but for other trees it is generally more appropriate to seek to maintain a more natural form. This can be achieved by retaining a framework of branches formed after crown reduction and carrying out a follow-up cycle of thinning and branch tip reduction. A system of this type was developed by F. Boddy of the London Borough of Ealing in the 1960s and later improved by H. Girling [59], who describes it as "shoot renewal pruning" .

In "shoot renewal pruning", the interval between the first crown reduction and the thinning of the new branches needs to be varied according to the species and situation. In the case of suburban roadside plantings of *P. x hispanica*, an interval of six years has been found sufficient. In some cases, cutting may need to be repeated at intervals of four years or even less, but this should be a reasonably simple and inexpensive operation compared with the original crown reduction.

6.4.3.2 Progressive crown reduction and thinning

If a tree is affected by a worsening defect, or if a site with a defective tree is destined for more intensive usage, a second phase of crown reduction, more severe than the first, may be desired to achieve acceptable safety. This would involve cutting below old cutting positions, at which the tree may have laid down carbohydrate reserves and defensive barriers. Removal of these defensive zones may lead to the development of extensive dysfunction and decay, especially if the tree is already affected by butt-rot or other decay. On the other hand, if a single but severe reduction is carried out, a high proportion of the tree's photosynthetic area will be lost suddenly, perhaps also leading to serious decay.

Experience has shown that a second phase of height reduction can sometimes be tolerated by the tree if it is done in a carefully staged manner. After an initial height reduction of perhaps two to three metres, the tree is given the opportunity to develop a new branch structure below the cuts. Later, if a further reduction of height and spread is required for reasons of safety, the new cuts can be made above the newly developed branches and foliage, so that a reasonably attractive but smaller crown is retained.

Plate 117 Street pollards of Tilia *with long, heavy new growth*

6.4.3.3 Treatments for neglected urban pollards

Pollards are developed by the removal of the leading shoots of trees, usually in immaturity, so that numerous small branches develop near the position(s) of cutting. The new branches are removed periodically so that the height and spread of the crown remain restricted. Swollen areas, known as pollard heads or knuckles, develop at the tips of the permanent branch framework. The frequency of the cutting cycle varies according to requirements, as discussed in Sections 7.8 (establishment of pollards) and 8.3 (maintenance of ancient trees). As far as urban pollards are concerned, the abandonment of the cutting cycle may lead to a situation where the size of the trees creates a nuisance or where heavy and weakly attached sprout-origin branches are a hazard (Plate 117).

For urban pollards that have been allowed to grow unchecked for many years, the main options are as follows:

- restoration of a cutting cycle, with removal of the neglected sprout-origin branches at the original pollard heads
- of a cutting cycle, with the shortening of the sprout-origin branches to form a new, higher set of pollard heads
- management as for free-grown trees in need of remedial action: e.g. crown reduction and thinning, followed by monitoring and *ad hoc* maintenance
- no action other than regular hazard inspection if the tree has developed a strong branch structure, with no indications of weakening due to decay, and is not too large for the site.

The third and fourth options are appropriate only if the trees are not to be managed as pollards in future, and will therefore not be discussed further in this section.

The first option provides an opportunity for the trees to be managed as originally intended, which may be desirable if they have become unacceptably large for the site. It will, however, result in the exposure of relatively old branchwood which, in some species, is quite susceptible to decay. There may also be a failure of new shoots to develop near the positions of re-cutting, perhaps followed by dieback of the pollard heads. This happens mainly when there are few viable dormant buds in or near the pollard heads, or if the species concerned does not readily produce adventitious buds.

The second option, to create a secondary set of pollard heads, exposes younger wood, which is generally less susceptible to decay than the wood at the bases of the sprout-origin branches. The retention of a relatively tall framework may, however, perpetuate a hazard if extensive decay is already present in the original pollard heads. In any case, this framework will probably require more work to maintain it, compared with the primary pollard structure. It should also be borne in mind that trees treated in this way can, arguably, seem very unsightly in the early stages of restoration.

There is no simple prescription for choosing between the above two options, other than to take account of experience with the type of tree concerned, and the condition of the individual trees. In the absence of formal research to compare the results of implementing the two options, it is not possible to compile information relating to tree species. There is, however, extensive experience with *T. x vulgaris* and *P. x hispanica*, two of the species most frequently used as urban pollards. Both have reasonably good resistance to the development of decay from pruning wounds. They also both readily produce new sprouts after cutting, and can therefore respond well to the removal of branches down to the old pollard heads. On the other hand, *A. hippocastanum* often develops quite large decay columns after severe wounding and is best not treated in this way.

Susceptibility to decay is not the only factor to be considered in the choice of the pollard restoration method. In particular, the mechanical properties of the sprout-origin branches are an important factor as far as hazards are concerned. The main fear with overgrown branches is that they will tear away from weak attachments in the pollard head, where there is often included bark and decayed wood. This can happen in any type of tree, but it appears to be far more prevalent in *Populus* and *Salix* spp. than in any other trees commonly grown in the UK. When neglected *Populus* or *Salix* pollards are to be restored on a high-usage site, they may remain hazardous if long branches are retained. Large wounds created by cutting such branches are not good either, but at least the old pollard heads of these species will usually produce abundant sprouts, which can be kept in check by the adoption of a frequent cutting cycle thereafter.

Observational evidence of failure in pollards of common species other than *Populus* and *Salix* suggests that splitting from weak attachments may be less of a problem than the snapping of thin, overcrowded sprouts just above the point of attachment, perhaps because of end-loading. On the other hand, if the main stem of a neglected pollard is extensively decayed, the increasing weight of the branches can split the tree apart. This is, however, mainly a problem of ancient rural pollards and the period of neglect is often 150 years or more before major failure occurs [136].

When restoration cutting is done, it is advisable with most tree species to retain the bases of the most recent generation of sprout-origin branches. As with drop-crotching, these cuts should be made immediately distal to a chosen side-shoot with a diameter of at least one third (preferably half) of that of the parent branch. This will help to prevent dieback by maintaining 'channels' of functional tissue and a nutrient 'sink'. Otherwise, the entire cross-section of the tree's functional wood will be exposed. Nevertheless, some trees, such as *Populus*, *Salix* and *Tilia*, usually produce vigorous new shoots with little dieback even after being denuded of all their branches.

The frequency of the cutting cycle following pollard restoration should not be so long as to allow the recurrence of any hazard from the formation of long heavy branches. It can be argued that no sprouts should be allowed to grow for more than two years, so that their eventual removal will not expose relatively old wood, which might not respond very effectively to wounding. The merits of this approach are discussed in Section 7.8 in connection with the use of pollarding as a formative treatment for hazard prevention.

Although people and property need to be protected from the possibility of decay-related failure in urban pollards, the pockets of decay which often develop within such trees have some value as deadwood habitats for wildlife. In most cases, the deadwood invertebrates at urban sites are unlikely to include endangered species, as these are mainly confined to certain rural areas where deadwood habitats have been continuously present for centuries. This is, however, not a reason for dismissing the value of urban deadwood habitats, and they should be protected wherever safety and other important considerations allow. The management of ancient pollarded trees, which are very important for wildlife, is discussed in Chapter 8.

6.5 Artificial systems for restraint or support

The main purpose of restraint systems, principally bracing, propping and guying, is to help prevent the mechanical failure of weak points through excessive motion or bending. This can also be achieved by lightening the load or shortening the lever arm. Treatments involving cutting are currently the most commonly chosen options, but they may detract from the aesthetic value of the tree, while also creating wounds which may be a source of dysfunction and decay. Particularly large wounds are sometimes left by the removal of heavy branches which are bending excessively under their own weight. The negative effects of treatments involving cutting can be minimised through skilled work, but it may also be possible to reduce or even eliminate the need for such treatments if the hazard can be mitigated using a restraint system.

Restraint systems are principally designed to help prevent specific types of failure, and are often very effective. They do, however, occasionally fail, and they are not in any case designed to prevent other, relatively unusual, kinds of failure. Examples outlined below include the 'cupboard door' or twisting failure of weak forks and the breakage of heavy branches due to upward or sideways movements. The possibility of eventual failure is not necessarily a reason for rejecting the use of artificial restraint but it must be carefully considered when such a system is being designed.

Another point that should be taken into account is that systems primarily designed to restrain movement may also replace the natural support of the tree to a greater or lesser extent. In some cases, parts of the tree are supported so much that their adaptive growth is poorly stimulated. As a result, the chance of failure may again increase in the course of time. If cable bracing is used, excessive support can largely be prevented by careful installation and subsequent adjustment. Such systems, which allow a certain amount of movement of the stems or branches involved, are technically described as flexible. Propping and rod bracing allow negligible movement and are described as rigid or inflexible.

As with other remedial treatments, a tree fitted with any kind of artificial restraint or support should be regularly inspected at intervals to be determined by individual circumstances. Normally, the interval should be not less than three years for the tree and five years for the hardware. Inspection should also be carried out after any severe storm.

Any practitioner who installs an artificial restraint or support system should have product liability insurance, in addition to the public liability insurance which is appropriate for tree work in general. Such cover is needed because the artificial system, like a new building, is deemed to be a product, at least by UK insurers.

In addition to the currently accepted kinds of system for restraining movement, the possible use of cavity fillings to resist failure by cross-sectional flattening deserves some mention. This has been tentatively suggested by Mattheck and Breloer [106], who point out that the pith of a one-year-old elder (*Sambucus nigra*) stem helps to support a structure whose outer shell of wood is less than one third of its overall radius. A light but fairly rigid filling (for example, one of the plastic foam materials that were introduced to arboriculture in the 1970s) might achieve the desired effect, provided that it had enough resistance to compression.

In the absence of experimental evidence to substantiate the idea of using fillings to resist cavity flattening, there is no good reason at present to alter the relevant guidance in the British Standard for tree work [193: Section 17], which currently does not recommend the filling of cavities. In any event, there is probably no justification for considering the use of dense materials, such as bricks or concrete, which were used many years ago in the largely unfounded belief that they would somehow add strength to the stem.

6.5.1 Rod bracing: general principles

Rod bracing is used mainly to resist tensile and sometimes also compressive stress in the immediate region of a defect or zone of weakness; usually a weak fork and occasionally a cavity. It can also be used to prevent rubbing between adjacent branches (Section 6.6.2). All components in a rod bracing system should conform to recommended specifications for strength. The current British Standard specifies the use of bright drawn steel rod [193: Appendix D2] and describes the use of two kinds of rod: a fully threaded rod which is screwed into the wood, or a bolt with screw threads at each end to which nuts and washers are attached. The bolt should be inserted into a pre-bored hole 1 – 2 mm wider than the bolt itself. Fully threaded rods are very time-consuming to fit and are in any case unsuitable for insertion into cracked unions because the thread resists closure of the crack.

Plate 118 Rod bracing of fork in Platanus x hispanica*; note growth of occluding tissues along rod*

6.5.1.1 Rod bracing for weak forks

Rod bracing for forks (Plate 118) is a long-established practice, but there have been doubts as to whether it reduces the likelihood of failure at weak unions. On engineering principles, Mattheck and Breloer [106] have now explained that this treatment does have some mechanical value, since it can arrest the propagation of splits in the wood below the zone of included bark. They also give advice on the positioning of the rod or bolt which, on engineering principles, should be about 10 cm above the tip of the bark inclusion (or of the split if one has already formed). One possible drawback is that rods or bolts tend to hold the limbs rigidly near their bases, so that the stimulation of adaptive wood formation by bending stresses may be reduced in this region.

Plate 119 Snap of Aesculus hippocastanum *stem, possibly associated with bolts which were inserted too close together*

If a split extends more than several centimetres, or if the tree is large, it is advisable to use two bolts, rather than one. The bolts should both be placed close to the split, but not in the same alignment [106], as otherwise the wood might crack between them. (The same danger arises with bolts or screw eyes inserted for cable bracing; Plate 119.)

If possible, any crack below the fork should be held in the closed position during the boring of the hole and the securing of the bolt with a nut and a large, thick washer at each end. It may be possible to close the crack by applying temporarily increased tension to a cable brace positioned in the crown above. Indeed, it is usually necessary to install permanent cable bracing higher up between the members of the fork as a supplementary form of restraint.

6.5.1.2 Rod bracing (bridging) of cavities

Rods or bolts may have some value in resisting compression from the cross-sectional flattening of cavities [67]. As this usage does not appear to have been evaluated mechanically, and is not included in the British Standard for tree work [193], it is not appropriate here to recommend any specifications relating to the type and number of bolts required, nor the means of fixing them. In theory, at least, this practice of 'rod bridging' might provide a means of retaining hollow trees without recourse to excessive crown reduction.

6.5.2 Cable bracing: general principles

Bracing with cables can help to prevent the splitting apart of the co-dominant members of a fork when they reach a certain size, which is especially likely to happen if the union contains included bark. Bracing can also be used to prevent the tearing away or fracture of branches which are weakly attached or subjected to excessive loading by their own weight or, potentially, by snow and ice. Except where the bracing system connects co-dominant stems of equal size, the general principle is that the limb requiring restraint should be cabled to a stronger limb or main stem of the tree. Otherwise, it may be necessary to possible to install one or more additional cables so as to spread the potential load to other parts of the tree.

It is important that both the hardware and the tree should be able to withstand the greatest loads that can reasonably be expected, considering all relevant factors. In particular, the stresses generated when braced limbs sway, either synchronously or asynchronously, will depend on the size and configuration of these limbs, as well as on the tree's exposure to wind. In case the tree itself proves unable to withstand these stresses, the bracing system should be capable of suspending any broken part safely. For this purpose a breaking load of twice the weight of the part concerned can be regarded as providing an adequate safety factor. A higher safety factor would be required in the event of the entire load being imposed suddenly on the system (a 'snatching' load), but the failure of a braced limb is believed usually to involve a less abrupt transfer of weight from the point of fracture to the artificial tether.

The cable used for bracing systems is available in different diameters, of which four are usually available in the UK: 4, 5, 9 and 13 mm. Each of these has a stated breaking load [193: Appendix D]. The cable is constructed from strands of high tensile galvanised steel wire, each containing nineteen filaments. Six such strands are wound around a central core, which consists either of fibre or of an additional wire strand. A fibre core provides better flexibility, but on very rare occasions seems to become compressed to the extent that the cable slips out of the wire rope grips that are used to secure it. Excessive tightening may in any case damage the galvanised surface of the steel, so allowing rusting [23].

The other components of the system, by which the cable is secured to the tree, must be of an appropriate size to suit the cable. In current practice [193: Section 16], each end of the cable is fixed to a threaded eyebolt (Plate 120) or screw eye (lag hook); (Plate 121). A table of compatible sizes for these components has been published [193: Appendix D, amended], but this does not include any information on breaking loads. In practice, it seems that the eyebolts or screw eyes are the weakest part of the system, for which reason the sizes stated in the cited table should perhaps be regarded as a minimum requirement. For example, an eyebolt of 13 to 16 mm diameter is stated to be compatible with 9 mm cable, but it is advisable to use a larger size in the range

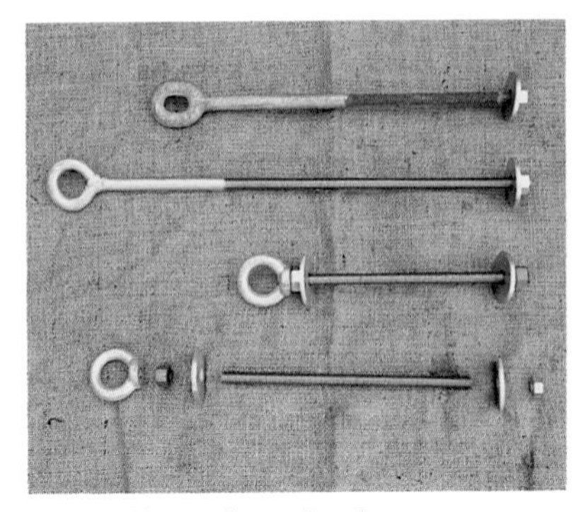

Plate 120 Bolts and rods

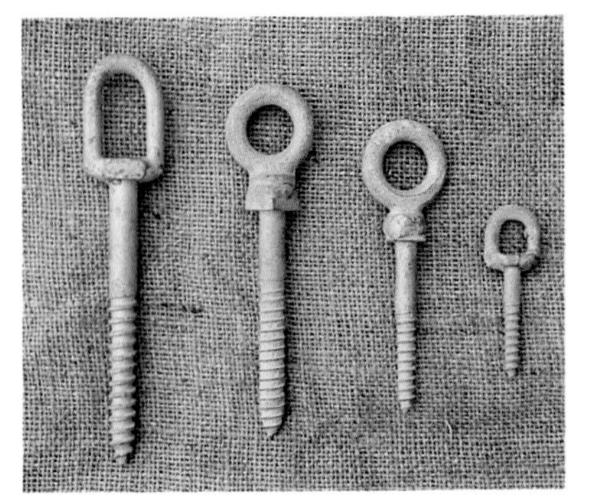

Plate 121 Screw eyes (laghooks)

16 to 19 mm if the load on the eye is likely to be higher than normal. This may, for example, apply in the case of 'through-cabling' (see below), where the bolt is loaded from each end.

In order to insert an eyebolt into a trunk or limb, a hole is bored with a clean, sharp auger all the way through the wood so as to be in line with the cable, as seen both in plan and from the side (Fig. 6.3). Straight alignment is desirable because it produces a 'straight pull' when the cable is under tension. However, it could to some extent conflict with the need to ensure that the bolt is safely held within the wood. A hole bored across the grain is thought to provide a stronger attachment than an oblique one, and it is therefore advisable to avoid deviating from a right angle by more than 45°. If, as a result, the bolt would not be aligned exactly with the cable, a larger size of bolt than usual should be employed so as to resist the bending loads that may occur. It may also be useful to spread such loads by means of a washer inserted between the eye of the eyebolt and the trunk or limb; this is described in Section 6.5.2.2 in relation to the bracing of individual branches.

The hole should be 1 – 2 mm wider than the bolt, which can thus be tapped right through to the other side until its eye is just in contact with the bark. A washer and nut must then be fitted to the other (threaded) end of the bolt. The washer, which should be round or oval, should lie flat against the wood (i.e. countersunk), for which purpose a small area of bark and perhaps a thin layer of wood must be removed from around the hole. The nut should apply pressure evenly over the surface of the washer [193], and it may therefore be necessary to insert a spacer of steel piping, with one end cut at the angle that the bolt makes with the trunk or limb (Fig. 6.3). After the nut has been tightened, the protruding end of the bolt should be cut to leave a length roughly equal to its diameter and hammered to create a burr so as to avoid loosening of the nut through swaying of the limb.

It has been advised that the eye of an eyebolt should never be fitted with more than one cable [e.g. 193], as the bolt might otherwise be overloaded or subjected to intermittent side-loading and hence metal fatigue. The latter problem may occur when two cables attached to the same eye pull in different directions. Safe results have, however, been obtained by limiting the angle

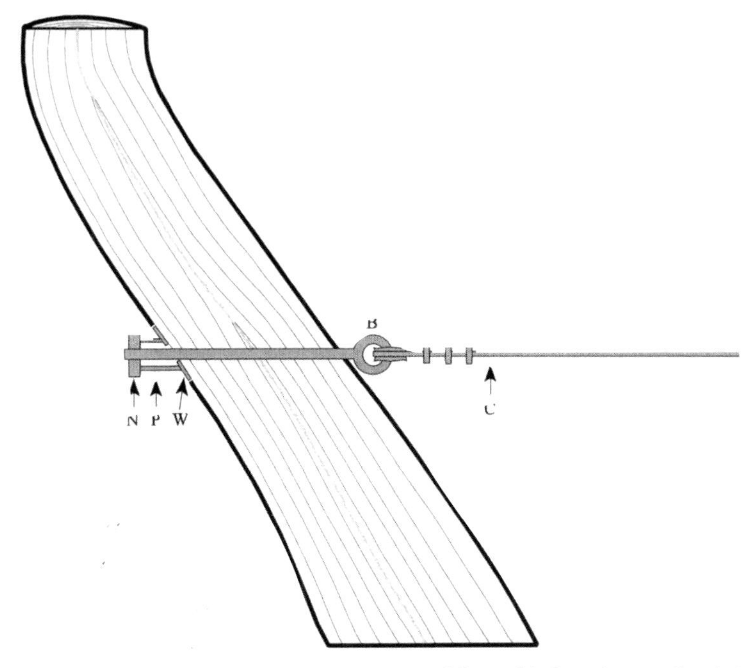

Figure 6.3 Position of a bolt or screw eye used for cable bracing so that it is aligned with the cable (C). In this example a bolt (B) is shown, and as the stem slopes a piece of piping (P) cut at an angle is inserted between the nut (N) and washer (W) to spread the load. The cable is attached via a thimble.

between two cables to a maximum of about 25°, and by using an eyebolt of the size that would normally be used for a cable one size thicker. One definite advantage of using double attachments, provided that these precautions are observed, is that fewer holes have to be bored in the tree. There have been cases where holes placed one above the other have led to the propagation of cracks, leading to mechanical failure (Plate 119).

Another method of attaching two cables to one eyebolt is employed in the system known as through-cabling, in which the attachments are made at opposite ends of the bolt. For this purpose the threaded end of the bolt is equipped with an amon nut (drop-forged eye nut) so that the second cable can be fitted. This type of system has been approved by the British Standards Institute [193].

Occasionally, bracing systems fail when bolts are pulled out due to the presence of decay, which weakens the anchorage of the nut and washer. Such failure can be prevented by adding a second washer and nut [158], which will become strongly gripped by new wood. It is advisable to use this additional safeguard either if decay is already present, or if the species concerned is known to be relatively ineffective in forming barriers against fungal colonisation (e.g. *Aesculus*, *Betula* and *Populus* spp.). Indeed, for such

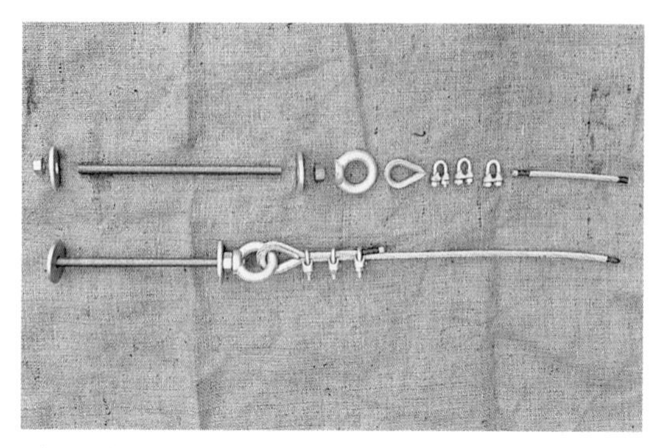

Plate 122 Bolts and eyes with cable attachments

species, the use of belt attachments (Section 6.5.3) may be a better option than a system involving bolts.

In some circumstances, screw-eyes (lag hooks) can be used as an alternative to bolts. Unlike a bolt, a screw eye is secured within the wood by means of its own screw thread and is inserted no deeper than half or two-thirds of the stem or branch diameter. It is screwed into a pre-bored pilot hole, which should be 1 – 2 mm narrower than the widest part of the screw-thread and usually no longer, or only a little longer, than the unthreaded 'shank' of the screw eye. In exceptionally hard wood, the hole may have to be enlarged very slightly so as to allow insertion of the screw eye. As with a bolt, the screw eye and the cable should be installed in a straight line, so as to help prevent the lag from being bent out of alignment [67]. Also the screw should be inserted to a position where the eye is vertically aligned and slightly clear of the bark [158].

Although screw eyes are capable of providing a firm attachment for cables, especially when they become gripped by new wood, it must be understood that their anchorage depends on the strength of the wood into which they are screwed. They should, therefore, not be used in trees with soft wood such as *Populus*, *Salix*, *Aesculus* and many conifers, nor in any wood where decay is present. Also, in order to avoid excessive loading, it is advisable not to use screw eyes when supporting stems or branches more than 150 mm in diameter.

The attachment of each cable end to an eyebolt or screw eye is made via a thimble, around which the cable is looped (Plate 122), and the loop is secured with a minimum of three wire rope grips or proprietary fastening devices (e.g. the "Eureka Wirelock" or the "Gripple" rope grip). These grips or other devices are supplied in sizes appropriate for the diameter of cable. Slippage of the cable from the fastenings is a possible cause of failure in the system, although – like the pulling out of eyebolts – this is a very rare event in properly installed systems (R. Finch, pers. comm). Slippage or, conversely, excessive compression of the cable should, as far as possible, be prevented by correct tightening of the grips or wirelocks.

6.5.2.1 Cable bracing for weak forks and co-dominant stems

Forks with included bark are inherently weak, and artificial restraint may therefore be justified if there is a risk to people or property. Cable bracing helps to restrain excessive movement of the members of such a union, so that they do not split apart during high winds or other adverse weather conditions. A potential disadvantage of bracing is that it may relieve the tree of stresses which would otherwise stimulate adaptive growth of wood. It is advisable to use bracing only where it is the most suitable remedy, either alone or in combination with another treatment. Co-dominant forks without included bark are generally considered to be less hazardous, but they are more likely than ordinary branch junctions to split apart [155]. It may therefore be a useful precaution at high-risk sites to brace such forks in cases where they carry a heavy lateral load or have a history of failure in the particular species of tree concerned.

Although cable bracing can be a very effective remedy, there are some circumstances where it is not sufficient on its own. In particular, it often needs to be combined with a reduction of crown height and sail area in forked trees with tall crowns exposed to strong winds. This is particularly important if the fork consists of no more than two members, and if site conditions allow strong gusts of wind to blow between them. Such gusts can sometimes cause a twisting motion which cannot be resisted by the bracing system, unless perhaps the union itself is braced with rods so as to resist failure likened to the opening of a cupboard door [106]. Rod bracing (Section 6.5.1.1) may also need to be used in combination with cable bracing if the fork is already splitting.

If a weak fork has three or more members, bracing between roughly opposite pairs can be very successful, especially as these structures are less

Plate 123 Box cabling

likely than two-membered forks to undergo 'cupboard door' failure. Similarly, multiple stems developing from a coppice stool can be braced, although allowance must be made for the fact that their attachments may become very weak owing to the development of decay in the parent stem base. It is also possible to link several co-dominant limbs or coppice stems by means of an outer ring of cables, known as box or rotary cabling [67], but the cables should be positioned so as not to rub against any part of the tree nor against each other. If there is a need to restrain lateral movement of the limbs, box cabling (Plate 123) may be useful in combination with the cabling of opposite members.

The bracing cable is usually attached so as to link co-dominant stems together at a position between three fifths and two thirds of their length, as measured from the point of union. A lower point of attachment may have to be used if the stems are so repeatedly branched that no wood of substantial diameter can be found within this height zone. Also, if cracking at the union has already begun, it is probably necessary to insert an additional brace near the union to arrest the development of the crack (see rod bracing, above).

The cables linking co-dominant stems should be attached neither too tightly nor too loosely. The tension should be just enough to keep the cable taut on a calm day in winter. Seasonal increases in moisture content or the presence of fruit or foliage will add weight and so increase the tension, perhaps very considerably if the foliage is wet or if there is a covering of ice or snow. A slack cable may fail to restrain movement sufficiently, and will allow an excessive jerking when the slack is taken up by movements. An excessively tight cable will interfere with the transmission of mechanical stress from the crown to the union, thus impairing the adaptive formation of wood. As the crown grows larger, the union may become progressively less able to bear the force from strong winds, so that a disproportionate amount of stress is eventually placed on the bracing system.

It is rather hard to achieve exactly the right cable tension in a braced fork; spring-loading might allow easier tensioning and would allow a more natural movement, but standards for this refinement have not yet been developed in Britain. James [89] states that the easiest way to provide the correct tension is to secure one end of the cable using the wire rope grips and then to adjust the system before the opposite end is secured. The best available method for doing this is to use a temporary cable system fitted to a draw vice winch for controlling the tension between the parts to be braced. The bark is protected from the winching cable by means of a soft sling.

If the tension on a bracing cable cannot be correctly adjusted before both ends of the cable are fastened, it may be possible to make a final adjustment by slackening or tightening the nut on one of the eyebolts. If, however, screw eyes are used, the tension of the cable must be adjusted before its ends are both fastened. Subsequent attempts to adjust tension by turning the screws will result in twisting of the cable. Bridgeman [23] suggested the use of one left and one right-handed screw eye, so that both screws could be turned in the same direction for adjustment of tension, but left-handed screw eyes appear to be no longer available.

6.5.2.2 Cable bracing for individual branches

Excessive downward bending in a branch can be restrained by bracing it with a cable attached higher in the tree. As such bending tends to be progressive in a heavy branch, the cable may become increasingly loaded, so that naturally optimised growth is impaired. In such cases, the branch tends to develop an abrupt thickening on the distal side of the support point. This tends to act as a stress notch and thus becomes a potential point of failure. Although progressive loading of the artificial system is almost inevitable in the case of propping, it can be avoided with a cable system, provided that this is installed and adjusted periodically so as to carry no weight except in the event of excessive movement.

Another problem that may occur in some cases with artificially restrained branches is that severe sideways, twisting or upward movements could occur, perhaps causing failure. In particular, a cable system should be capable of operating like a 'safety net', by keeping the branch suspended in the event of failure. Even so, it must be borne in mind that a branch with a single suspension point will swing if it breaks proximally, perhaps thereby causing harm. Maintenance of the system is also important, as in the case of braced weak forks. Thus, it is necessary to carry out regular inspections to monitor the condition of the branch and of the system itself.

The location of cable attachment points is often less straightforward for the restraint of individual branches than for the bracing of forks. Important requirements are as follows:

- to make the upper attachment to a part of the tree which can safely take the maximum potential load,
- to make the lower attachment at the furthest place along the branch where the diameter is sufficient to allow load-bearing without breakage or obvious bending, and
- to ensure that the cable forms an angle of not less than 45° either from the branch [23] or from the vertical. (Both angles will of course be 45° if this requirement is observed in the case of a horizontal branch cabled to a vertical stem.)

Also, the cable must run entirely free from obstructions such as other branches. In complex cases, or where the branch is very long, special designs (e.g. the use of more than one cable for a single branch) may achieve the required degree of safety. Otherwise, another form of remedial action may have to be applied.

The importance of achieving a suitable angle for the cable may need some explanation. If the angle between the cable and the restrained branch is much

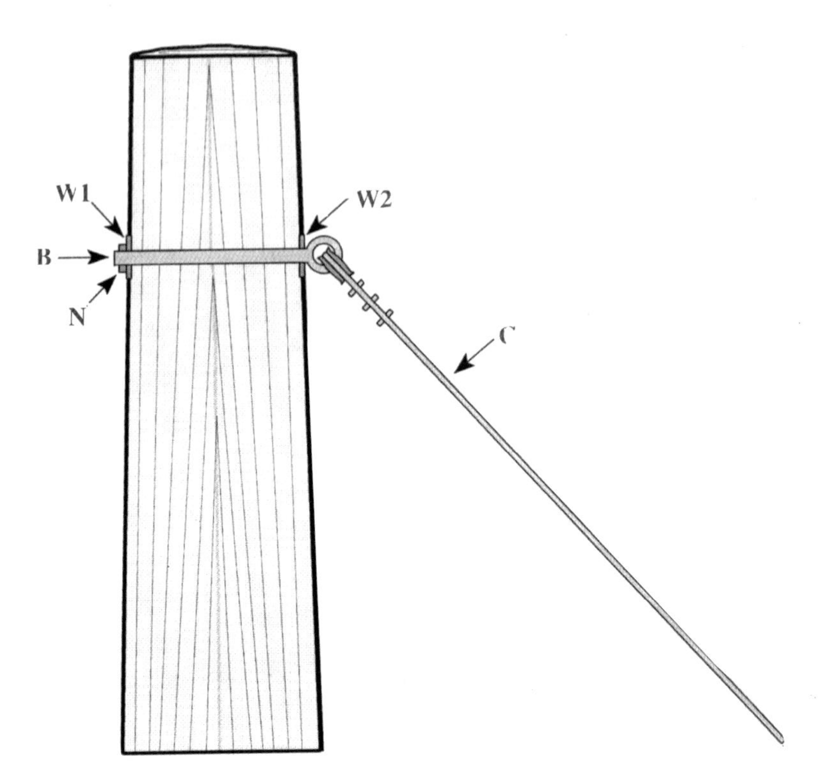

Figure 6.4 Branch bracing: attachment of the cable to the main stem, when the bolt needs to be inserted other than in direct line with the cable (based on information from R. Finch). B = bolt, one size larger than normal for the diameter of cable and with the eye close to the stem and orientated vertically, N = nut, W1 = washer inserted as normal between nut and stem, W2 = second washer inserted between stem and eye, C = cable attached via a thimble

less than 45°, downward bending may be insufficiently controlled. Also, if the attached bolt or screw-eye is placed in line with the cable, its angle within the wood may be too shallow to provide a strong fixture. As mentioned in Section 6.5.2, the alignment of bolts with their cables is a general recommendation, together with the insertion of angled spacers between nuts and washers if appropriate [193]. If, on the other hand, the cable is inclined at less than 45° from the vertical, the potential downward loading on the cable system could become excessive.

If it proves necessary to install a cable at less than 45° from the vertical, a bolt of a larger diameter than usual should be used at the upper attachment so as to help resist downward loading (Fig. 6.4). Also, if this attachment is made to a vertical stem, it is advisable not to align the bolt with the cable as is usually recommended, since the bolt would then be mounted at too shallow an angle to the grain of the wood. Horizontal insertion may lead to the bolt being subjected to a bending load, but this should not be excessive provided that the bolt is thick enough and that its eye is in the vertical plane and is close to the stem surface. It may also be useful to insert a washer between the eye and the stem, so as to help prevent the eye or shaft from being pulled downwards into the tissues. This washer should be in firm contact with the eye and, like its counterpart on the opposite end of the bolt, should be seated flat on an area of exposed wood.

The selection of the upper attachment point for the cable will depend not only on the need for adequate strength, but also on the structure of the tree. This attachment may need to be made high in the tree, so as to meet the requirements for optimising both the angle and the lower attachment position of the cable. The main stem, if there is one at the required height, should be used in preference to a branch. If there are a number of substantial ascending limbs rather than a single stem, one of these may be used. The chosen limb should not have any included bark or other indication of weak union at its base. It is also important not to use a branch which is too small or excessively loaded already.

Plate 124 "Double belt bracing system"

6.5.3 Bracing systems incorporating belt attachments (Plate 124)

Bracing with belt attachments, which has been developed in continental Europe [143, 144], is used mainly for restraining excessive movement in forked trees. The members of the fork are fitted with polymer belts which are linked via a steel cable or polymer rope. The use of belts avoids the need to bore holes for the insertion of bolts. No interference with cambial activity due to belt pressure has been reported, even from systems which have been installed for seven years [145]. The possible occurrence of such damage and of jerking movements can in any case be reduced by the incorporation of a shock absorbing device. This may consist of an elastic insert in a polymer cable or a metal spring in a steel cable. The spring is linked in parallel with a slack loop in the cable so that the cable becomes taut when the spring is stretched to its safe working load.

The belts used for attachment can easily be repositioned or removed for inspection, but are rather unsightly and expensive compared with bolts. Some designs of belt seem rather prone to slipping from their points of attachment, but the more expensive types are secured to each limb by a supplementary internal belt. Examples of belt systems have been installed only since the early 1990s, and some aspects of their performance, such as their durability in ultraviolet light and the continuation of adaptive growth in the braced stems may require further evaluation. Various polymers have been tested for strength and durability under experimental conditions [145] but there is currently no British Standard covering their use in belt bracing.

6.5.4 Propping

Propping is used mainly to restrain the downward movement of heavy or very long branches within a few metres of the ground. For such branches, propping may be a worthwhile alternative to cable bracing, although it has the disadvantage that there is usually no means of making adjustments to prevent the excessive transference of weight from a progressively sinking branch on to the prop. Also, lateral or upward movements of the branch are perhaps more likely to lead to failure, due to the prop being dislodged in the process. This problem can, however, be avoided by securing the prop to the branch.

If propping is chosen for a low branch, the position at which the prop should be placed should be determined by the curvature and orientation of the branch. For very long or contorted branches, more than one prop may be needed, but this must be judged individually in each case. If a single prop is used, it should preferably be placed between three fifths and two thirds of the way along the branch, provided that the branch is thick enough at this point to bear a load.

The prop can be made of wood or metal and should be robust enough to bear the weight of the branch [212]. It should also be treated to avoid rapid deterioration, with a pressure-impregnated preservative in the case of wood or with an anti-rust coating for steel. Some metal props have the advantage of being adjustable for height. The top of the prop should be equipped with a 'U'- or 'Y'-shaped attachment to prevent the branch from sliding off sideways

Plate 125 Propped branch of Platanus x hispanica*; note the distorted growth in the zone of contact.*

(Plate 125) or fixed to the branch to prevent it being dislodged. A manufactured prop may incorporate such a device while, in the case of a timber prop, a piece of a tree limb with a natural fork could be used for this purpose [89] provided that it is taken from a species with highly durable wood (e.g. yew, *Taxus baccata*), or is treated with a preservative.

The prop should be inserted securely in the ground at right angles to the propped portion of the branch and within the plane of potential downward bending of the branch. Thus, for a branch which is more or less horizontal at the propping position, the prop should be driven into the ground vertically – which should aid the depth adjustment – or fixed vertically to a solid base, i.e. concrete or a paving slab. Ideally, a prop should just prevent the branch from snapping, and not exert a significant support. If, however, the increasing weight of the branch comes to bear more heavily on the prop, its growth in diameter near the support point may be distorted so that a mechanical stress notch develops there (Plate 125).

For a branch with a complex weight distribution, an A-framed prop may be necessary to provide adequate stability. Such a prop can also be used to support an entire tree with an unstable lean if the species is relatively small (e.g. mulberry, *Morus* sp.). This will cause less damage to the root system than an attempt to right the tree and guy it (see next section).

6.5.5 Guying

If a tree has become hazardous (or even windthrown) due to movement of the root-plate, it may be possible to guy it in its original position for a number of years, in the hope that adequate root anchorage might be re-established. For trees that are large enough to represent a serious hazard, guying is quite a major engineering task, involving several cables anchored over a substantial ground area. The anchors employed are usually of the 'duckbill' or 'deadman' type [193, 212]. Precautions would have to be taken to prevent pedestrians or riders from tripping over the cables. Also, in view of the costs and inconvenience of such a system, a tree would need to be of exceptional value to deserve guying.

Guying has been carried out for columnar trees as high as 10 – 12 m and for trees of lesser height but with heavy broad crowns. However, too few cases have been documented to provide much information on the success rate. Success depends partly on the ability of the residual root system to supply enough water to the crown, for which reason a reduction of the leaf area to lessen transpirational stress has been tried in some cases. This also reduces the sail area, which may be necessary for mechanical reasons if the tree is quite large. In the longer term, success also depends on the ability to re-establish adequate natural anchorage by the growth of new roots. This ability appears generally to decrease with age, and may be very poor in mature and 'over-mature' specimens. This further limits the usefulness of guying as a hazard remedy, as the trees that can be most easily and successfully guyed are often too small to represent a serious hazard.

As long as a guyed tree lacks good root anchorage, the guying system must support it in strong winds. There are no current UK guidelines for the erection and maintenance of remedial guying systems, but the recommendations for the support of transplanted root-balled trees [194] are relevant. The cables should each lie at an angle of 45° to the trunk and should carry equal tension. In order to encourage mechanically adaptive growth, the tension should be reduced progressively after the tree has begun to show signs of regaining its natural anchorage. However, there should be enough restraint of movement to prevent visible rocking of the root-plate during gales, as breakage of new roots might otherwise occur.

The sounds produced by partial failure, involving the breakage of roots or the loss of cohesion with the soil, can be detected by means of buried microphones [34]. It is conceivable that microphones could be used to test the stability of a guyed tree whenever the cable tension is reduced. Otherwise, the movement of the tree could simply be observed during high winds so as to help judge whether there is any need to increase the cable tension again. If good anchorage is eventually re-established, the guying system can eventually be removed.

One possibility, which deserves some consideration, is that a non-destructive pulling test to detect root-plate tilt might help to evaluate the re-establishment of anchorage in a guyed tree. There are, however no standards for such a test, at least in the UK, and it would therefore be advisable to use this rather debatable method only if it can be evaluated further than has been achieved at the time of writing. It is, in particular, important to avoid causing new failure by tree pulling; this could be monitored with microphones. Another point to consider is the potentially high cost of using complex equipment to test the stability of guyed trees, even allowing for the fact that guying would in any case be used only for a particularly valuable tree.

Another system also sometimes known as guying involves the underground anchorage of root-balls. This is sometimes used for newly planted trees, and is mentioned as a preventative technique in the next chapter. It cannot, however, generally provide enough support for larger trees that have been uprooted.

6.6 Enhancement of natural processes to help limit or redress loss of strength

Although there is often no safe alternative to a remedial treatment involving the removal of branches or the use of an artificial support, it should be remembered that a tree may have considerable ability to strengthen itself through the addition of new annual increments or to delimit the extension of weakening from decay. It is therefore of some interest to examine some ideas and techniques which might be of value in enhancing these processes.

6.6.1 Encouragement of new root development (see also Section 7.2)

After a tree with a damaged root system has been made stable by crown reduction or guying, it is desirable to promote root growth so as to restore absorptive root area and anchorage. The soil conditions most important for good root growth are adequate water and good soil aeration. Mineral nutrients are also essential, but do not usually need to be artificially supplemented if the tree was growing well before the damage occurred.

Watering is beneficial if the soil becomes dry, and also helps to wash soil particles into contact with loosened roots. It is, however, important to remember that waterlogging must be avoided, and that superficial wetting of the soil may have the undesirable effect of encouraging shallow development of roots. Mulching with composted bark to a thickness of 80 to 150 mm helps to conserve soil moisture, but thicker layers of mulch may impair the diffusion of oxygen to the roots. A badly damaged root system is usually unable to absorb enough water to meet the transpirational demands of the crown, so that the tree will become moisture-stressed even if watering and mulching are carried out. Prompt pruning or even the removal of individual leaves, so as to reduce the leaf area by about one third, should help in such circumstances.

Improvement of aeration may be helpful if the site has become compacted or if the soil level has been raised. If there has been recent infilling, the original soil level should be restored if this is feasible. As root activity is usually greatest in the top 300 mm of the soil, hollow-tine aeration may be worthwhile on sites with surface compaction. Machines for injecting high-pressure air at depths of a metre or more are also available (e.g. the "Terralift"), but it is not clear whether their effects are generally helpful [84]. More radical measures such as soil ripping and subsoiling are usually appropriate on sites being newly planted, rather than on sites where soil disturbance could harm existing trees. As on dry sites, mulching will encourage the development of roots, but not of deep roots which are important for stability.

Fertilisation may produce an increase in growth rate, but fertilisers with a high nitrogen content tend to reduce the root:shoot ratio and may also induce a deficiency of micro-nutrients. Phosphate-rich amendments, such as bonemeal, tend to enhance root development.

6.6.2 Self-grafting

In Chapter 2, it was mentioned that a union with included bark can eventually become stronger by the fusion of its two members, which thus unite to form a single stem. This is a form of self-grafting, which occurs when the members are in tight contact but are not rubbing against each other. Continued rubbing will prevent fusion from occurring, but can sometimes be prevented by rod bracing, the normal purpose of which is to help prevent failure by preventing the members from splitting apart (see above). It is also possible to stabilise the movement of two independent branches that are crossing, either by bolting them together or by bracing them apart with a rod inserted into a piece of piping as a spacer [133].

The contact points will to some extent remain as stress notches, even after bracing, but their potential for fracture may diminish if the branches eventually unite. The prevention of rubbing should also lessen the chance of decay developing at the contact point. This type of bolting may be an alternative to cutting back one or both of the branches, but the need for any such treatment is best prevented by early formative pruning.

6.6.3 Treatment of decayed wood and cavities

It is often found that a zone of decay or cavity formation is currently not large enough to warrant remedial pruning. Nevertheless, there may be grounds for suspecting that the decay has the potential to extend further. This is quite likely to happen if the decay is being caused by one of the major root and butt-rot fungi, such as species of *Ganoderma* or *Armillaria*. The same applies in the case of some above-ground decay fungi, such as *Inonotus hispidus* or *Phellinus igniarius*, which have the ability to grow extensively within the volume of wood that was present at the time of the initiating event. In such cases it would perhaps be desirable to be able to slow down the further development of decay, and it may be of some interest to consider whether this is feasible.

6.6.3.1 Control of aeration in decaying wood

Since the decay process depends on aeration (see Chapter 3), the idea of hermetically sealing the surface of exposed decaying wood has some appeal. In practice, however, this is very difficult to achieve in the long term. It is difficult even when the exposed wood is initially sound and could in theory provide a stable base for the adhesion of a wound paint. Breakdown of adhesion, cracking of the surface or permeability of an artificial covering tend eventually to allow aeration of the underlying wood. At the same time, a sealant retains more moisture within the wood than if the surface had been untreated, and may therefore prolong fungal activity in the outer layers of wood which might otherwise have become too dry for decay to remain active. Nevertheless, wound sealants do appear to reduce the rate of decay development over a period of a few years [17], and the possibility remains that regular re-treatment, if practicable, could sustain this effect in the longer term.

The natural sealing of an entry wound by occlusion, unlike the application of artificial sealants, appears to arrest decay in many cases, although incomplete occlusion tends to produce the same combination of aeration and a relatively high moisture content that can favour decay behind painted surfaces. The development of occluding tissues can be speeded up by applying various wound dressings around the edges of wounds, but this is not necessarily a good thing, as the rapidly growing tissues often tend to become inrolled, forming a 'rams-horn' (Plate 14) which may create mechanical stress and perhaps a resulting crack in the new wood (see Section 3.4.3).

Fillings have sometimes been used with the intention of promoting the natural closure of open cavities through occlusion, which could cut off the air supply to the decay column. A filling can certainly divert the growth of the occluding tissues so that they might eventually form a complete shell across the cavity opening, instead of forming an inrolled margin around its edges. Although this shell could indeed reduce aeration it may remain very narrow, perhaps providing less mechanical support than an inrolled margin.

The aeration of decay columns can become naturally restricted not only by the total occlusion of entry wounds or cavity openings, but also by the accumulation of rainwater in cavities. For this reason, the drainage of permanently wet cavities probably does more harm than good in most cases. Also, the insertion of a drainage pipe breaches boundaries between the sound and decayed wood. If a cavity dries out during dry weather, the alternating wet and dry conditions may encourage the further development of decay. In this situation, it is sometimes suggested that a filling could usefully prevent temporary accumulations of rainwater. To achieve this, the filling would need to adhere to the wood so as to prevent seepage of water between the two materials. It is, however, not clear if any filling material exists that could adhere in the long term.

Fungal fruit bodies are sometimes removed from decaying trees on the supposition that the growth of the decay fungus would thereby be weakened. This, however, is not likely to be achieved, as the bulk of the fungus consists of mycelium within the wood, and will not be reduced by the removal of a fruit body. The mycelium in the wood might, on the other hand, be affected in a rather different way by the removal of fruit bodies, as there is a possibility that they provide a route for the loss of excess moisture which would otherwise hinder the decay process. This is now suspected to occur at least in species that exude water drops, such as some *Inonotus* spp. [146, 152].

6.6.3.2 Removal of partially decayed wood as a fungal foodbase

The development of decay is thought to be favoured by the availability of a large foodbase (i.e. an energy source) for the fungus, in the form of wood that it has already partly utilised. The removal of soft, decayed wood from the surface of a cavity or other decaying region of the tree, may therefore help to reduce the supply of food to the fungus, and so reduce its ability to extend beyond barriers that may be restricting its further spread within the tree. No attempt should, however, be made to cut into sound wood (as advised in older textbooks), since this procedure could breach boundaries between sound and decaying wood. In any case, it should be borne in mind that cavity formation is a normal process in old trees, and provides both wildlife habitats and a system for the recycling of mineral nutrients locked up in the wood. In some cases, adventitious roots grow down into cavities and may even become large enough to fill it and add support to the tree, at least in the case of yew (*Taxus baccata*).

If the decayed wood surrounding a cavity is very dry or friable, it is probably no longer supplying energy to the fungus anyway, but it can be removed together with other inflammable matter in the interests of protecting the tree against arson, if this is a real threat. The cavity opening can then be closed with wire mesh, ideally secured to the inside, to help prevent the build-up of twigs and leaf litter. If arson is not a major consideration, the conservation of deadwood habitats associated with cavities should take precedence as long as the tree can be retained [51, 52]. This consideration is not included in the current edition of the British Standard for tree work [193].

Dead, decaying branches are usually occupied by fungal species that are adapted to a relatively dry environment. These species, many of which exist as endophytes in sound wood, lack the ability to cause decay under the very moist conditions that occur within living parts of the tree. Major decay fungi rarely grow in dead branches unless the branches are too large to dry out very much in the summer, or unless the climate is very cool and wet. For this reason, the removal of dead branchwood will not usually deprive decay fungi of a foodbase if they are already established in the tree. It may, on the other hand, allow occlusion to occur at the branch bases, although this happens anyway if the branches are allowed to fall naturally. The hazard that can be created by dead branches is a quite separate matter, which must be dealt with if necessary.

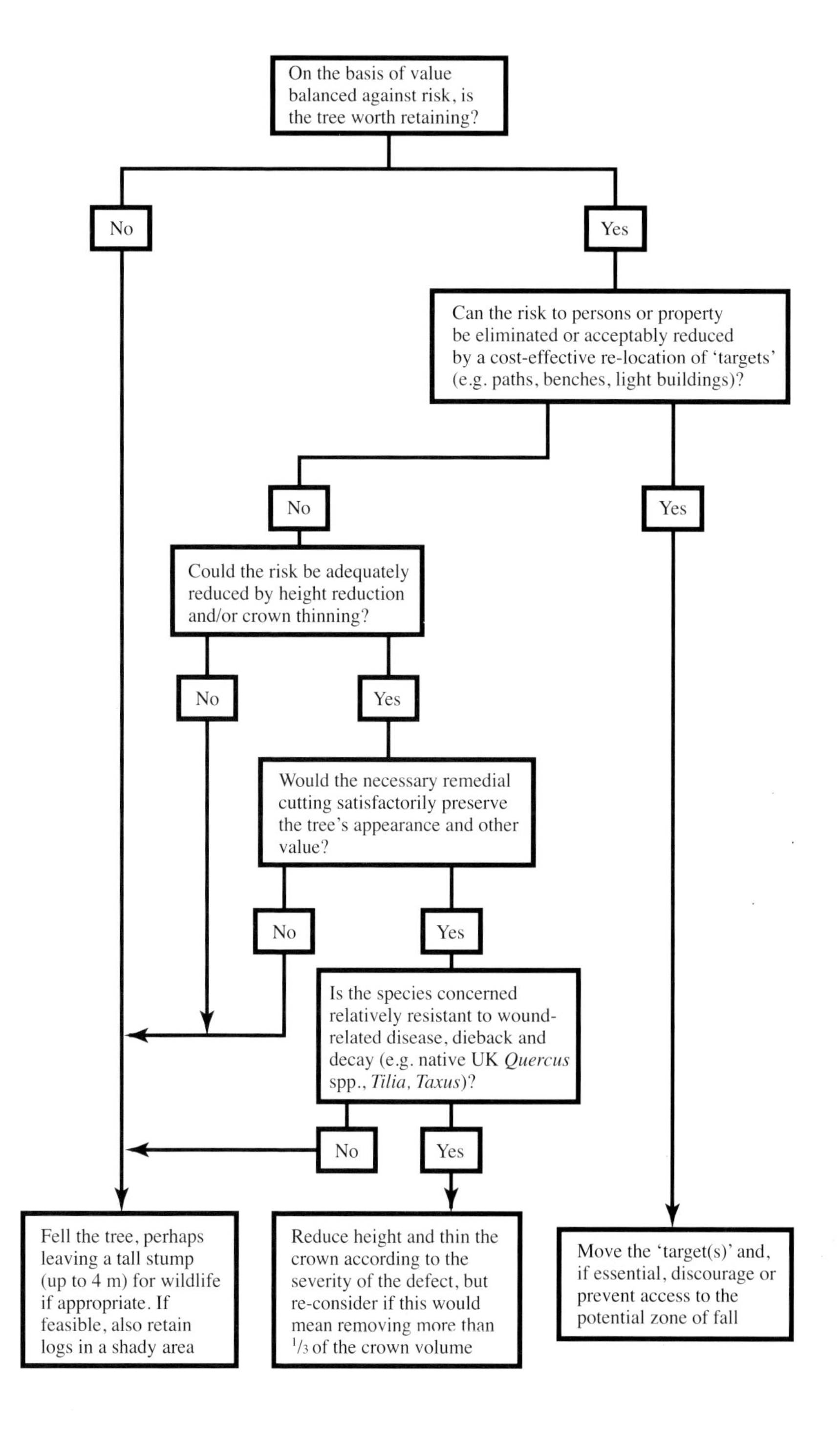

Figure 6.5 Deciding options for remedial work on trees

Chapter 7 Prevention of hazards

Defects in trees often originate from preventable damage or avoidable circumstances. In tree hazard management, as in most affairs of life, prevention is better than cure (Plate 126). The neglect of preventive management may prove to be a false economy if it eventually brings about a need for costly remedial action. Apart from the obvious expense of remedial work and the planting of new trees, a long-lasting environmental cost is incurred when well-established trees have to be removed or harshly cut.

Plate 126 Roof of house damaged by fallen Quercus robur *(The tree had root decay and was on an unstable bank: preventable damage.)*

Ideally, the aim of preventive management should be to achieve a situation in which trees require very little remedial work, except perhaps to deal with hazards caused by branches that die back as a result of normal competition for light within the canopy. In practice, trees may become hazardous due to events or processes which are beyond our control (e.g., weakening due to the natural establishment of decay or partial breakage in storms), but there are also many instances in which hazards are caused by inappropriate treatment or site management.

Hazards can originate at any stage of a tree's life, and indeed before the tree is even planted. Preventive tree care should therefore start with the production of good nursery stock. It should continue with careful handling of the stock between the nursery and the planting-out site [109], good ground preparation and an appropriate choice of species for the locality. If the area is to be much frequented by people, the development of mechanical defects should be further prevented by protecting trees from wound-induced decay and by forestalling the growth of structurally weak formations. Such measures are of value throughout the life of a tree, but managers often have to deal with trees which have already become hazardous and which therefore require a combination of remedial and preventive action.

At sites where people and trees are often close together, the need for rigorous safety requirements should be met by preventive management in preference to remedial action. This approach involves not only the careful maintenance of existing trees, but also a choice of reasonably 'trouble-free' species or cultivars for new planting schemes. At sites that are much less used by people, it is neither feasible nor desirable to place so much emphasis on safety standards for individual trees. This means that hazard prevention must depend quite a lot on other aspects of the management of such sites. For example, where there is a population of valuable trees with some mechanical imperfections, it is unwise to bring people and property closer to them by altering site usage. If there is a compelling need for such a change, there may be little alternative but to remove the trees rather than to hope or pretend that they can somehow be safely retained.

Site management often involves the installation or maintenance of utilities and amenities, the design of which ought to take into account the long-term welfare of surrounding trees. For example, trees within hard surfaces should be provided with planting spaces which allow for growth, thereby avoiding constriction of the trees or damage to the surface. Trees within soft verges suffer damage from improper car parking (Plate 127); a predictable problem which could for example be prevented by barriers. Another problem in streets is the severance of tree roots when underground pipes and cables are installed or maintained. Integrated planning for utilities and trees could allow them to co-exist more happily. One possibility is the installation of permanent conduits to house different services which could subsequently be renewed or augmented without extensive re-excavation.

On many sites, trees co-exist with other vegetation rather than with man-made structures. In such situations they represent perhaps the most costly and long-term site investment and should be protected under an integrated system of vegetation management. This should provide them with protection from foreseeable kinds of damage, such as competition for moisture or various types of injury caused for example by cultivation, mowing and animal activity.

Long-term planning is an essential aspect of preventive management. If mechanically sound trees are in place to succeed others that become hazardous in old age, it may be easier to accept the eventual loss of the older generation. Planting schemes should be phased so as to help reduce gaps in the succession during future decades and centuries. Also, within individual schemes, plans are needed for the management of pioneer or 'nurse' species which, if left too long, may adversely affect the development of other trees intended for long-term retention. The investment placed in such trees may be largely wasted if they are suppressed or drawn up in their growth so that they fail to become well adapted to wind exposure. In large planting schemes, a broad-brush approach is sometimes more appropriate than an emphasis on the

Plate 127 Root damage to Tilia *due to uncontrolled car parking on road verge*

care of individual trees. Silvicultural methods such as selective thinning are often cost-effective.

Planning is also important where changes in land use could harm existing trees. If a site is being considered for development, everyone who is potentially affected, including local residents, ought to realise that trees can be damaged not only by construction work, but also by intensified use of the site afterwards. This consideration ought to be a factor in the granting of planning permission, at least with regard to the requirement for new trees to be planted in succession to others that may have to be removed.

Many aspects of tree establishment, tree care and land management are relevant to hazard prevention, but it is beyond the scope of this book to describe them all in detail. Useful sources of additional information in English include *Trees in the Urban Landscape* by Bradshaw, *et al.* [19], *Urban Forestry Practice*, edited by Hibberd [79] and *Principles and Practice of Planting Trees and Shrubs* by Watson and Himelick [177].

7.1 Planning for the co-existence of trees, people and property

The risk of injury or damage from mechanically defective trees can be greatly reduced by moving 'targets' (i.e. persons or property) away from the danger zone. It is, however, preferable to avoid situations in which targets are placed next to trees with a relatively high hazard potential. Thus, wherever possible, new access routes, buildings or other facilities should not be constructed in the vicinity of any trees which are already defective or likely to become so, unless it is clearly accepted that the trees will probably have to be removed or cut back as a result. Local experience and the application of general principles can help in the recognition of species or cultivars that have a propensity to fail under particular circumstances of tree age, soil type and wind exposure. Old trees in general require special attention, as do species which have relatively weak wood or a reputation for frequent failure (e.g. poplars, *Populus* spp., Silver maple, *Acer saccharinum* and Box elder, *Acer negundo*). It must also be remembered that construction work may make previously sound trees hazardous (see Section 7.4).

On roadsides, railways, waterways or near overhead cables, the crown development of trees often has to be restricted in order to prevent interference with traffic or utilities. Substances that regulate plant growth have been used for keeping power lines free from vegetation, but periodic cutting back of trees is usual in most of the above situations. As with cutting for other purposes, this should be planned and carried out so as to minimise the size of pruning wounds and to avoid making the crown mechanically unsafe by excessive one-sided cutting. Such work can be more cost-effective and less damaging than the alternative approach of using vehicle-mounted machinery. It is possible to carry out machine cutting without doing serious damage if it is repeated on a short cycle (e.g. one or two years), so that only twigs are removed. However, there have been far too many cases in which flail cutters have injured the main stems of trees (Plate 128).

The damage that tree roots can cause to structures is a very important consideration both for planting schemes and for construction work near existing trees. For example, it is unprofessional and foolish to plant trees in paved areas, without leaving room for their stem bases and buttresses to expand. A more expensive mistake may result if a tree species with a high water demand is planted too close to a building on a shrinkable clay soil. Equally, a great deal of damage can be done to trees, with consequent hazards, if they are not properly protected during construction work, or permission is granted for construction work that proves to be incompatible with their protection.

7.2 Young trees and their establishment

Defects that originate early in the lives of trees account for many of the problems which require remedial action, or which cause accidents at heavily used sites. In some cases, the defects are of genetic origin, for which reason preventive management should begin even before the raising of nursery stock. This requires care in the choice of species, cultivars and propagation stock,

Plate 128 Flail cutter damage on stem of roadside Betula pendula

Plate 129 Young tree of Tilia *sp. with co-dominant leaders, which could be managed by formative pruning*

some of which have mechanically undesirable traits, such as the frequent formation of forks or branch crotches which contain included bark.

7.2.1 Nursery and pre-planting practices

This section briefly highlights aspects of plant quality which are relevant to the future safety of trees at the planting-out site. Even amongst genetically suitable nursery stock, defects may develop due to poor practices. These include the following: overcrowding, retention within under-sized containers, bad or insufficient pruning, the use of unsuitable rootstocks for grafting and the careless or unnecessary use of stakes and ties.

Managers of planting schemes need to be aware of the various defects that may be present in nursery stock, and should be prepared to visit nurseries in order to select trees that meet their requirements. By doing so, they may encourage some nursery firms to improve the quality of trees on offer. The following notes on the more prevalent defects in young trees may be of some guidance.

Girdling roots tend to develop when the root system is confined for too long (e.g. in a container), or when a seedling is raised in compacted soil. Such conditions should be avoided, and any girdling roots that develop despite precautions should be removed during a subsequent stage of transplanting.

Instability in a grafted tree may occur when the scion is grafted on to a rootstock whose capacity for root development is too limited to provide good anchorage. Examples include the grafting of *Sorbus* spp. (whitebeams and rowan) on to *Crataegus* (thorn) rootstocks, or of ornamental *Malus* spp. (apples) on to dwarfing rootstocks intended for fruit growing. Weakness at the graft itself (see Section 2.1.2.4) may be an additional problem.

Weak forks (Plates 1–6 & 129) or excessively acute branch crotches are the chief example among those defects which are partly of genetic origin and which may be a feature of particular cultivars or provenances within a species. For example, although *Platanus* x *hispanica* (London plane) is generally one of the least failure-prone of broadleaved trees, this hybrid includes at least one commonly propagated form which tends to undergo weak fork failure on reaching semi-maturity. Similarly, this type of failure is generally rather uncommon among *Tilia* spp. (limes), and yet is said to be typical of the cultivar *T. cordata* 'Greenspire'. As a general rule, trees which are known to have a tendency to undergo failures at weak unions (see Appendix 2) are best not planted in areas which are to be managed formally or much frequented by people.

Very acute forks and branch unions are a typical feature of many fastigiate types of tree, such as *Populus nigra* cv. 'Italica' (Lombardy poplar) and *Fagus sylvatica* cv. 'Dawyck' (Dawyck beech), but their upright and compact branching habit often restricts excessive movement at unions unless the branches become excessively long and begin to splay out from the crown. There is therefore generally no need to avoid the planting of fastigiate trees except where experience with particular species or cultivars dictates otherwise. On the other hand, some species which tend to form long branches at more than about 30° to the vertical (e.g. Horse chestnut, *Aesculus hippocastanum*) frequently fail at weak forks.

Although the occurrence of weak forks in nursery stock is partly of genetic origin, it can also result from the loss or removal of leading shoots. In particular, if the crowns of trees are trimmed or 'headed back' indiscriminately in the nursery, they will often develop co-dominant leaders with bark inclusions at the point of union. It is advisable not to accept such trees for planting unless they are to be regularly cut. It may however be possible to develop a better crown structure through formative pruning (see Section 7.6.1).

Stems may develop with **insufficient taper** or with a generally poor girth:height ratio if nursery stock is raised under excessively crowded conditions [82] or with excessive staking. When trees are removed from such conditions, they are liable to break or bend. The development of adequate girth and taper should be encouraged by giving plants adequate space in the nursery to branch outwards and by keeping any artificial support to the minimum needed. Also, the lower part of the stem can be encouraged to develop a stronger taper by retaining its branches. The removal of low branches may eventually be required in order to produce 'standard' trees, but this should preferably be done selectively over a number of seasons so as to avoid the creation of numerous wounds at one time, or of excessively large ones. Flush cutting should be avoided, as it may have serious biomechanical and physiological effects.

Plants with **inadequate root systems** tend to be generally unhealthy after planting, at least in the first few years. Their poor growth and their tendency to die back can be prolonged by wind-rock, which breaks newly formed roots. As far as future hazards are concerned, such trees may develop a pronounced lean, which in a small proportion of cases gets worse later in life and leads to instability (see Section 2.2.3). It is important to retain as much as possible of the root system when the plants are lifted, and also to protect it from frost, desiccation and rough handling. Container-grown plants should be 'potted on' or offered for use before they have outgrown their containers. Otherwise, their root systems will be inadequate both for water uptake and anchorage, as well as tending to develop girdling roots (see above).

Due to the difficulties of lifting and transporting trees with large root systems intact, the problem of a poor root:shoot ratio tends to increase with the size of nursery stock. Large plants also require more costly site preparation and aftercare if they are not to be checked in growth. In practice, 'standard' or larger trees tend to survive less well in the medium term than smaller plants [39], sometimes markedly so [163]. These are perhaps good reasons for choosing the smaller categories of stock, unless an instant effect is required. It is, however, possible to achieve acceptable results with semi-mature or even mature trees if funds are available for the use of special machinery and techniques for lifting, transporting and planting them, and then providing many years of after-care [177].

The need to provide nursery stock with better root systems has stimulated the development of new products and techniques. For example, the use of root bags may help to produce plants with intact root-balls, rather than the severed bases of major roots with soil loosely attached. The practice of undercutting the root systems of nursery plants may alternatively be of some benefit in stimulating the development of new fibrous roots. Those who specify requirements for nursery stock need to be aware of currently available methods, and of the need to evaluate their long-term consequences for the health and stability of transplanted trees.

7.2.2 The right tree for the right site

If a site is planted with species or cultivars unsuited to it, their root systems may become mechanically unstable in later life (Plate 130), or their branches may die back and become hazardous. In many instances, however, the main problem is the failure of the trees to thrive, so that they might even remain too small to become hazardous. In any case, there is a resulting waste of money, especially if the older and more costly categories of nursery stock have been planted. It is particularly important to take account of the properties of the soil, including soil texture, compaction, the depth of soil horizons, pH, water-holding properties, and the occurrence of any mineral deficiency or toxicity. Some of these properties can if necessary be ameliorated (see Section 7.2.3). Other important site-related factors include exposure to wind, the severity and type of air pollution and the deposition of salt, either from sea spray or from the de-icing of roads and other surfaces [45, 55].

Climate is another important consideration, mainly because factors such as temperature, rainfall and sunshine and the incidence of early and late frosts determine the range of species that can be grown successfully. Climate also interacts with site conditions so that, for example, sandy or gravelly soils can be very drought-prone in relatively dry districts, but less so elsewhere. In hard-paved areas, stress due to high summer temperatures may be a problem, perhaps aggravated by restricted rooting conditions. Apart from affecting the health of trees, climatic factors such as wind strengths and snowfall may limit the suitability of certain species. In particular, evergreens with a horizontal branching habit, (e.g. *Cedrus libani*, Cedar of Lebanon) tend to be damaged by the weight of heavy snow.

The **space available** and the current and future usage of the site are very important considerations for the choice of trees, especially if there is any plan to use species with the potential to grow very large. Unsuitably large trees may either have to be felled prematurely or subjected to severe crown reduction or topping (Plates 116 & 131), sometimes at the risk of causing severe decay associated with large wounds. Large, fast-growing trees such as *Populus* spp. are nevertheless useful for a rapid effect or as nurses for other trees, but they

Plate 130 Upturned root-plate of mature Tilia *sp., growing on a site with impeded rooting depth (note the water in the rooting zone)*

Plate 131 Severe lopping of Tilia x vulgaris. *(Despite the resulting xylem dysfunction, the trees were healthy eleven years later.)*

must then be removed or brought under a system of pollarding before they become a nuisance or a hazard in confined areas. Requirements for future management, including formative pruning, should be set down in writing at the planning stage.

At sites where the most rigorous safety standards must apply, it is often advisable to avoid planting types of tree that have a history of frequent failure (see Appendix 2). Care should also be exercised when choosing trees which could become hazardous in ways unconnected with mechanical failure. Poisonous fruits are, for example, a potential hazard if they are likely to be eaten by children. The deposition of honeydew, slippery fruits or autumn leaves can also be somewhat hazardous, but can perhaps be classed within a range of relatively minor problems, mainly causing inconvenience, which can to some extent be tolerated.

Among site-related problems, **restricted rooting** is perhaps the most directly relevant to safety hazards. On some sites, tree roots are able to take up enough water and nutrients to support considerable growth in height, but cannot attain the depth or spread needed to provide good stability. This problem sometimes occurs in built-up areas, when root growth is impeded by underground structures. It is also a feature of various soil types in which only a superficial layer provides good rooting conditions, so that the roots tend not to penetrate deeply enough to provide adequate anchorage. In many such cases, the main factor limiting root development is the availability of oxygen within the soil profile. This can be determined by measuring the rate of rusting of steel rods driven into the soil [28, 85].

The choice of species is important for soils with poor aeration at depth, as some are more able than others to root into the deeper and less well aerated soil horizons [35]. For example, *Fagus sylvatica* (beech) and *Quercus rubra* (Red oak) on surface water gleys tend to be uprooted during extremely wet and windy weather whereas this rarely happens to *Q. robur* (English oak), which can root more deeply into this type of soil.

7.2.3 Amelioration of the site

If site conditions are so hostile that even the most tolerant species are likely to grow very poorly or to form unstable root systems, some form of amelioration may be necessary. Compaction and poor drainage can be alleviated by soil ripping or subsoiling during the summer months. Surplus moisture can to some extent be extracted by the trees themselves, especially fast-growing species, such as *Populus* and *Salix* spp., which may be used as pioneers in advance of other species which require drier conditions. A lack of moisture may result from competition by a grass sward, and may be lessened by the planting of shrubs which suppress the grass while intercepting relatively little moisture in their own right.

Mulches are another aid to tree establishment, as they suppress competing vegetation and reduce the evaporation of moisture from the soil surface. The area mulched around a newly planted tree should extend to about three times the diameter of the root-ball [177]. Various mulching materials are available, including wood chips, composted bark and plastic mulch mats [38] for individual trees.

Organic mulches should be laid to a depth of 50 to 100 mm but not on waterlogged soils, where they may impede aeration. They gradually contribute to the humus content of the soil and yet cause little or no depletion of nitrogen, unlike organic amendments which are mixed with the soil itself [178]. A humus layer provides habitats for woodland fungi, some of which may form a beneficial mycorrhizal association with the tree roots. On the other hand, if honey fungus, *Armillaria* spp., is already prevalent on the site, organic mulches may support its development, although they also encourage the growth of cord-forming fungi which are antagonistic to it. Even on sites where *Armillaria* is present, it is frequently one of the less aggressive forms (e.g. *A. gallica*), which tend not to cause damaging infections unless the trees are under stress. If *Armillaria* has been found to be a problem, it may be worth referring to a list of tree species which have good resistance to honey fungus (see Section 4.3).

At sites with a naturally high water table – a localised situation in Britain, mainly confined to valley bottoms – waterlogging may persist for many months of the year, despite the uptake of water by trees and other vegetation [73]. Under such conditions, deep rooting can be encouraged by planting the trees on mounds of well aerated soil, but the mounds need to be wide and deep enough to accommodate the mature root systems of the chosen species, as the natural soil beneath is unlikely to dry out very much. This could be an expensive undertaking for large species. Also, interference with natural drainage or topography could be ecologically damaging at some of these sites, and it is then better to choose species to suit the conditions. In very wet soils, only a few genera such as alders or willows may be suitable and it should be borne in mind that too much reliance on a few species increases the risk of losing tree cover through diseases such as Phytophthora disease of *Alnus* spp. (alder) [57].

If there is a lack of topsoil, the development and function of roots in the upper soil horizons can be improved by the addition of materials rich in organic matter, such as pulverised refuse fines or sewage sludge, provided that it has a low content of heavy metals [19]. In formal settings, where cost is not a major consideration, topsoil could be imported and laid to a depth of 400 mm or more. Soil replacement, rather than addition, may be necessary at exceptionally inhospitable sites where highly toxic materials or extreme pH values predominate so much that even the most tolerant species will not thrive. Inhospitable conditions may also prevail in hard-paved areas such as urban streets and car parks. In such areas, it is important to provide planting-pits of sufficient depth and volume to provide both anchorage and an adequate supply of moisture and mineral nutrients (see Section 7.2.4). Trees in inadequate pits often grow deceptively well at first, but their roots eventually become restricted, leading to poor health and perhaps instability.

Detailed information on site amelioration is available from various sources, including Moffat [115] and Bradshaw *et al.* [19]. Also, for further specific information on the choice of trees to suit local conditions, various guides are available. A particularly useful book, which provides illustrated descriptions of many species, together with a table of their suitability for various conditions, was compiled by Mitchell and Jobling [114]. This table has been reproduced by Hibberd [80]. Additional information is provided in British Standard 5837 [197].

7.2.4 Planting procedures

Faulty planting is often responsible for the development of instability in trees, as well as poor growth. If the roots are too closely confined within the planting notch or pit, some of them may grow in a circle and girdle the stem base in years to come. The same can happen if container-grown plants are not removed from their containers before planting, even if these are of a biodegradable type. Such roots should be unwound and spread within the planting-pit, or removed if they are too woody and stiff. It is also advisable to relieve compaction in the bottom and sides of the pit, especially in clayey soil, so that the roots will grow out freely and provide good anchorage. Preferably, the tree should be planted in a large volume of cultivated soil, extending laterally to at least three to four times the diameter of its root spread or root-ball. If a number of trees are to be planted, it is worthwhile to cultivate a large enough area for a group-planting and to dig the individual pits within it.

A planting-pit within inhospitable ground should preferably be large enough to accommodate the root-plate of the tree throughout its life, thus aiding stability. Unfortunately, however, this may be unachievable within many existing urban streets. As a rough guide, the volume of such a pit should comprise between 0.3 and 0.5 m^3 for each square metre of the expected 'footprint' area of the crown at maturity. The backfill material should be formulated to provide good aeration, root penetrability, moisture retention and mineral nutrient availability. It may also be necessary to incorporate layers of aggregate in order to support the weight of traffic passing over the hard surface. In other sites, where the natural soil is of good quality, it can be used for backfilling [194]. If, however, the tree has been container-grown in a peat-based compost, its roots should be surrounded by a mixture of similar material and mineral soil, so as create a transition through which they should readily extend beyond the initial ball.

The depth of planting may affect stability, both in the short and long term. If the tree is planted so that its roots are deeper or shallower than they were in the nursery, its stability could be impaired because of a re-distribution of wind-induced stresses on its developing stem. The best guide for the depth of planting is the root flare, which should sit immediately above the soil surface.

It is wise not to rely on the mark (if any) left on the bark by the soil surface; such a mark may have formed during a period of 'heeling in' after the tree was dug from the nursery bed.

If a tree is planted at the wrong depth, the process of adaptive growth can to some extent compensate for the resulting alteration in mechanical stresses [106] but instability sometimes seems to persist indefinitely, especially if the primary root architecture has already been laid down, as in older planting stock. Small plants such as 'whips' are better able to adapt to an altered planting depth. Similarly, unrooted cuttings or 'sets', as used for poplars and willows, eventually tend to develop root systems at a depth which confers stability, provided that they have been inserted to at least one third of their length.

The formation of a buttress zone above ground level is a normal feature of tree growth and is necessary for strength and stability. It may, however, become hazardous to pedestrians in paved areas if the buttresses push up the surface. It is advisable to leave an area of unpaved ground around each tree, large enough to accommodate its stem base and buttress zone throughout life, and slightly sunken below the level of the pavement. Large metal grids, sometimes supported on rims, are available for covering and demarcating these unpaved areas. They help to protect the planting medium from compaction while allowing rainwater to reach some of the roots, but care is needed in the design of the hard surface to prevent water contaminated with salt, oil or petrol from running into the planting place. Accumulation of litter can be reduced by the inclusion of thick wire mesh under the grid. It is highly advisable to choose grids which are made up from removable sections, so that the central hole for the tree can be enlarged when necessary to prevent bark contact. For the same purpose, it is important to place the tree centrally within the grid.

In some tree establishment schemes, especially those involving group planting, 'nurse' species (e.g. Scots pine, *Pinus sylvestris*) are useful for protecting others that are sensitive to adverse conditions when young (e.g. *F. sylvatica*). Apart from the resulting improvement in the survival rate, the leading shoots receive some protection from frost and are less likely to die back and give rise to forks. For the reasons outlined in Section 7.2.1, nurse trees should be thinned and eventually removed before they become too large. Details of the use of nurse crops and other techniques for the planting and establishment of trees are described in standard textbooks. Some useful guidelines are summarised by Potter [134].

7.2.5 Artificial support and protection

Injuries after planting can lead to the development of mechanically weak branch formations and may initiate decay and cracking. Single injuries are usually 'walled in' by the growth of new wood, and are not necessarily a cause of extensive decay if they occur when the tree is young and has the potential to add greatly to its girth. In many cases, however, injuries recur repeatedly at the same point (e.g., machinery injuries near the stem base), sometimes causing extensive defects which may become hazardous. Appropriate forms of temporary support, together with protection against injury, can help to produce healthy and mechanically strong trees. If, however, such installations are used inappropriately or carelessly or are poorly maintained, they may contribute to the formation of defects.

7.2.5.1 Staking

Artificial support is usually necessary for trees which have too small a root system or root-ball to provide good anchorage at the time of planting [212]. This imbalance between the roots and the aerial parts of the tree is common in the larger types of nursery stock, including 'standards' and 'heavy standards'. Such trees usually need some form of support, usually provided in the form of staking, until they have established good root anchorage.

One of the drawbacks of staking is that it restricts the swaying of the stem in the wind. The resulting flexure would otherwise help to stimulate the formation of a mechanically optimal taper when the stem grows in diameter. This problem should preferably be minimised by securing the stem at a point no higher than one-third the height of the tree [123, 134]. A low stake often suffices to prevent excessive movement of the roots while they are developing their own anchorage. This can be achieved within two growing seasons if the tree has been well planted and is free from moisture stress, so that the stake can then be removed.

Another mechanical problem, which is not entirely avoidable, is the tendency for a tree to break at the point of attachment to a stake when it is under bending stress. This may appear more likely with low staking which, despite its advantages for adaptive growth, presents a long lever arm above the attachment point. This is not a serious problem for a tree which has a sturdy, well-tapered stem, but some nursery-grown trees have rather weak stems. Rejection of such a tree may be the best option, but otherwise a system for high staking may be necessary. Such a system should support the stem safely near the crown while allowing some flexing lower down, preferably by means of three stakes placed around the tree. High staking is also used to reduce wind-rock in trees which are too large to be entrusted to low staking alone (e.g. 'extra heavy standards'), but this can sometimes be achieved by artificial anchorage of the root-ball (see below).

The manner in which trees are staked is another important consideration. Poorly executed staking and tying can lead to chafing or constriction of the stem. The tree should be secured to the stake(s) using ties of a recommended design [194], and no stake should be so placed that the tree can rub against it. Ties should always be adjusted to provide room for diameter growth, while preventing excessive movement. If they become too tight, constriction of growth leads to an abrupt change in stem diameter which acts as a stress notch where snap could occur. Similarly, if tree tags are used for identification, care

Plate 132 Ingrown tree tie causing severe constriction of stem

should be taken that they neither constrict growth, nor chafe the bark by whirling in the wind. An extreme example of constriction by a tie is shown in Plate 132.

Support for newly planted semi-mature trees is sometimes provided by guying the trunk or scaffold branches with ropes or cables [194]. Care should be taken to minimise bark injury from pressure at the attachment points; one way of achieving this might be to use belts of the sort available for the bracing of weak forks (Section 6.5.3). The term guying is also sometimes used to describe a system at or below the ground which restrains the rocking of the root-balls of standard or larger trees. Such a system can be constructed by surrounding the stem base with a triangular wooden frame anchored on the ground surface with posts or rods. The frame can easily be removed before it interferes with the growth of the stem base or buttresses. There are other systems, available commercially, which secure the root ball with underground cables. It seems possible that such cables could interfere with the growth of major roots as they are not usually designed to be removed without damaging the roots in the process.

7.2.5.2 *Tree guards and shelters*

Small plants such as 'whips' or seedlings are usually provided with guards or shelters to protect them from physical damage [212]. Such protection initially helps the leading shoots to grow beyond the reach of gnawing or browsing animals. If translucent tree shelters are used, the resulting greenhouse effect may enhance growth so that the young trees more rapidly emerge above competing vegetation [50]. Guards or shelters, retained after this stage or used on larger trees such as 'standards', protect stems against injuries. Such injuries could lead to the development of mechanical defects and associated hazards later in the life of the trees.

Among the more frequently used types of protection are rigid tubular shelters or plastic mesh guards, usually 1 m in height and supported by a stake [130]. These devices are useful if the leading shoots are within reach of browsing animals, but simpler forms of protection may suffice if the main threat of damage is from gnawing animals such as field voles (*Microtus agrestis*) near ground level [212]. Protection can then be provided by means of a plastic guard of the helical ('spiral') type. Longitudinally split tubular plastic guards at least 250 mm high have, however, been found to exclude voles more effectively [41, 42]. In built-up areas, various metal guards, including mesh types and wrought iron ornamental constructions, are used to protect stems from accidental abrasion and vandalism.

Some types of guard or shelter can constrict stems unless they are used with care and are not left in place for too long. This can be a problem especially with metal guards, which are durable and rigid. If rigid designs are used, special care should be taken to ensure that the trees are centrally placed within them, as growth may otherwise be affected very soon. The implications of using high metal guards for long-term protection are discussed in Section 7.3.2. As far as plastic guards are concerned, the 'spiral' types are designed to unwind with the expansion of the stem but may fail to do so if they become fixed to the stem by shoots growing through their ventilation holes. Tubular guards and shelters are nowadays often made from photo-degradable plastics which are intended to become brittle and fall apart by the time that the stem becomes thick enough to fill the tube cross-section.

Chafing is another problem that may be caused by tree shelters if they have rough edges which could abrade the emergent stems. It is therefore advisable to use shelters which are designed so as to avoid such injury and to erect them according to the manufacturer's instructions. It is important, as far as possible, to secure the shelters against wind-rock and to deal with any that have blown over. Otherwise, the stems may be damaged or develop a lean.

Although tree guards and shelters are not primarily intended to provide mechanical support, the latter reduce the swaying of stems in the wind, which would otherwise help to stimulate diameter growth. The stems thus tend not to be very sturdy. The rapid height growth of the trees and the lack of lower branches may also help to make them top-heavy. For these reasons, a young tree deprived of its shelter may bend over, even under its own weight. It is therefore useful to leave the shelters in place long after the tops of the trees emerge, as they may continue to provide some support. A few years' diameter growth after this stage will usually produce stems that are strong enough to require no further support.

All trees that are provided with guards or shelters should be inspected periodically for signs of chafing or constriction, so that adjustments or removal can be carried out if necessary. Inspection is advisable even if the equipment concerned has been designed to avoid such problems.

7.3 General protection of established trees

The need to use guards or other forms of protection is not confined to young trees, since various agents of damage can affect trees of any age. Indeed, there is one such agent, namely lightning, which is more likely to injure large trees. It may be worthwhile to equip particularly valuable specimens with lightning conductors [139]. More common agents of damage include vehicles and other machinery [125] and large animals such as horses which have a habit of stripping bark. In some cases, it is possible to erect guards (e.g. against strimmer damage) immediately around the lower part of the stem, but better protection can generally be provided by means of an exclusion zone or enclosure at some distance from the trunk. Some options for providing such protection are outlined below.

In the event of injury to the stem, the risk of consequent decay or cankering can be lessened by scribing the wound so as to remove injured bark and wood, together with any soil or debris [158]. The wound should not be unnecessarily enlarged, deepened, nor shaped into a vertical ellipse. No cuts should be made into 'callus' surrounding the edge of the wound, and cutting is best delayed if it has not yet begun to develop around an injury inflicted during the current growing season. If the injury is both very recent and shallow, a covering of plastic wrap or moist moss might encourage new tissues to develop on the still-living wound surface [158].

7.3.1 Protection against machinery, grazing animals and competing vegetation

Some of the most frequent and most recurrent injuries are caused by basal abrasion from mowers and strimmers, leading to the development of decay and cracking over much of the stem cross-section. Heavy mowers can cause serious damage even on the thick-barked buttresses of mature specimens. Damage is very prevalent on young trees of all species, and also occurs on mature individuals of species that do not usually form a thick outer bark. These forms of damage should be prevented by proper supervision of operators and facilitated by retaining a zone of mulched, grass-free soil around the bases of the trees.

A number of factors should be considered in the demarcation of grass-free protection zones. For the purpose of avoiding damage to the bases of trees, it is advisable to allow at least 500 mm of clearance from the buttresses of every tree. On this basis, the exclusion zone needs to be enlarged as the tree grows, but the idea of progressively extending a circular zone around each tree may often be impracticable. As far as grass control is concerned, it is probably more practicable to incorporate the exclusion zone(s) within a 'flame-shaped' area, around which mowers can be manoeuvred without the need for awkward and time-consuming turning. Such an area could easily be made large enough to accommodate the basal growth of the tree(s).

Another benefit of a grass-free protection zone is the reduction of competition for water and mineral nutrients, which greatly improves tree growth in early years [40]. If, however, herbicides are used in the maintenance of the zone [108], great care must be taken to avoid harm to the tree. This can lead to severe dieback or complete death, with consequent hazards in the case of large trees. There are frequent cases of damage from certain herbicides, partly because some site owners or managers fail to realise that they can be absorbed through thin bark both above and below ground. Some herbicides can also cause damage by being absorbed by foliage in the vapour state during hot, still weather. It is possible to reduce the exposure of non-target plants to herbicides by the use of hand-held direct applicators [92].

Plate 133 Mower damage on shallow roots of Prunus *sp.*

Plate 134 Shallow roots of Prunus *sp. protected from mower damage*

The exclusion of machinery from the immediate vicinity of trees helps to avoid damage to their major roots, as well as to their stem bases. There are however, many types of tree (e.g. *Prunus* and *Betula* spp.) which produce very shallow roots at a considerable distance from the stem base (Plate 133). Such roots are easily damaged by mowers, and can then become diseased or decayed so that hazards may eventually occur. In the example shown in Plate 134, individual protection has been provided for roots of a *Prunus* sp., which have expanded considerably above soil level. Such intricate measures may often be impracticable, but the only other means of protecting the tree satisfactorily (assuming that it is to be retained) may be a large protection zone. If the roots are only just above the surface, mowing can be permitted within the area of the tree canopy, but only if the frequency is reduced and if the blades are always raised to the maximum cutting height.

With suitable training for operators, trees can be protected from machinery without the need for physical barriers. Such barriers may, however, be essential in the presence of large herbivores, such as cattle, sheep, horses and deer, which may cause both above-ground injuries and compaction of the soil, leading to root damage. The type of barrier required will depend largely on the type(s) of animals concerned. As a general guide, each tree should be surrounded by a sturdy wooden or metal enclosure, high enough and wide enough at the top to prevent the animals leaning across to the stem.

The spaces in the framework of a permanent tree enclosure can be covered with plastic or wire mesh to exclude smaller mammals such as rabbits, but such an enclosure cannot prevent de-barking by grey squirrels, which can rarely be prevented other than by controlling the squirrel population. In forest plantations this is done using warfarin bait in feed hoppers of approved design, which are installed by approved operators [169]. Such hoppers do not allow the poisoning of non-target vertebrates, but poison bait is often perceived as unsuitable for use in amenity areas.

7.3.2 Protection against vandalism

Vandalism is often more difficult to control than accidental damage, but there are several ways of discouraging it. It is helpful in the first instance to recognise sites where vandalism is likely to be a problem, so that management can be modified if necessary. Some places, such as the vicinity of fast food outlets and public houses attract loitering, while there are others that tend to be used for informal play, such as skateboarding.

The size and form of a tree may influence not only its susceptibility to damage, but also its attractiveness to vandals. Newly planted 'standard' specimens are frequent targets for vandalism, so that the supposed advantages of using them for an instant effect can in reality be nullified. Trees which are planted as 'feathered' stock, or which have grown on-site from seedlings or 'whips' often seem less subject to vandalism. In areas where vandalism is rife, but where small trees are not acceptable, the use of heavy standards or even larger trees should be considered, as their trunks are usually too thick to be snapped easily.

The use of staking is another factor which needs to be considered in relation to vandalism. The choice of high or low staking is discussed in Section 7.2.5.1, mainly in relation to wind-rock and the snapping of stems in the wind. Low staking is generally better for stem development, provided that the stem is initially sturdy enough not to be easily snapped above the tie. Unfortunately, even a well formed stem could be a target for vandals, so that

Plate 135 Damage caused by failure to remove an old metal tree guard

high staking may be a safer option at some sites, especially if the tie can be placed beyond easy reach (i.e. at least 2.5 m above ground).

High metal guards provide a certain degree of protection, except against determined vandals, but they can be misused as litter bins or even filled with paper which is then deliberately set on fire. Like other kinds of tree protection or support, guards should be designed and installed so as to help prevent them from interfering with growth (Plate 135) or otherwise damaging the trees which they are intended to protect. The trees should be regularly inspected for such damage, and the guards should be removed, repositioned or replaced with larger ones as necessary. Unfortunately, guards or planting grids are all too frequently placed eccentrically around trees, so that bark contact occurs within a few years of installation. Even if the tree is centrally placed, swaying of the stem can lead to abrasion against the guard. Such movement can be restrained by the use of ties high on the stem. The larger types of guard are sometimes equipped with attachment points for two or more ties of a sling design, which may allow enough movement to encourage adequate diameter growth in the lower stem.

The overall management of the planting scheme and of the site generally may help to discourage vandalism. Casual acts of vandalism may to some extent be deterred by simply not planting trees too close to areas where potential vandals are likely to pass or congregate. Also, some observations indicate that formality in the form of a mown sward surrounding the new trees tends to attract vandals. It might therefore be better to allow a rather more natural vegetation cover to develop around the trees, or to establish them within a matrix of shrubs (see Section 7.2.4). Also, species which readily grow again after being broken (e.g. *Populus* and *Salix* spp.) can be used as a foil to surround more vulnerable trees.

A positive way of discouraging vandalism is through education and the participation of local people, including children and adolescents, in tree planting and maintenance. For example, relatively little vandalism seems to be inflicted on trees that are planted through individual donations. Even if the trees are planted by a local authority, local householders can be encouraged by schemes under which they 'adopt' individual specimens. As well as watering such trees in dry weather, the participants in such schemes may feel inclined to guard them.

7.3.3 Protection from root decay

The biology of most root decay fungi is not understood well enough to indicate whether trees can be protected against them, except by the avoidance of serious injury to the roots (see Section 7.4). There has, however, been a considerable amount of work on *Armillaria* spp. (honey fungus) and on *Heterobasidion annosum* (the cause of Fomes root and butt rot) which shows that these fungi can penetrate uninjured roots. The various species of honey fungus are common in plantings of amenity trees although some, such as *A. gallica*, tend only to attack trees that are otherwise stressed or in poor health. There is, however, evidence that *A. mellea* and *A. ostoyae* are able to kill and decay the roots of previously healthy trees. In situations where this seems likely to happen, infection can be prevented by the removal of infested material or the isolation of infection sources in the soil by means of plastic-lined trenches. More information on these measures is provided in Section 4.3 and by Greig, Gregory and Strouts [64].

Mechanical damage to roots is thought to allow the development of decay fungi, especially if root function is simultaneously impaired due to soil

Plate 136 Root severance during trenching for cable laying

Plate 137 Failure of tree with roots damaged by trenching for the construction of a wall and path

Plate 138 Deliberate severance of major roots and removal of soil

Plate 139 Severe damage to Fagus sylvatica *on construction site due to failure to impose a zone of protection against compaction, dumping etc.*

Plate 140 Root damage: Cedrus atlantica *crowns still alive during construction of a roundabout*

Plate 141 Root damage: Cedrus atlantica *crowns dead, subsequent to the scene in Plate 140*

Plate 142 Decline of Acer pseudoplatanus, *with snapped dead branches, following raising of soil level*

compaction or other disturbance of growing conditions. Also, a wise presumption is that the probability of serious infection by decay fungi increases with the number and size of wounds. For these reasons, it is important to avoid as far as possible all forms of direct mechanical injury and of disturbance or compaction of the rooting area. This form of preventive management is addressed in the following section.

7.4 Avoidance of damage from construction work, trenching and ditching

Construction and other work involving excavations can cause very severe damage to trees, especially mature or over-mature ones which are much less able to adapt to an altered environment than young specimens. Above-ground damage, caused by **fires**, **impacts with machinery** or unauthorised 'tree surgery' may be fairly obvious. Root injuries are usually less obvious, but they may have very serious consequences for tree health. Direct damage involving root severance can be caused, for example, by the digging of **trenches** and ditches (Plates 136–137), **the stripping of topsoil** or **dredging** near waterside trees. In some cases, there is also the deliberate cutting or 'shaving' of major roots and buttresses to make way for vehicles (Plate 138). The causes of indirect damage, which may also be very serious, include **soil compaction** from vehicles (Plates 139–141), the dumping of foreign materials (Plate 139), the **raising of soil levels** (Plate 142), the **laying of impervious surfaces** and the alteration of **drainage patterns**.

Ignorance of the characteristics and requirements of tree root systems contributes to the damage that is so often done to them. Many people imagine that tree roots extend more deeply and much less widely than is usually the case. As a result, they seem to assume that the effects of root damage will only be serious for a tree if very deep holes are dug close to its trunk. This misconception is perhaps reinforced because excavations more than a few metres from the trunk of a tree seldom expose roots that are thick enough to appear important to the uninformed lay person. It would be a major step forward if all those whose work affects trees were aware of some simple facts, such as the following:

- There is no clear relationship between the above-ground size of a tree and the spread of its roots. It is, however, quite common for the roots to extend to between 1.5 and 2.5 times the spread of the crown; much more if the crown is fastigiate or columnar.

- Outside the root-plate of a tree, most of the roots are quite slender; even a root less than 25 mm across may carry a substantial part of the fine root system, extending outwards for many metres.

- The root spread of many trees is not symmetrical.

- Typically, most of a tree's roots occur in the top 600 mm of the soil, although some may penetrate to 1–2 metres or occasionally more.

- Roots need air as well as water, and may be killed by changes that reduce aeration; e.g. compaction, infill and interference with drainage.

Detailed information on tree root systems is available in various articles and papers [e.g. 53, 131], and in a booklet by Helliwell & Fordham [74].

Root severance can give rise to an immediate windthrow hazard if it affects major roots in the root-plate area. A root-plate, as a fairly distinct mass of interwoven roots and soil particles, is rarely more than three or four metres across but is thought to provide most of a tree's anchorage. This view is supported by the theory relating to fastenings in engineering components [61]. On this basis, the shape of the root-plate, as a coherent heavy mass with a disc- or inverted dome-like shape, probably makes a far greater contribution to stability than the cord-like 'outer' roots, which break off or pull out when the tree is uprooted. Nevertheless, the anchoring capacity of these outer roots seems not to have been tested rigorously in the field, and site managers should not always assume that they can be damaged with impunity as far as stability is concerned. Indeed, both theory and practice indicate that widely spreading roots play quite a significant rôle in very shallow-rooted trees.

Although construction work sometimes renders trees immediately unstable due to major root severance, the serious loss of physiological root function appears to be a much more frequent problem, with long-term consequences. In many cases, soil compaction is the main cause of such damage, as it greatly reduces gas exchange and penetrability even when, by the criteria of civil engineering, the soil is not even classed as compacted. The effects on the tree as a whole may range from fairly rapid death to a permanent or merely temporary reduction in vigour and vitality. In many cases, the loss of vitality is sufficient to cause dieback in the crown, which tends to create a hazard from dead branches. In later years, problems of instability may occur due to the decay of damaged roots. If such hazards occur, these should be detected and dealt with as advised in Chapter 6. It is, however, far better to prevent the damage in the first place.

Damage from construction and trenching or ditching can to some extent be controlled through compliance with current regulations or codes of practice [124]. In Britain, two major documents in this category are British Standard 5837 [197] for tree care on construction sites and a booklet from the National Joint Utilities Group (NJUG) which outlines some methods by which roots can be protected during trenching operations [201]. British Standard 5837 additionally gives fairly detailed guidance concerning the laying of hard surfaces (if these are required) within the protected area after construction has been completed. A continuing review of published recommendations or regulations can help to identify any areas of guidance that may need to be strengthened or added.

The various guidelines state the need to protect roots above a diameter of about 25 mm if these are exposed as a result of necessary excavations. Such roots are important because they are in a sense the main 'arteries' of the root system. If, however, some of them are severed, they will often produce vigorous lateral roots near their cut ends. This process of recovery depends on the ability of the tree to manufacture abundant photosynthetic products, which in turn depends upon the retention of a full crown, served by a predominantly intact root system. The formation of new lateral roots can be stimulated by the application of various plant hormones and humic acid preparations to the wound surfaces [78], but it is not clear whether such treatments provide worthwhile benefits in the long term. In any case, the prevention of injury is the best option, especially in the case of large roots which could become a seat of decay.

Compliance with protective measures requires an appropriate legal framework. In the UK, the planning authorities have a duty under the Town and Country Planning Act [195] to provide adequately for the 'preservation' of trees by imposing conditions for site development. Planning conditions can be adequate only if they include appropriate specifications for the protection of individually identified trees before, during and after the construction work. These specifications should be based on advice from an arboriculturist with appropriate knowledge and experience.

The survey of trees before development is particularly important, as it can avoid unnecessary conflicts and expense [6, 32, 70]. Some guidance for survey procedures is included in BS 5837 [197], but there is a strong case for adopting a more structured approach, by which the trees on a site are accurately recorded and designated according to their suitability for retention in the short, medium or long term. A pre-development assessment procedure has been developed by Barrell [6, 7], based on the concept of "Safe Useful Life Expectancy" (SULE).

Large trees whose "SULE" would probably be rather brief after site development could be scheduled for removal before development, so as to avoid the unnecessary cost both of protecting them and subsequently removing them. Equally, however, the procedure can be employed to identify trees which would have a long SULE, were it not for the proposed development. If such trees have considerable amenity, wildlife or other value, this should be taken into account by the planning authority. On the other hand, for young or small trees which may theoretically have a long SULE, replacement after site development may be an acceptable and cost-effective option.

When trees have been selected for retention, it is important that the written provisions for their protection during site development should be adequate and easy to understand. Also, these provisions should not conflict with other specifications (for example concerning the siting of underground services) which may be the responsibility of different departments of the planning authority. Proper implementation of the specified protective measures is also very important. This cannot be achieved unless adequate supervision is maintained throughout all stages of work on construction sites. Under UK provisions, the developer is responsible for supervision, jointly with the local authority, and is best placed to ensure that the site workers know what is required of them. It is usually through ignorance or poor communication that serious damage is done.

The prevention of damage to trees on development sites should be seen as a matter for co-operation, but it needs to be enforced through the provision of effective penalties. In Britain, fines can be imposed if damage is done to trees protected under Tree Preservation Orders and within Conservation Areas. It is also very desirable to have provision for heavy penalties for infringements of planning conditions.

Despite the existence of planning controls and guidelines, there have been many instances where trees have received little if any protection. In such cases, potential objections to site development may have been withheld on the basis of assurances that existing trees would be retained. Such assurance is worthless unless there are effective means to protect the trees and their environment, and to prevent them from being rendered hazardous.

7.4.1 Specific methods for protection

Detailed guidance for tree care on construction and cable-laying sites in the UK is provided in British Standard 5837 [197] and in guidelines from NJUG [201]. An outline of the principles involved is given here for general information.

7.4.1.1 Protection of the rooting area during construction work

A tree or group of trees on a construction site should be surrounded by a strong fence throughout the work, thus protecting them from above-ground injury, root severance, compaction or stripping of soil, chemical contamination and the dumping or storage of materials. Guidance on the **minimum** distance that should be allowed between the fence and the tree is given in British Standard 5837 [197]. This distance is determined on the basis of the tree's trunk diameter, its stage of maturity and its "vigour", all of which should have been assessed by an arboriculturist at the pre-planning stage. The size and maturity categories are intended to take account of the root spread of the tree, while the vigour category allows for its tolerance to disturbance. In this context, the term "vigour" should probably read "vitality".

It is important to realise that the minimum allowable sizes of the protection zones advised in BS 5837 represent a compromise, as the typical root spread of most tree species extends far beyond the recommended distances. When a protective fenceline is established at such a distance, there is often an assumption that a foundation trench can be safely dug immediately outside this line. In theory, this allows compliance with the recommendations, provided that the protected zone remains completely undisturbed.

Nevertheless, it should be appreciated that a trench in this position will sever the distal part of the root system, thus probably causing more damage than soil compaction alone. Also, if construction is allowed on the very edge of the protected area, it may be impracticable to deny access to the area itself. In such cases compaction inside the fenceline can be minimised by providing access via scaffolding of a recommended design [197].

Another important consideration is that root systems are often highly asymmetric, so that an arbitrarily designated circular protection zone may be inadequate on one side. It is often impracticable to map the distribution of roots, but major asymmetry should be suspected if the ground is sloping or if there are existing roads or buildings nearby. Asymmetry is an especially important consideration if there is a desire to establish the protective fenceline closer to a tree than is recommended in Table 1 of BS 5837. A clause in BS 5837 allows the tabulated minimum distance to be reduced by up to a third on one side of the tree only, subject to the judgement of the arboricultural adviser, provided that the fenceline is placed further away in other directions by way of compensation.

If there is no room to accommodate all access routes, equipment and materials outside the recommended protection zone, it may still be possible to protect the soil from compaction and contamination by laying down suspended platforms. In such circumstances, special consultation with the planning authority and with specialist advisers in arboriculture and civil engineering should be regarded as essential. The laying of a reinforced concrete slab, as described in BS 5837, is intended only to support temporary access by vehicles. Similarly scaffold boards, placed over a geotextile fabric, are intended only to support pedestrian access to scaffolding. Another option, which for reasons of cost may be appropriate only for small sites, is to avoid storage on-site and to use materials as soon as they are delivered. In any case, the close proximity of equipment and new buildings to trees will often impose a high risk of other kinds of damage during or after the construction work.

It is usually essential to ensure that the proposed siting and construction of a new building are compatible with the procedures normally recommended for protecting trees chosen for retention. In rare circumstances, however, it may be appropriate to employ special construction methods which allow the retention of trees very close to new buildings. Helliwell [70] illustrates such a case, in which a holiday chalet was erected on steel girders supported on concrete piles, with service trenches being hand-dug so as to leave tree roots intact.

7.4.1.2 Long-term protection of the rooting area

Following the completion of the main construction work, it is very important to continue to protect tree roots thereafter. Even if the original surface has been properly protected during and immediately after construction, the new use of the site could result in damage through soil compaction or root severance. Such problems may not appear to come under the heading of construction-related damage, but it is only realistic to take them fully into account when planning permission is being considered.

In some projects, for example in the garden of a newly built house, it may be intended to retain a natural soil surface. If so, there ought to be no attempt to alter the soil level within the area previously enclosed by the protective fence. If, however, the level has to be raised, any resulting root asphyxiation can often be lessened by first building a permanent tree-well, in which the old soil surface is preserved over the central part of the root system [158]. There is no precise guideline for matching the diameter of the well to the size of the tree, but the larger the better. Outside the well, aeration at depth can be enhanced by the incorporation of coarse material within the infill layers.

If it is intended to lay a hard surface over part or all of the rooting area of a tree, direct or indirect damage to roots should be avoided as stringently as during the main construction work. The guidelines given in BS 5837 [197] refer to protection of the area previously enclosed within the protective fence. The main requirements that are embodied within this guidance can be summarised as follows.

- Physical damage is to be prevented by avoiding the skimming or stripping of soil and by avoiding or controlling excavations and cultivation so as to prevent injury to large roots.

- An unpaved strip 250 mm wide should be provided around the base of each tree so as to allow for growth.

- The paving materials must allow the penetration of rainwater and the exchange of gases; i.e. an impermeable material such as concrete should not be laid as an unbroken sheet.

- The slope of the surface should not cause the excessive accumulation of water.

- If salt or other toxic materials are likely to contaminate surface water, an impermeable surface should be laid, with a highly permeable sub-base to allow lateral diffusion of air and water: see also Dobson [45].

The need to protect roots from direct damage during the laying of the surface is perhaps more obvious than the need to avoid deleterious changes in the movement of water and gases. Sometimes, attempts to adhere to guidelines such as those in BS 5837 may not produce the desired result when put to the test by the weather. If a newly paved or tarmac-covered area diverts the flow of rainwater so that the roots of existing trees receive too much or too little, it might be possible to correct this by altering the slope or providing seepage points. In general, drainage and compaction problems can be hard to deal with on sites where established trees are present [83]. If the construction work has led to a serious impedance of drainage, there may be a need to lay new drains, but great care should then be taken to avoid severing roots as a result.

7.4.1.3 Pipe and cable laying

In most trees, about 90% of the root system lies above a depth of 600 mm and it is thus all too easy to cause very severe damage by the cutting of trenches. Only the larger roots are thick enough to be easily noticed when trenches are dug, so that there is often a false impression that little damage has been done. The relevant guidelines [201] define a 'precautionary area' by laying down minimum allowable distance between machine-dug trenches and the bases of trees of various sizes. If the only feasible route for a cable or pipeline would intrude into the precautionary area, special techniques are advised. Trenching within this area should be done by hand, and must not result in the cutting of any roots more than 25 mm in diameter. Also, all exposed roots should be covered with sacking or horticultural fleece to protect them from desiccation or frost before back-filling.

Trenching within an otherwise protected zone is allowable under British Standard 5837 [197], provided that it is done along a radius from the tree. The assumption is that primary roots run mostly in a radial direction and will therefore be damaged less than by trenching on one side of the tree. Over a distance of one metre on either side of the trunk, the radial excavation must take the form of a tunnel, which should preferably be not less than 750 mm deep, according to BS 5837. The use of tunnelling, known as trenchless technology or thrust boring, may be of value in various situations where pipes or cables have to be laid closer to trees than is generally desirable. The effect of such work on tree roots has, however, not been properly evaluated at the time of writing.

Another situation requiring extra care arises when pipes or cables are to be laid near trees in the pavements or verges of roads. Roots are usually unable to grow beneath the carriageway, and this means that street trees often have very asymmetric root systems and therefore depend on roots growing away from the road for their anchorage and water-absorbing capacity. The precautionary measures outlined above are therefore of particular importance where such roots are concerned.

7.5 Prevention of damage to man-made structures by trees

Tree roots can cause direct damage by disrupting or distorting underground services or structures with shallow footings as they grow in girth. They can also grow into conduits and drains if these are defective [197: Section 10]. Indirect damage occurs when roots dry out shrinkable clay soils beneath the foundations of buildings, thus causing subsidence. This can be an expensive problem, although it rarely amounts to a safety hazard and is sometimes blamed on trees even when seasonal shrinkage unconnected with tree roots affects inadequate foundations. Existing buildings may be protected from such damage by preventing the establishment or full crown development of any trees that are judged to be capable of causing shrinkage beneath the foundations. This judgement depends on the species of tree, the distance from the building, the type of soil, the climate and the depth of the foundations. The assessment of these factors is described by Biddle [11, 12].

Tree-related subsidence in new buildings can be prevented by laying foundations below the depth where tree roots are likely to extract substantial amounts of moisture. In Great Britain, local authorities can stipulate that foundations should be adequate to allow the retention of trees without risk of subsidence. In some cases, for example near mature poplar trees on a shrinkable clay soil, this may necessitate the use of deep foundations or piles. Some guidance on advisable foundation depths for new buildings, taking into account factors such as soil type and the distance from various species of tree, is available to builders [198]. Also, the relationships between tree roots and buildings have been examined in detail by Biddle [12].

The lifting of pavements and shallow structures can be prevented by providing trees with planting spaces which are designed to allow for growth, while allowing the safe passage of pedestrians or other traffic. This approach is mentioned in Section 7.2.4 in relation to new planting.

Underground services, including some kinds of rigid pipework, can occasionally be damaged by the movement of roots when trees sway in the wind. In very rare cases, it is possible for serious accidents to result if gas escapes are involved. However, most kinds of pipework that are being installed nowadays are flexible and are supplied in long lengths which require relatively few joints. The probability of breakage in new systems is therefore very low [21] but, as pointed out by Mattheck and Breloer [106], it is advisable in principle to ensure that pipelines lie beyond the area where structural roots are likely to occur. Failing this, the amount of any movement should be relatively small if the pipeline passes directly under the tree at right angles to the prevailing wind direction.

7.6 Preventive management for growth-related weaknesses

Growth-related weaknesses, as distinct from the weakening of existing wood by decay, are caused by factors that interfere with the natural tendency of tree growth to optimise the distribution of mechanical stresses [106]. Such interference can be lessened through appropriate management, as outlined below. Certain factors – such as the tendency to produce unions with included bark – have a genetic basis, and can therefore be made less prevalent by the selection of propagating and planting stock (see Section 7.2).

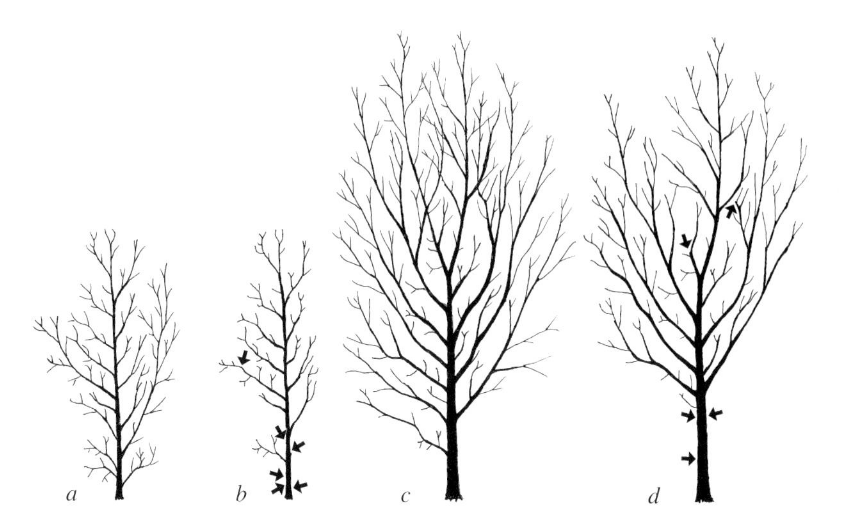

Figure 7.1 Formative pruning, positions arrowed

7.6.1 General principles of formative pruning

In many intensively used areas, it is desirable for trees to have a branch structure which is mechanically sound and generally free from potentially hazardous features. The development of such a structure should be encouraged through formative pruning while trees are young. The style of pruning may be determined by special management objectives such as the establishment of street pollards, or the removal of low branches which could be broken by vandals or eventually obstruct a thoroughfare. If a more natural growth habit is to be encouraged, the only need at amenity sites is to remove formations which could become hazardous, such as crossing limbs and forks with included bark.

Usually, only twigs and small branches need to be removed in formative pruning (Fig. 7.1), so that there should be little or no need to remove major branches when the tree is older, with the attendant problem of creating large, decay-prone wounds. Formative pruning should begin in the nursery, as mentioned above. In this context, it is advisable not to accept planting stock which has already been structurally compromised, for example by the removal of central leaders.

One of the principles of formative pruning can be summed up by the phrase "little and often". Unwanted branches can be removed when they are still very small; indeed smaller than is indicated in Fig. 7.2. It is often useful to prevent the development of unsuitably placed branches by selectively pinching out young shoots by hand. If this degree of individual attention is feasible, it is also worth encouraging the formation of branches from desired buds by notching the stem just above these positions.

7.6.2 Formative pruning for unions containing included bark

As explained in Section 2.1.2.3, trees often develop mechanically weak regions of bark-to-bark contact, due either to a genetic trait or to the development of co-dominant leading shoots following the loss of the primary leader. Once such a formation has developed, its tendency to fail depends partly on the species or cultivar concerned (see Appendix 2). Exposure to wind is another important factor, since trees in groups or forest stands provide shelter and mutual support, so that weak forks are rarely a hazard in these situations. The greatest chance of failure occurs when a tree with one or more weak unions is newly exposed to the wind, e.g. by the removal of adjacent trees.

In heavily used sites, the first line of preventive management is to avoid planting cultivars or provenances with a genetic tendency to produce excessively acute-angled branches (Section 7.2.1). Failing this, potential hazards can be avoided to some extent by formative pruning. Such action may, in any case, be appropriate where a fork begins to develop as a result of the loss of a leading shoot, rather than due to genetic predisposition. Although the development of forks can be forestalled, it is clearly impracticable to remove all acute branches. If, however, any such branches show the potential to form scaffold limbs, they can usefully be removed before the resulting pruning wounds would be very large.

The removal of potentially weak formations at an early stage can prevent hazards from developing (Plate 129). By the time that a tree is semi-mature, the removal of a limb from a weak fork could create serious crown asymmetry, together with a wound large enough to allow the development of extensive decay. In such cases, remedial action in the form of bracing or crown reduction may be necessary. Otherwise, an approach that has been suggested by some practitioners is to encourage one member of the fork to become dominant. This involves shortening the other member, so that it will eventually become over-topped. The union may continue to have some potential for failure, owing to a concentration of stresses in this region. This tendency should diminish in future years, with the gradual formation of a substantial shell of new wood around the union.

7.6.3 Downward bending of heavy branches

The progressive downward bending of large branches under their own weight is often countered by the formation of reaction wood. Such bending may, however progress until breakage becomes likely, (see Sections 2.3.2.1 and 5.2.1.4), perhaps with a consequent hazard. Branch propping or removal may then become advisable, but these remedies may bring their own problems. Heavy lower branches often develop on open-grown trees (Plate 16), since they are not shaded by neighbouring trees and can thus survive and grow up to form part of the main crown in maturity. If retained, the lowermost branches might in many cases come to rest on the ground without bending excessively, while also supporting branches above them. Their removal makes it possible for somewhat higher branches to bend down, sometimes far enough to break. Browsing by animals is another activity which prevents branches from coming to rest on the ground, although it does at least relieve them of some of their weight.

For reasons of site usage, it is sometimes potentially hazardous or impracticable to allow low branches to grow until they come to rest on the ground. If so, the next best option is probably to remove them through formative pruning when the tree is young. However, this practice can detract from the appearance of an open-grown tree in the landscape and has come in for some justifiable criticism, even though it is preferable to excessive 'crown lifting' of trees after they have reached maturity.

7.7 Pruning in relation to hazards

Formative pruning helps to prevent the development of hazards related to growth-related weakness (see Section 7.6). On the other hand, pruning in general is a form of wounding and can initiate the development of decay (see Section 3.3), as well as perhaps removing too much leaf area. It is therefore important to prune only with good reason and to use techniques which cause the least damage to the tree. These techniques, which are outlined below, are feasible because pruning wounds are made in a controlled manner and they are usually created in places where wound-induced dysfunction can be arrested at anatomical boundaries. For convenience, the term 'pruning' will be used in this section to describe all kinds of work in which twigs or branches are removed or shortened. The term 'lopping' is often applied when large branches are removed, but this distinction is not made in the present context. Special considerations apply in the case of pollarding, topping and crown reduction, which are discussed elsewhere (see Sections 7.8 and 8.3).

7.7.1 Justifications for pruning

Trees are pruned for a wide variety of arboricultural and horticultural purposes [22], many of which are not directly concerned with the risk of mechanical failure. For example, there may be a need to restrict the size of trees in confined areas or near thoroughfares. Also, there may be a desire to create artificial shapes or to encourage flowering and fruiting. Pruning may take place below ground, as well, as above – for example when there is a need to remove unwanted stems arising from roots ('suckers'), especially in grafted trees. As far as hazard management alone is concerned, the main purposes of pruning are as follows:

- the 'singling' of forked leading shoots (see Section 7.6.2)
- the removal or shortening of branches which would in time become

excessively long and heavy (see Section 7.6.3)

- shortening branches so as to manage excessive end-weight
- removing or shortening branches which are:
  - weakly attached
  - dead
  - detached but hanging
  - cracked
  - seriously decayed or bending down excessively (see Section 6.3.2)
- removing or shortening branches which, although sound, are hazardous in other ways (e.g. through obstruction or potential poisoning of children)
- balancing the crowns of storm-damaged trees
- crown reduction and thinning to reduce the lever arm or the sail area of hazardous trees (see Section 6.4.1)

7.7.2 Considerations for minimising pruning-related defects (incorporating text from Lonsdale [96])

7.7.2.1 Size of wounds

The larger the wound, the greater the risk of decay. The reasons for this may be less obvious than they seem, and there is some evidence that size *per se* is less important than the relative sizes of the severed branch and its parent stem. There is no precise formula for calculating an acceptable size limit for wounds, since many additional factors can influence the development of decay. In particular, the age of the exposed wood is an important consideration because old central wood differs considerably between tree species in its decay-resistance. Obviously, large wounds tend to expose older wood than small ones. A rough guide, based on current knowledge, is that the removal of a branch should preferably create a wound not larger than about one-quarter to one-third the diameter of the parent stem or branch.

A stem or branch may need to be shortened, rather than being cut back to its base. This obviously results in the exposure of the entire cross-section, which results in dysfunctional changes proximal to the cut surface. The likelihood of extensive dysfunction may be reduced by making the cut immediately distal to a daughter branch whose diameter is at least one third that of the parent. This practice also helps to retain a reasonably natural appearance, compared with the retention of very small branches adjacent to disproportionately large wounds.

The size of a wound not only affects the extent of dysfunction in the xylem, but also the rate at which it is occluded by the growth of new wood and bark around its edge. The larger the wound, the greater is the distance across which the new tissues must grow. This simple relationship is, however, complicated by the fact that the rate of growth increases with the proportion of stem circumference occupied by the wound.

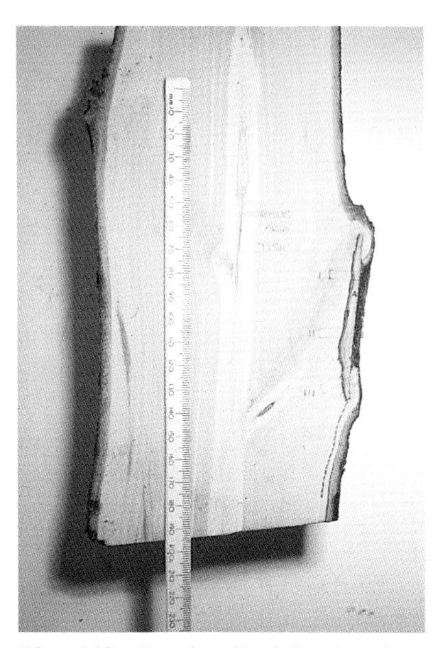

Plate 143 Very localised discoloration behind a pruning wound on Sorbus aria

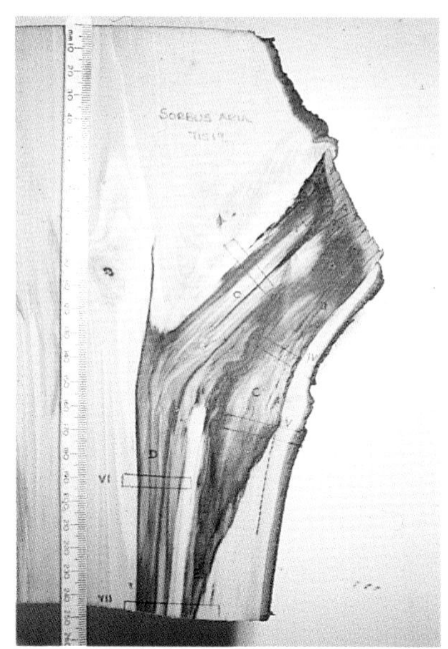

Plate 144 Extensive discoloration behind a pruning wound on Sorbus aria

7.7.2.2 Number of pruning wounds per stem

Decay associated with single wounds is very often confined to within a few centimetres of the wound surface (Plate 143), but it sometimes extends towards the centre (Plate 144). Extensive decay, often in the form of a central column, seems to occur more frequently where a number of wounds have been created on a single stem or branch (Plates 36–37), especially if they are large and perhaps even more so if they date from about the same time. The reason for this is probably that, like individual large wounds, multiple wounds severely disrupt xylem function. Another effect of excessive pruning is the sudden exposure of the parent stems or branches to solar heat, which may increase the extent of drying from the wound surfaces. It is not possible, in the current state of knowledge, to give guidance on the maximum desirable number of wounds on a given length of stem, but it is important to be aware of the risks inherent in multiple wounding and to avoid the practice wherever possible.

Crack formation is another problem that can occur after a number of pruning wounds are made close together on the same stem. The tree's responses to wounding, especially flush-cutting, may lead to the induction of radial cracks within the inrolling wood formed after wounding, or of circumferential cracks between the old and new wood (see Chapter 2). If there is only one wound, any cracks that form are quite likely to remain localised, but they are more liable to join up and become extensive if a number of wounds are present.

A more immediate hazard can be created when numerous branches are removed from the lower portion of a stem. This shifts the distribution of weight towards the apex, so that the problem of end-loading (Section 2.2.1.1) may arise. No definitive guidelines can currently be given for the amount of lower branch removal that can be allowed without creating a significant hazard. This will almost certainly differ between various tree species and cultivars.

7.7.2.3 Position of pruning wounds in relation to the branch junction

The position of a pruning wound is a major factor in determining whether or not the wound will seriously harm the tree. If we look at natural processes of dieback in trees, we see that boundaries between living and dead tissues often coincide with anatomical boundaries, especially branch junctions. In some species, these junctions contain pre-existing boundaries such as vessel endings, and perhaps also a concentration of starch reserves which can be converted into defensive substances. If an entire branch dies back, perhaps due to lack of light, the live/dead boundary often forms at or near its base, rather than a long way down into the parent stem. Defensive substances are laid down in this zone, forming a reaction zone (Plate 145), so that the tissues of the parent stem are protected from dysfunction and decay.

The removal of a live branch is a more sudden event than the process of natural dieback, but the damaged tissues near the wound will similarly form a reaction zone. The reaction zone may, however, be weak and ineffective if the cut is made too close to the parent stem. Such a cut injures or removes the zone where the boundary would otherwise have formed. If, however, the cut is made too far out along the branch, the more distal tissues will usually die back some way, forming a dead stub which will obstruct the process of wound occlusion (Fig. 7.3).

The optimum pruning position might seem difficult to define exactly, but it is marked by a natural feature in the axil of the branch; i.e. the branch bark ridge (Plate 146, Fig. 7.2). This ridge (or groove in some species) is usually visible, unless it has been obscured by the formation of very thick outer bark or by a bark inclusion. It marks a plane of separation between two sets of tissues; those which belong only to the parent stem and those which join the branch to the stem [155, 157]. When a pruning cut is made, it should not damage the ridge, but should pass immediately distally to it (Fig. 7.2). Cuts of this type are termed 'natural-target' cuts [158], whereas those that damage the ridge are termed flush cuts. The other kind of cut, a stub cut, can be defined as one which retains part of the branch distal to the ridge.

The branch bark ridge provides a simple guide for locating the best position for the top edge of a pruning cut, but the optimum angle for the cut is less easy to define. The tissues which belong only to the parent stem can be regarded as continuing all the way around the base of the branch as a sort of 'collar' [156]. The cut should be just distal to this collar, which is sometimes visible as a distinct bulge. Such a bulge develops if the diameter growth of the branch is disproportionately small in relation to that of the parent stem. This happens

Plate 145 Section cut through a stem of Quercus robur *at the junction of a dead, suppressed branch; the dark region near the branch base is the protective 'reaction zone'*

Plate 146 Branch base of Castanea sativa *with visible collar*

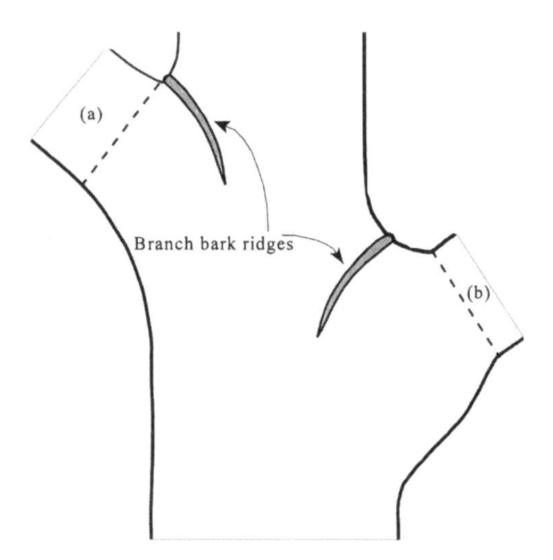

Figure 7.2 Natural target pruning: (a) without the presence of a conspicuous branch collar; (b) with a conspicuous collar (dotted lines show positions of final cuts)

more in some species than in others. The bulging collar may extend a short distance along the branch, in which case it should not be removed by the cut (Fig. 7.2), even if a stub appears to remain. Another useful guide can often be found at the base of a horizontal or downward-sloping branch in the form of an encircling bark ridge.

Sometimes, a branch base has a visible collar only on its abaxial side, in which case the optimum position of cutting is marked by the branch bark ridge

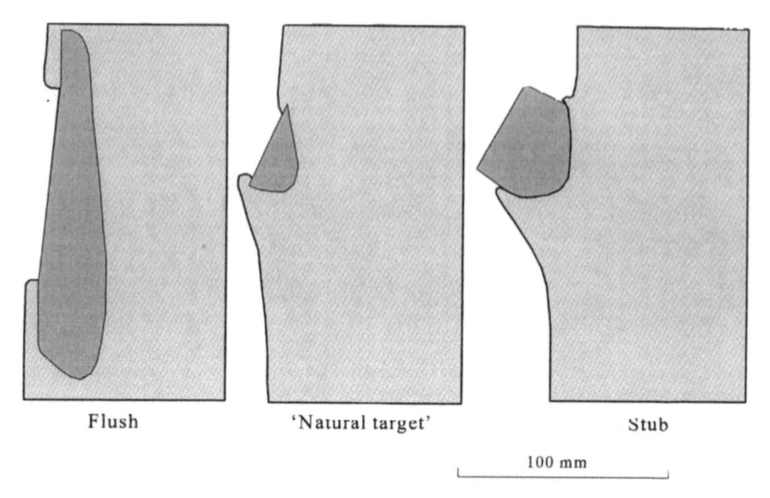

Figure 7.3 Mean extent of wood discoloration or decay four years after flush, stub and natural target pruning in *Fagus sylvatica*

Plate 147 Old flush pruning cut on Fagus sylvatica, *showing partial occlusion almost entirely from the sides*

Plate 148 Pruning cut with undamaged branch bark ridge on Fagus sylvatica, *showing almost circular pattern of occlusion*

above and by the distal edge of the collar below. If no visible collar can be distinguished, an approximate guide is to make the angle of cut equal to, or slightly steeper than, a mirror image of the angle between the parent stem and the branch bark ridge [157]. For a particular tree species or indeed for an individual tree, the best guideline may sometimes be found in its responses to previous cuts. If 'callus' growth has been poor around the lower edge of a cut (Plate 147), instead of developing strongly all around the wound (Plate 148), the reason might be that this part of the cut was made too close to the parent stem. If, however, a dead snag protrudes beyond the 'callus', the cut was probably made too far away from the parent stem (Fig. 7.4).

If we look at old wounds that have been created by natural-target pruning, we soon see that there is room for error in trying to predict the natural position

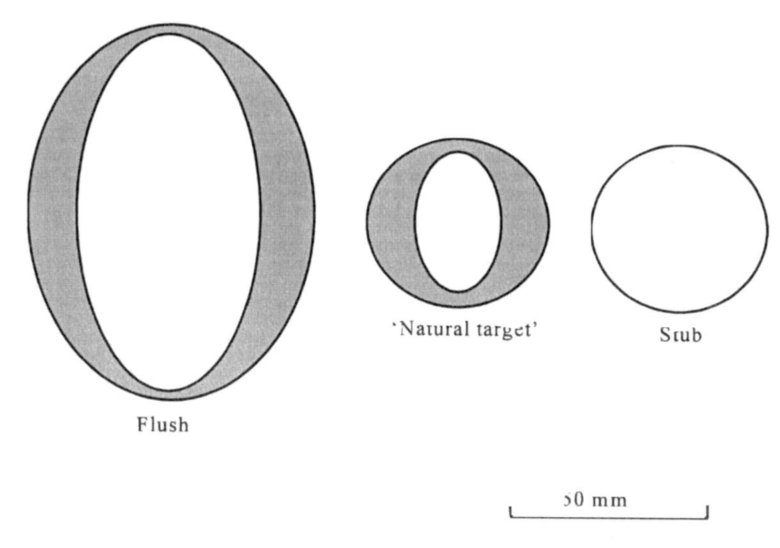

Figure 7.4 Extent of wound closure four years after flush, stub and natural target pruning in *Fagus sylvatica*

of boundary-setting. This problem has led to suggestions that there might be some advantage in pruning in two stages, so that the tree has a chance to set its own visible boundaries after the first stage. In such a procedure, known as '**phased natural-target pruning**', a stub cut is made initially, and the stub is removed just distal to the dead/live boundary a year or more later. In view of the extra cost and complexity of adopting phased natural-target pruning, it may prove to be of largely academic interest. It may, however, be practicable in some circumstances, and the following observations may therefore be of interest.

It seems clear that, if natural-target pruning is phased, it provides a more accurate definition of the correct pruning position than can often be achieved in a single procedure. On the other hand, it remains uncertain which of the two methods is more likely to allow colonisation of the parent stem by micro-organisms. It is often said that a stub provides these with the foodbase required to breach the reaction zone and thus colonise the parent stem. This 'springboard' hypothesis has not been tested by long-term experiments but, in a relatively short-term study lasting four years, experimental stub cuts and 'natural-target' cuts on beech trees did not differ as far as microbial colonisation of the parent stems was concerned [100].

One of the main objectives of natural-target pruning is to avoid removing the region of the branch junction which is physiologically primed to lay down an effective barrier (i.e. a reaction zone) to decay fungi. In some cases of natural branch dieback, as in Plate 145, the reaction zone forms at a short distance along the branch, in a region that might be removed by one-stage natural-target pruning. On the other hand, there is some reason to suspect that phased natural-target pruning might damage a barrier that has already formed. With regard to the development of decay, some observations indicate that damage to a reaction zone in previously cut tissues could be more harmful than the original cutting of the tissues when they were fully functional.

Although, in general, dead stubs should not be permanently retained, this does not mean that all branches should be cut back to their bases. Indeed, there are many branches which would leave extremely large wounds on their parent stems if they were to be removed entirely. The shortening of such a branch may be a better option, provided that it can be cut back to a junction with a healthy side-branch which is not excessively shaded. A similar procedure is appropriate in the re-cutting of old, lapsed pollards, as mentioned in Chapter 8. If cuts are made too close to the ancient trunks of such trees, serious dieback is likely to occur. If a stub is left, the boundaries of dysfunction and decay may be confined within the stub, near to a side-branch or new shoots. Decay within the distal part of the stub is ecologically desirable in such circumstances.

One general point that seems appropriate here is that the final cut in branch pruning should be made only after most of the weight of the branch has been removed by preliminary cutting. This is standard practice, and helps to avoid any tearing or pinching of bark on the parent stem or branch. Heavy or awkward branches may need to be dismantled in several sections.

7.7.2.4 Susceptibility of different species to decay and cankering following pruning

Species, and indeed cultivars and individuals within species, differ in their ability to form effective barriers at pruning wounds (Section 3.4), but too little research has yet been done for anyone to provide a reliable 'league table' of susceptibility. To some extent, the differences between various types of tree are related not only to their relative ability to lay down natural barriers, but also to their resistance against certain disease-causing organisms. For example, many members of the Rosaceae and some *Acer* species are susceptible to infection by canker fungi, especially *Nectria* spp. Another common disease-causing organism which affects the Rosaceae, as well as many other families, is the silver leaf fungus, *Chondrostereum purpureum*, which can cause decay or be replaced by other decay fungi.

There are some species which form a durable heartwood containing substances which inhibit invasion by decay fungi (see Section 3.4.2). No kind of heartwood is, however, immune from decay; some fungi are specialised degraders of heartwood, e.g. *Laetiporus sulphureus*, which attacks several genera and is common in oak (*Quercus* spp.), yew (*Taxus baccata*) and False acacia (*Robinia pseudoacacia*).

7.7.2.5 The influence of time of year on pruning-induced decay and bark dieback

A seasonal cycle of change occurs in several of the factors that are believed to influence the defences of wounded tissues. These factors include the following: cell growth activity in the bark and cambial zone, total carbohydrate reserves, the starch:sugar ratio, moisture content and gas content. Many of the micro-organisms that colonise wounds also show seasonal patterns of growth and dissemination. Apart from these cyclic patterns in the tree and in micro-organisms, there may also be changes brought about by seasonally varying and fluctuating external factors such as atmospheric humidity and temperature.

Although data exist on most of the seasonal changes outlined above, prediction of good and bad times for pruning is difficult, since different factors affecting tree defences may, in effect, be working against each other. Nevertheless, the nett effect of these factors appears to change during the year, so that some periods can be judged more favourable for pruning than others. For convenience, these periods can be defined in terms of the conventional four seasons of temperate climates. They would, however, be better defined on the basis of biological criteria, including the annual cycle of the individual tree.

Autumn, despite tradition, can be judged on balance to be a rather bad time to prune trees. Components of active defence that depend on cell growth are clearly less effective at this time than in spring and summer. Also, wood moisture is at its lowest in many species during the autumn. A low moisture content in wood equates with increased aeration, which favours the activity of many decay fungi. Finally, autumn is the time when a high proportion of decay fungi are releasing their spores (presumably, an advantageous evolutionary adaptation), and therefore tend to colonise new hosts during this period.

Predictions for winter, spring and summer are more difficult. In **winter**, the tree is at its least active, but so are most micro-organisms. In maritime climates like that of Britain, as well as in the subtropical and warm-temperate zones, microbial growth in winter may nevertheless be considerable even when the tree's defences are not very effective. Another factor which can result in winter damage is the occurrence of freezing temperatures. In severe cases, dieback may develop from pruning cuts, perhaps because water is lost from the frozen surface by sublimation of ice without being replenished by the transpiration stream.

In **mid-spring**, when the tree's food reserves are being depleted by flushing and perhaps by flowering, the availability of sugars for conversion into defensive chemicals is almost certainly reduced. On the other hand, defences involving cell growth can operate better than in autumn or winter. It has therefore been suggested that the best time to prune is at the end of winter when the tree's defence systems are about to become active, but before its food reserves are depleted by flushing [155]. The above proviso regarding desiccation in very cold weather should be noted, especially in the case of evergreens which can lose moisture from their leaves as well as from pruning cuts.

If cuts are made in late winter or early spring, they often exude fluid owing to the development of positive xylem pressure before flushing begins. This so-called bleeding is particularly marked in certain genera such as *Acer*, *Betula*, *Carpinus* and *Juglans*, and is often cited as a reason not to prune them during this period. There is, however, no danger of water depletion, although there is a slight loss of dissolved sugars. Indeed, the positive pressure probably helps to prevent the ingress of fungal spores.

In **mid– to late summer**, the tree is active, wood moisture is fairly high and food reserves have been restored by photosynthesis following their depletion in spring. This appears in principle to be a good time for pruning, and this was borne out many years ago by experimental work in which wounds on plum trees were exposed to infection by the fungus which causes silver-leaf disease of rosaceous fruit trees, *Chondrostereum purpureum* [24]. This is a fresh-wound parasite (see Section 3.4.1), which was found to be largely incapable of infecting wounds more than a month old. Wounds made in June, July and August become infected much less often than those made in other months. Different results were, however obtained in recent work by Spiers *et al.* [166] in New Zealand. They found that in cuttings of *Malus, Pyrus, Prunus* and *Salix* spp., xylem tissues were at their most resistant to invasion by the fungus during May, June and July, which make up the late autumn to midwinter period in New Zealand. Peak susceptibility was in November; i.e., late spring.

No seasonal comparisons appear to have been carried out experimentally for individual wood-invading fungi other than *C. purpureum*, but some workers have measured the general extent of microbial colonisation behind pruning wounds created at different times of year. In interpreting their results, it seems reasonable to assume that a small zone of discoloration indicates a highly effective delimitation of wound-induced dysfunction. In a study on nine tree species, Lonsdale [99] created pruning wounds without introducing specific fungi. After twelve months, measurements of the extent of discoloured wood behind the cut surfaces showed significant differences between dates of pruning (e.g. Fig. 7.5, showing data for hornbeam, *Carpinus betulus*). However, the species differed in their periods of peak 'susceptibility'. Seasonal differences in the extent of xylem discoloration have also been reported from a study involving increment borer wounds in stems of *Fagus sylvatica* [48].

The extent of cambial dieback is another property of pruning wounds which is affected by the season of cutting. In all nine species studied by Lonsdale [99], the seasonal differences were statistically significant but the 'best' and 'worst' times of year differed between the species. The autumn was the worst time for only two of them; gean (*Prunus avium*) and Norway maple (*Acer platanoides*). It is, however, known from numerous other studies that wounds created in the autumn are generally the most likely to result in extensive cambial dieback if certain pathogens are present. This is because such organisms can then attack the tissues over several months while the tree is dormant and has little ability to defend itself.

As cambial dieback is affected by the season of pruning, it could be expected that 'callus growth' would show something of an inverse seasonal relationship due to its being delayed by extensive dieback. This effect was to some extent borne out by the study conducted by Lonsdale [99]. Seasonal differences in the rate of wound occlusion were also measured by Liese and

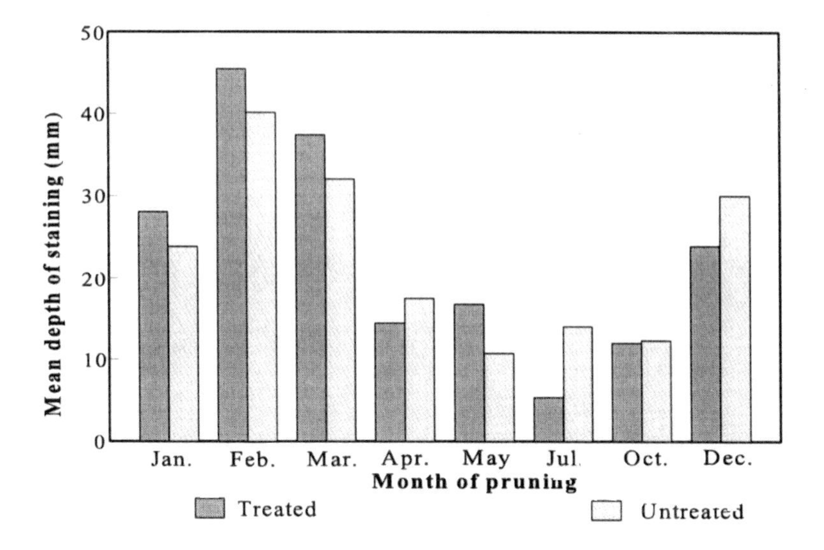

Figure 7.5 Extent of discoloration beneath pruning wounds of *Carpinus betulus*, created at different seasons

Dujesiefken [94], but their 'good' and 'bad' times differed from those found by Lonsdale [99] for three species common to both studies.

In view of the long-term nature of the decay process, there is perhaps a need for further research to see whether seasonal differences detected in one-year tests would be maintained beyond the first year. It is possible that further progression of wood discoloration could override short-term differences. Rather more reliance can, however, be placed upon one-year data as far as cambial dieback is concerned, as it seldom progresses after 'callus' has begun to form around the edge of the dead area. There is equally a need to determine whether the results so far obtained are reproducible on different sites and in different years and to define 'good' and 'bad' times of year more exactly, perhaps by reference to tree phenology (e.g. times of bud-burst and leaf-fall) rather than the calendar date.

In the present state of knowledge, it seems important to avoid dogmatic statements about good and bad seasons for pruning, but the above review of evidence should provide some relevant indicators. Except in periods when the moisture or carbohydrate reserves of trees are particularly low, there seems little objection to pruning trees when the job can be done most effectively. For example the thinning or reduction of crowns in the dormant season may help to show the worst of any unsightly effects which would otherwise be masked by foliage.

7.7.2.6 Pruning tools

A smoothly cut wound is thought to be better than a rough one with regard to discouraging fungal growth and dieback, although there are many reports to the contrary. Both bow-saws and the modern kinds of pruning saw provide a smooth cut, and the choice of which type to use will depend mainly on other considerations. Tests carried out on various broadleaved and coniferous species indicate that the very narrow bow-saw blade provides some advantage with regard to the time and effort required for cutting (D. Lonsdale, unpublished data). On the other hand, pruning saws are better suited for insertion into tight crotches, and are also considerably more convenient and safer to carry when climbing. Chainsaws may be necessary for the removal of large branches if this is essential, but their use for routine pruning can tempt operators to create larger cuts than might be advisable.

Pruning tools are not generally regarded as a means of cross-infection between diseased and healthy material. There is, however, some reason to believe that such transmission could occur if the pathogen concerned is both highly aggressive and exists in the form of sap-mobile cells or spores. The agents of virus diseases, vascular wilts (e.g. Verticillium wilt) and bacterial blights (e.g. fireblight) could fall into this category. As a precaution, it is therefore advisable to sterilise blades after using them on any stems or branches which have wilted or died back rapidly, or which are believed to have a serious virus disease.

For sterilisation, a general disinfectant such as "Dettol" or "Jeye's Fluid", diluted according to manufacturer's instructions, will kill most fungi and bacteria. Sodium hypochlorite, available as household bleach, is also very effective and is additionally active against viruses. Industrial or laboratory solutions of hypochlorite contain 10 to 14 % available chlorine and should be diluted one hundred-fold with clean water; this working solution should be kept in a clean, non-metallic container. As the solution loses its effectiveness during use and storage, it should be made up freshly every day. Some commercial forms of hypochlorite (e.g. "Chloros") are mixed with potassium permanganate, the purple colour of which fades as a warning that the hypochlorite has been exhausted.

Tools must be cleaned before sterilisation, since dirt or grease will render the sterilant ineffective. A few minutes' immersion will suffice for sterilisation. To prevent metal corrosion and possible damage to plant tissue, the sterilised tools should be rinsed in water or swabbed after immersion. It should be noted that oily tools such as chainsaws cannot be properly sterilised and should preferably not be used on such plant material. Thorough cleaning of the saw may, however, remove most of the contaminating material.

7.7.2.7 The use of wound dressings

The above practices may reduce the risk of extensive decay developing from pruning wounds, but they cannot eliminate it. In the past it was assumed that wounds could be protected by dressings, but experimental evaluations of various research projects have generally failed to support this view, even though certain materials are valuable as short-term protectants against fresh-wound parasites. The results of these projects have become widely known, so that the use of wound dressings has been discontinued by most practitioners in the UK. It has been widely assumed that wound dressings can never be of value, but this conclusion is not wholly justified on the basis of the research that has so far taken place. Conclusive findings are very hard to obtain, for reasons which include the variability of the trees that are available for experiments and the need for very lengthy trials [98].

In practice, it is reasonable to decide not to use wound dressings except in cases where fresh wound parasites are a particular threat. However, practitioners should bear in mind that the case against wound dressings is not proven in principle. For the present, any continuing hope for an effective wound treatment is largely of academic interest, since legal requirements for pesticide registration have made it uneconomic for companies to offer products with a small market potential. Nevertheless, anyone who is interested in this subject should be aware of the reasons why various types of dressing should or should not be expected to work.

A wound dressing could in theory be expected to work in one or more of the following four ways.

1. Prompt treatment of the wound surface with a sealant might exclude infection by fresh wound parasites.

2. The incorporation of a chemical fungicide or a biological control agent into the formulation could help to prevent the growth of harmful micro-organisms.

3. An impermeable dressing could reduce gas exchange, thus inhibiting the growth of harmful micro-organisms.

4. If the dressing encourages the growth of new bark and wood across the surface of the wound, total occlusion and hence the arrest of decay development could be hastened.

A cosmetic covering to the wound may also be desired.

Most of the evidence on physical sealants and on materials containing fungicides suggests that their ability to exclude harmful micro-organisms by physical or chemical action lasts only for a short period (less than one year). Short-term protection may be very useful where the main risk is from a fresh wound parasite, such as *C. purpureum* (Section 3.4.1) or one of the more pathogenic canker fungi. It is not likely to help much against most decay fungi. It is also possible that chemical protection might inhibit the growth of beneficial micro-organisms which are antagonistic to decay fungi.

A somewhat longer-term protection may be available from biological control agents, particularly species of the fungus *Trichoderma* [98, 112]. In experimental work, it has been easy to establish this fungus in the wood behind wounds by applying it as a spore suspension by brush or even via chainsaw oil. Before the implementation of stringent procedures for product registration in the UK, at least one product containing *Trichoderma* was at various times commercially available for treating tree wounds.

The control of the wound micro-environment, particularly the capacity for gas exchange, is also difficult to achieve in the long term, owing to the degradation of the dressing materials. Nevertheless, there is evidence that materials with this mode of action may slow down the development of decay from basal trunk injuries over periods of about four or five years [17]. There is probably some potential for the development of more durable treatments, as indicated by promising results that have been obtained with a novel wound treatment based on a polyurethane preparation, currently marketed as a roof repair compound [98]. Such a material would, however, require further evaluation before its registration as a plant protectant could even be considered.

The occlusion process is enhanced for up to about three years by some sealants, but this is likely to be of little use on very small wounds which can be occluded rapidly anyway, or on very large wounds which may never become occluded. Experiments show that sealants containing the fungicide thiophanate methyl are particularly good at enhancing the short-term growth of occluding tissues. This fungicide has little activity against most decay organisms, although it inhibits attack by many canker fungi. In any case, it is now becoming widely accepted that acceleration of occlusion can do more harm than good, since it sometimes results in the rolling over of the new bark and wood to form 'rams-horns'. The resulting mechanical stress tends to cause cracking.

7.7.3 A checklist for pruning

- Prune only if there is a good reason
- Minimise pruning on species that are particularly susceptible to fresh-wound parasites (see Sections 3.4.1 and 8.2.2), and treat such species with a wound paint if an effective one is available
- Do not make flush cuts, and follow up-to-date advice on the correct position of pruning
- Where possible, avoid the removal of branches which are large in relation to the parent stem
- Avoid making wounds close together on the same parent stem, unless they are all very small
- Make use of information about 'good' and 'bad' times of year for pruning
- Try to avoid pruning drought-stressed trees, especially if the resulting wounds would be large

7.8 Pollarding in the management of urban trees

Some of the tree species that were traditionally planted in urban areas, for example lime (*Tilia* spp.) and London plane (*Platanus* x *hispanica*), have the potential to outgrow the space available to them and to obstruct traffic. There may also be problems of excessive shading, blockage of gutters with fallen leaves, interference with underground utilities and the subsidence of buildings due to the drying out of shrinkable soils. In many sites, such species have therefore been subjected to various forms of periodic cutting to restrict their growth.

In view of the costs of managing potentially large trees in small spaces, the trend in more recent decades has been to choose species which are unlikely to outgrow their surroundings when they reach maturity. This option was made possible partly by the greater commercial availability of these trees in the nursery trade and partly by the control of coal burning, which formerly restricted the choice to pollution-tolerant species.

Although the use of smaller-sized trees avoids the need for expensive and possibly harmful cycles of cutting, there remain many specimens of potentially very large size whose growth still has to be kept in check. Also, there is some desire to continue planting large species which arguably provide greater aesthetic benefits and the capacity to reach a worthwhile size rapidly. Even from a purely practical point of view, the larger species can more satisfactorily provide the height of clear stem that is needed to allow the passage of vehicles along major roads. Large-growing species will therefore need to be managed in urban areas for the foreseeable future, in many cases by a system of pollarding.

Pollards must be cut periodically in order to keep them within their desired size and shape. Apart from this requirement, the development of long or heavy branches from the pollard heads sometimes represents a hazard which has to be managed. Although it is quite expensive to maintain the regular cycle of re-cutting, the cost is hard to compare with that of maintaining very large trees which may need complicated *ad hoc* remedial work at a much greater operating height. Another problem is that many people find pollarded trees unattractive in the winter. Nevertheless, there is sometimes a positive desire to grow trees as pollards because they represent a traditional feature of the formal landscape or townscape.

If lapsed urban pollards become unacceptably large or hazardous, re-cutting may be required as a remedy (see Section 6.4.3.3), but this could lead to extensive decay if the wounds thereby created expose old central wood with poor resistance to microbial colonisation. Provided that the pollard heads are capable of supporting new growth, such neglected trees can be brought under renewed preventive management in the form of regular cutting. Some other aspects of pollarding, mainly as it concerns ancient trees, are discussed in Section 8.3; these include the effects of environmental conditions and the ability of different tree species to respond to re-cutting.

Chapter 8 Environmental implications of hazard and disease management

In areas where trees exist alongside people and property, there is generally a need to manage them so as to avoid any unacceptable risk of personal injury or other damage. For this reason dead or decaying trees or branches are often removed or destroyed, to the extent that many urban and recreational sites are almost devoid of dead wood. From a conservation standpoint, such a situation represents a serious gap in biodiversity because deadwood habitats are vital for a wide range of plants, fungi, animals and micro-organisms. Many woodland areas abound in dead wood, but this is very often of small diameter due to the utilisation of most of the larger material for timber or fuel. Also, it is the practice in some woodlands to remove dead wood because of the largely mistaken belief that it harbours pests or pathogens.

Even in areas which are managed primarily for timber production or for intensive public access, there is usually scope for providing a deadwood resource. This is, however, limited at some urban sites where the retention of standing deadwood would create an unacceptable risk, and where other considerations may make it impracticable even to retain much fallen deadwood. In rural sites of recreation where members of the public have access to ancient trees, safety is similarly an important requirement but it can often be achieved by means which do not deplete the deadwood resource. In yet other situations, particularly in remote woodland areas, trees that are not required for timber can be allowed to age and decay naturally without placing anyone at appreciable risk.

The richest deadwood habitats are usually associated with old trees, since they usually contain decaying wood in larger volumes and in a greater variety of states than young ones. Also, their bark is usually a better habitat for lichens, mosses and liverworts. Furthermore, many people take pleasure in the sight of massive or bizarre, gnarled old trees (Plate 149), or indeed revere them. Such interest has grown in Britain during the 1990s, with the formation of the Ancient Tree Forum and the launch of the Veteran Tree Initiative by English Nature. There is, however, a long national tradition of valuing particular ancient trees which are exceptionally large or which have historical associations. Examples include the Major Oak in Sherwood Forest (Plate 150) and the Machen Oak in the Forest of Dean (Plate 151).

The desire to retain old trees can sometimes lead to difficulties if it takes no account of the need for safety and for providing conditions for the healthy development of future generations of trees. Managers of ancient trees must

Plate 149 Bizarre living remnant of a pollard of Fagus sylvatica*; this gathering of people at Burnham Beeches, Buckinghamshire exemplifies a growing interest in 'veteran' trees*

Plate 151 The Machen Oak, Forest of Dean, adequately supported by outer wood, despite the decayed core

Plate 150 The Major Oak, Sherwood Forest; massive ancient trees are traditionally venerated in the UK (note the arguably excessive propping)

take all requirements into account, but they should resist any irrational desire for 'tidying away' specimens that do not fit some dendrological ideal of vigour and flawless form.

The maintenance of health in trees sometimes depends on the control of diseases and 'pests'. Control may in turn prevent the development of hazards where these might otherwise arise due to the embrittlement, decay or altered growth of diseased or damaged trees. This chapter outlines some of the situations in which pest or disease control may be desirable, while also identifying circumstances in which such measures may be unnecessary, counter-productive, or harmful to wildlife. If control is being contemplated, it is important to diagnose the problem correctly. There are a number of books which are useful in aiding diagnosis, and some of those available in the UK are listed below. Expert advice is also available from several sources, which are listed in Appendix 4.

- H. Butin, *Tree Diseases and Disorders*: see main list of references
- S.C. Gregory and D.B. Redfern (1998). *Diseases and Disorders of Forest Trees*. Forestry Commission Field Book 16. The Stationery Office
- T.R. Peace (1962). *The Pathology of Trees and Shrubs, with Special Reference to Britain*. Oxford (out of print)
- D.H. Phillips & D.A. Burdekin (1992). (revised edn.) *Diseases of Forest and Ornamental Trees*. Macmillan
- W.A. Sinclair, H.H. Lyon and W.T. Johnson (1987). *Diseases of Trees and Shrubs*. Comstock Publishing Associates (a North American book)
- I. M. Smith, J. Dunez, R. A. Lelliot, D. H. Phillips, S. A. Archer, eds. (1988). *European Handbook of Plant Diseases*. Blackwell Scientific Publications
- R.G. Strouts & T.G. Winter, *Diagnosis of Ill-health in Trees*: see main list of references
- T.A Tattar (1989). *Diseases of Shade Trees*. Academic Press (a North American book)
- H. Wormald (1955). (3rd edn.) *Diseases of Fruits and Hops*. Crosby Lockwood & Son Ltd (out of print).

8.1 The need to conserve biodiversity in the deadwood fauna and flora

Dying and dead wood provides one of the greatest ecological resources in a natural forest, and is equally important in many managed stands where it has been allowed to accumulate. In stands where fallen timber and partially decayed trees are removed, the diversity of animals, lower plants and fungi can be seriously impoverished. There are many different forms of wildlife that depend directly or indirectly on deadwood or on old trees. The major groups to which these species belong include beetles, flies, solitary bees and wasps, insectivorous birds, bats, fungi, mosses, lichens and liverworts. They include some species, such as woodpeckers (*Picus* and *Dendrocopus* spp.), the stag beetle (*Lucanus cervus*) and various hoverflies (*Syrphidae*), which are well known and attractive to naturalists.

Among the species that depend on deadwood habitats, some have very limited powers of dispersal, having evolved in primeval forests where they did not need to disperse more than perhaps a few metres between suitable niches. Over many centuries, woodland clearance and the exploitation of trees has led to the severe depletion and isolation of deadwood habitats, thus greatly reducing the geographic range of the species that depend on them.

Managers in both rural and urban areas should, at the very least, work to conserve existing deadwood habitats. Where possible, the deadwood resource should be enhanced by avoiding its unnecessary removal for firewood or in the interests of tidiness. Standing deadwood can, of course, sometimes pose a hazard for public safety, but it too should be retained at sites where persons and property are not thereby put at an unacceptable risk (Plate 152). Where there is such a risk, judicious tree surgery can often make it possible to retain trees that might otherwise be hazardous, while retaining much of their deadwood habitat. For example, decaying branches can often be made safer by shortening them, rather than removing them completely. The wood that is cut from such branches should not be burnt or removed from the site, provided that the owner can accept its retention.

Deadwood habitats are extremely varied, and it is therefore important to conserve variety as well as quantity. To some extent, this can be achieved by the retention and sensitive management of large, over-mature trees, especially pollards (see Section 8.3). These often have exceptional importance for wildlife. As a general rule, the diversity of deadwood habitats in a standing tree increases with the age of the tree and with the progression of the decay process: oak, ash and beech rarely begin to provide deadwood and rot-holes before they are about 100 years old. Birch is useful in that it reaches old age at about 70 years.

Some of the main kinds of deadwood habitat are listed as follows.

Dead limbs on living trees

Dead sun-baked limbs generally support fewer invertebrate species than moist deadwood deep within standing trunks or lying on the ground, but they are essential for a range of invertebrates and fungi which need dry conditions. They also provide nest sites and an invertebrate food source for various bird species. Such limbs are therefore an important part of the deadwood resource which is not provided elsewhere.

Decay columns in boles and main branches of standing trees, living or dead

These are very important for a very wide range of deadwood species, especially on living trees, where the rot may provide a continuity of habitat for many decades. An especially valuable kind of rot, which often has a very rich fauna, is ‘red wood’ in the centres of living broadleaved trees. Red wood has not been studied enough to define it in terms of the principal kinds of decay that are outlined in Chapter 3, but it seems often to be associated with the later stages of brown-rot caused by the fungus *Laetiporus sulphureus*. Such rot may be extensive in large ancient trees but is not confined to these since its formation can start at an early age and continue throughout the life of the tree.

Rot holes on standing trees, especially beech

Holes where large old stems have snapped and partially filled with water often have a very interesting fauna, including some very rare invertebrate species. Old coppice stools also frequently contain rot holes, which sometimes lead to the coppice stems becoming unstable. If the stems need to be cut, either for safety or for other reasons, the rot holes should be protected from damage and desiccation.

Fallen deadwood: boles and large branches

This supports a succession of invertebrates and fungi which contribute to the gradual humification of the wood. Contact with the soil and the associated moist conditions create a range of habitats which are rather different to those found in standing trees. It is therefore important to allow large items of deadwood to accumulate in all states of decay (Plate 153). Such deadwood is also believed to be of benefit to the health of standing trees, since it supports cord-forming fungi which can compete with honey fungus, *Armillaria* spp. and other potentially pathogenic fungi. These beneficial fungi depend additionally on a good litter layer, which also provides a natural mulch for the roots of the standing trees.

The burning of naturally fallen wood for fuel or for 'tidiness' destroys not only a valuable wildlife resource for the future, but also incinerates invertebrates that have already colonised it. This practice is especially harmful to species which remain in their immature stages for several years within individual pieces of wood. The retention of the larval habitat for merely a year or two is clearly of no value to such species, and should not be regarded as some sort of compromise in favour of wildlife. Also, there are some species which may colonise wood many years after it has fallen. For these reasons, the removal or burning of wood that has fallen naturally should be avoided wherever possible and is best regarded as taboo in sites of special importance for deadwood fauna.

Fallen deadwood: small branches and twigs

Although generally of value to fewer species than larger material, small fallen deadwood has an important part to play and should not be removed without good reason; even a piece of wood the size of a person's arm has been known to support twenty or more deadwood invertebrate species.

Plate 153 Retention of fallen deadwood in parkland, Dunham Massey, Cheshire (note also the tyre-like bulges on standing stems of Quercus *sp., indicating innocuous fibre buckling)*

Plate 152 Death and decay of a specimen of Fagus sylvatica, *allowed to occur naturally, providing deadwood habitats; Dunham Massey, Cheshire (note also the internal roots)*

Stumps and buried roots

In addition to supporting a specialised fauna of their own, stumps and roots may provide habitats for many of the species that are also found in fallen deadwood and standing trees. The stag beetle, *Lucanus cervus*, one of our most spectacular deadwood invertebrates, often spends its larval stages in the stumps and large roots of various broadleaved trees.

Sap runs

Sap runs are exudations of fluid from cracked or microbially colonised areas of bark and sapwood. They do not necessarily indicate the presence of decay, but they are an important source of moisture and dissolved sugar for many insects, including butterflies and hoverflies.

Fungal fruit bodies

Fungal fruit bodies are not merely indicators of decay; they are also an essential habitat for many invertebrate species, especially beetles and flies, and should not be removed without good reason. They are sometimes broken off in the hope that this will help to arrest the decay process. As most of the fungus is present as a mycelium in the wood, there is generally no justification for such action, although it seems possible that the fruit bodies of certain fungi, such as *Inonotus* species, might aid the decay process by pumping excess water out of the wood [146].

8.2 Sanitation versus conservation

Some people hold somewhat fundamentalist convictions about sanitation within stands of trees. On the one hand, there is a notion that disease and decay can best be controlled by tidying away all dead and diseased material. By contrast, there is a philosophical view of nature as a balanced system in which disease and decay organisms are always kept within limits by competitors and antagonists. Both these approaches hold a certain amount of truth, but it is misguided and simplistic to hold unwaveringly to either of them. For example, although pests and pathogens can thrive when over-zealous sanitation creates an excessively simple 'ecosystem', they sometimes also cause serious harm to trees under more natural conditions. This can happen either due to the inherent aggressiveness of some of these organisms, or to the effects of environmental changes (e.g. drought-stress or fire) which can help them to overcome the defences of the tree or the natural controls exerted by other organisms.

It is not necessary to carry out sanitation unless there are specific disease or pest problems which are known to be alleviated by such action. Unnecessary attempts at sanitation destroy wildlife habitats without any economic benefit. For many pests and diseases, control is either impracticable or best achieved in other ways. In some cases, reliance on natural control processes may be the best option. Appropriate decisions can be made if the problems are properly diagnosed, if necessary with the aid of expert advice. It is beyond the scope of the present book to give guidance on diagnosis of disease, but the main kinds of problem for which sanitation might seem appropriate are outlined below. For information on the techniques of diagnosis, an excellent starting point is the companion volume in this series by Strouts and Winter [173].

8.2.1 Leaf diseases and leaf-feeding insects

Leaf diseases affect most tree species, but the damage that they cause is mainly limited to the disfigurement of foliage and a reduction in vigour, which are of no direct concern for hazard management. The same comments usually apply to damage from leaf-feeding insects, although certain aphid species at urban sites can cause an additional problem by depositing honeydew [29]. In rare instances, defoliation or leaf damage due to insects or leaf fungi can be so severe that branches or even entire trees die back due to the depletion of starch reserves, often in combination with frost damage or secondary attack by bark-infecting fungi. A hazard may subsequently result from the presence of dead standing timber.

For amenity trees, it is usually best to avoid controlling foliar pests or diseases unless they are causing unacceptable disfigurement or sufficient dieback to cause a safety hazard. Occasionally, a pest can cause a human health hazard, as in the case of the irritant hairs of the brown-tail moth, *Euproctis chrysorrhoea* [168]. In the case of various leaf-infecting fungi, which overwinter on leaf litter, some degree of control can be achieved by removing the litter. Examples include leaf blotch of Horse chestnut (*Aesculus* spp.) caused by *Guignardia aesculi*, apple scab caused by *Venturia inaequalis* and tar-spot of sycamore (*Acer pseudoplatanus*), caused by *Rhytisma acerinum*. A negative aspect of this method of control is that it removes a potential habitat for various invertebrates and the birds that feed on them. It also deprives the trees of a natural mulch and, in some situations, it might encourage the development of fungi with the ability to cause root disease, by suppressing their natural competitors.

8.2.2 Insects and diseases which affect shoots, stems or branches

Insect damage which affects the leading buds or shoots of young trees may lead to the development of distorted stems or of co-dominant stems with consequent structural weakness. A notable example of an insect which causes such damage is the Pine shoot moth, *Rhyacionia buoliana* (see *Pinus* in Appendix 2). Insecticidal control may sometimes be justified in tree nurseries.

Structurally weak formations can develop following shoot killing by diseases, as well as by certain insects. Also, if the bark, cambium or wood of large branches or the main stem are damaged by disease, they can become hazardous due to subsequent embrittlement or decay. Sanitation can be worthwhile for the most serious diseases and takes the form of removing and burning infected parts of trees, or in some cases fallen parts on which the causal organism is surviving. The main examples are fireblight, caused by the bacterium *Erwinia amylovora*, silver-leaf, caused by the fungus *Chondrostereum purpureum* and coral-spot caused by the fungus *Nectria cinnabarina*.

Fireblight is a wilt and branch dieback in apples (*Malus* spp.), pears (*Pyrus* spp.) and other members of the rosaceous subfamily Pomoideae. The ornamental trees that it affects include rowans and whitebeams (*Sorbus* spp.). Information on the diagnosis and control of this disease is provided by Strouts [171] and by Strouts and Winter [173], who also describe a rather similar serious disease on cherries, plums and other *Prunus* spp., caused by the bacterium *Pseudomonas syringae* pv. *mors-prunorum*. In the case of the cherry cultivar 'Kanzan', it remains uncertain whether this or a similar bacterium is the cause of dieback [170]. Sanitation is a recommended control for fireblight but has not been evaluated against bacterial dieback of *Prunus*.

Branches that have died back due to fireblight can be cut back well beyond any sign of discoloured tissue. This can sometimes eliminate infection from the affected tree, and some degree of sanitation is achieved by burning the prunings. Also, hawthorn (*Crataegus* spp.) in hedges can become a reservoir of infection, so that there may be circumstances where valuable specimen trees are at such risk that removal of the hawthorn should be considered. This is not generally desirable, since hawthorn is of considerable value for wildlife – especially for insects which feed on its flowers [52].

Silver-leaf disease is caused by a fungus, *Chondrostereum purpureum*, which is described in Chapter 4 as the cause of decay in a wide range of tree species. In certain genera; notably members of the Rosaceae, *Eucalyptus* spp. and sometimes maples (*Acer* spp.), the fungus also causes the dieback of branches and sometimes the death of entire trees. It is ubiquitous and can infect potential hosts wherever they have sustained sapwood injuries. Its attacks are, however, more prevalent where its fruit bodies are locally abundant on dead woody material or on standing trees. The removal of such material may have some value for sanitation at sites where valuable specimen or orchard trees are at risk. The pruning of individual infected branches may also have a curative effect. In many situations, however, attempts at sanitation will harm the deadwood habitat without providing significant protection for valued trees.

Coral-spot is a canker, in which the causal organism, *Nectria cinnabarina*, develops within a localised area of bark, rather than growing along extensive lengths of the affected branch like the organisms which cause fireblight or silver-leaf. The cankers can nevertheless kill shoots, branches and small main stems of many tree and shrub species by girdling. As with the above diseases, pruning out and burning the affected parts can to some extent provide both a curative treatment and a means of reducing local sources of inoculum. There are many other canker diseases for which similar comments may apply.

8.2.3 Vascular wilt diseases

These diseases can kill branches and entire trees by causing extensive loss of water-conducting capacity in the sapwood. The causal organisms do not decay the wood, but the dead parts can become a hazard due to embrittlement or to secondary invasion by decay fungi. The main examples of such diseases in Britain are as follows: Dutch elm disease, caused by the fungi *Ophiostoma novo-ulmi* and *O. ulmi*; Verticillium wilt, caused by the fungi *Verticillium dahliae* and *V. albo-atrum*; watermark disease of willows, caused by the bacterium *Erwinia salicis*.

Dutch elm disease (DED) has killed most of the large elms (*Ulmus* spp.) in Britain, except in the far north, following the accidental importation of the aggressive form of the causal fungus, *Ophiostoma novo-ulmi*, in the late 1960s. It is, however, still sporadically killing young trees that have grown up from root sprouts since the first wave of the epidemic, and some of these are large enough to become an eventual safety hazard after death. Sanitation can be effective in areas such as Brighton, Sussex, which are geographically isolated from external sources of infection.

The objective of sanitation against DED is to prevent the fungus from being transmitted from the bark of infected trees to previously healthy ones, a process which involves beetle vectors of the genus *Scolytus*. The beetles feed as larvae in such bark and the emerging adults carry the fungal spores to their adult feeding sites on previously healthy twigs during the following spring and early summer. The bark overlying infected sapwood must therefore be burnt before adult emergence if sanitation is required. The disease develops so rapidly that the bark of an entire tree must often be dealt with in this way, but individual infected branches can be pruned out and dealt with if infection is still localised. This represents both a curative treatment and a means of sanitation.

In areas where the disease has not been kept under control, sanitation is not appropriate, and so the dead wood can be left to provide a wildlife habitat where other considerations allow. On sites where falling stems would not endanger persons or property, the dead trees can be left standing. Even where sanitation is needed in order to maintain a control campaign, it can be achieved while conserving the deadwood resource to some extent. This involves stripping the bark from the main stems and larger branches and then burning it together with the brash. In practice, the cheaper option of burning the whole tree is often chosen, due either to shortage of funds or ignorance of the importance of deadwood conservation.

Verticillium wilt affects a wide range of trees, especially species of *Acer, Fraxinus, Castanea, Tilia, Robinia, Catalpa, Cercis, Rhus, Sorbus aucuparia* (rowan) and *Prunus dulcis* (almond) [26]. The causal fungi occur as strains, each of which usually attacks only a limited range of host species. Wilting and subsequent dieback initially occur on branches scattered within the crown, but the entire tree can die in some cases. The standing dead wood can become a safety hazard, but sanitation cannot be effected by removing or destroying it, as the fungus is soil-borne. It can persist for many years, at least in the case of *V. albo-atrum*, which forms durable resting structures (sclerotia). Thus, the only way to prevent recurrence is to select resistant or tolerant species for re-planting. The disease is most prevalent in nurseries, and it seems likely that some cases of infection originate from nursery stock, rather than from the soil at the planting site.

8.2.4 Damage to roots, other than wood decay

A wide range of fungi, insects and nematode worms can damage the fine non-woody roots of trees, and there are also some that can damage the bark of woody roots. If root damage becomes extensive, the affected tree usually shows overall signs of poor health, including the thinning and dieback of the crown. Safety hazards may ensue if the damage is severe enough to kill the tree, or if the external damage to woody roots allows decay to develop.

Phytophthora root diseases are caused by several species of the fungal genus *Phytophthora*, some of which (especially *P. cinnamomi*) have a very wide range of hosts among woody plants. These microscopic fungi kill non-woody roots and some of them can extend into the cambium and phloem of woody roots and sometimes into the stem base. The term root-rot (or collar-rot if the stem base is the main site of damage) is often applied, although no decay of the wood occurs until secondary infection by decay fungi such as *Armillaria* ensues. From then on, safety hazards may become an important consideration.

Primary infection by *Phytophthora* is effected mainly by motile zoospores, which swim in water or soil moisture films surrounding the roots and are chemically or electrically attracted to the root elongation zone or to wounds. Both the attractiveness of the roots and the susceptibility of the host plant to infection tend to be increased by environmental stress. For these reasons, outbreaks of disease are especially favoured by successive periods of drought and heavy rain. The fungus persists during dry periods by means of resting spores (oospores or chlamydospores) or other dormant structures, and these may survive for several years so that replanting with the same type of tree or with other susceptible species is often inadvisable.

Most occurrences of *Phytophthora* diseases in Europe were fairly localised until recent years, although devastating attacks by *P. cinnamomi* have long affected eucalypt forests in Australia. Perhaps due to greater extremes of drought and heavy rain, stands of oak (*Quercus* spp.) in parts of southern Europe have been quite extensively affected by disease. Also, a previously unknown Phytophthora disease of alder (*Alnus glutinosa*) was discovered in the mid-1990s to be killing numerous riverside trees in Great Britain and was subsequently found in other parts of northern and central Europe.

Other root-infecting or root collar-infecting fungi, including species of *Fusarium* and *Rosellinia*, are common on woody plants, but most of these pathogens appear to cause overt disease only in seedlings or small saplings. The same may apply to various microscopic or near-microscopic nematodes (thread-worms), which feed by sucking contents from the outermost cells of non-woody roots. On the other hand, the fungus *Rhizina undulata* kills coniferous trees up to or occasionally beyond thirty years of age as a result of extensive root attack. This is primarily a problem of forest plantations. The resting spores of the fungus are activated by heat, so that outbreaks tend to occur near the sites of fires. Finally, it should be noted that some of the fungi that cause wood decay in roots (see next Section) can also enter and kill unwounded outer root tissue in the primary stages of attack; this has been demonstrated with *Armillaria mellea*, *A. ostoyae* and *Heterobasidion annosum*.

8.2.5 Root- and butt-rots

Nothing is known of the infection biology of most of the fungi that cause root- and butt-rots. However, many of them appear to enter the tree via the root system, leading to the suspicion that sources of infection in the soil are involved. This has been clearly established in the case of honey fungus, *Armillaria* spp., which colonises new hosts by means of bootlace-like rhizomorphs which grow from roots and stumps that it has previously colonised. Also, *Heterobasidion annosum*, a fungus that is known more from conifer plantations than amongst stands of amenity trees, passes from tree to tree via root contacts. These fungi are described in Chapter 4.

If either *H. annosum* or one of the more aggressive forms of *Armillaria* is detected in standing trees or in stumps, it is possible within formally managed areas to protect nearby trees by sanitation or by constructing a barrier in the soil, as mentioned in Chapter 4 regarding *Armillaria* [64]. Sanitation involves winching out the infected stumps, together with their major roots. Burning this material will help to ensure that no infection sources remain on-site, but on some sites it may be possible to pile up the material away from standing trees and thus to conserve its value as a wildlife habitat.

For other root- and butt-rot fungi, there is insufficient evidence to justify sanitation. It is probable that some of them are present in the soil independently of woody debris. This has been demonstrated in the case of *Phaeolus schweinitzii*, which survives in spore form and can attack trees following initial attack by *Armillaria* spp. [8].

8.3 Old pollards and 'veteran' trees as an environmental asset

As indicated above, old pollards and other ancient trees are often exceptionally valuable as wildlife habitats. They have provided deadwood habitats continuously over hundreds of years and have therefore sustained populations of specialised deadwood invertebrates which have died out elsewhere. Many ancient trees occur in areas which are already recognised for their ecological importance, but some are surrounded by intensively managed farmland or commercial forest plantations. In an increasing number of cases, such trees exist within areas scheduled for urban or industrial development and may therefore be threatened unless the need for conservation is taken adequately into account [205].

8.3.1 The longevity of pollards

Pollarded trees often live longer than is normal for the species concerned. One possible reason for their longevity is that they tend less than maiden trees to develop tall crowns whose maximum water demand exceeds the absorptive capacity of the roots and the conductive capacity of the xylem. Also, since a pollarded tree has more scaffold branches than a maiden tree, there is a correspondingly larger number of vascular connections between the branches and the bole (Plate 154). These 'branch-traces' are in effect anatomical compartments within which the development of pathogenic organisms tends to be confined [159]. It is therefore rare for the entire tree to be overcome by disease or decay before it has reached a very advanced age.

Plate 154 Ancient pollard of Fagus sylvatica, *with discrete living channels of tissue, Burnham Beeches, Buckinghamshire*

Another important advantage of multiple branching is that the individual branches are in many cases fairly small relative to the diameter of the bole, so that the breakage of a few does not make the tree unstable or expose it to overwhelmingly extensive decay. This advantage can, however, be lost if the discontinuation of a re-cutting regime allows branches to become very large and heavy. Such branches often tend to break away from the bole eventually; this happens partly because they become crowded as they increase in girth, so that bark inclusions form and then lead to splitting. When breakage occurs, the bole may be so badly damaged by the tearing-out of wood below the branch base that it fairly soon breaks up further or dies from loss of functional sapwood due to drying and microbial attack.

Some main stem decay inevitably develops in association with pollarding cuts, but any weakening effects that it may have are usually offset by the small sail area and short lever-arm of the reduced crown relative to the stem diameter [106]. Indeed the decayed core becomes a long-term ecological asset by virtue of its value for wildlife dependent on dead wood [51], albeit one which can eventually decrease in value if new growth becomes heavy enough to pull the tree apart.

8.3.2 Reasons for success and failure in the rejuvenation of lapsed pollards

In the 1950s, the managers of various sites in England began to realise that lapsed pollards with large, heavy limbs were in many cases breaking up and dying. Remedial re-cutting was attempted at some of these sites, but there was perhaps insufficient understanding of biological principles to ensure that this was done in a successful manner. Also, many of the traditional management practices [135] which reflected these principles, had by then been forgotten or were inappropriate for such trees. In some of the early attempts to 'rejuvenate' old pollards, entire crowns borne on very large branches were removed. This method had very little chance of success, for reasons that can be understood by considering the physiological and pathological changes that occur in sapwood and inner bark after wounding.

Whenever a stem or branch is cut, the columns of liquid in the conductive cells and the cytoplasmic connections between living cells are broken across the entire woody cylinder. The severed cells become almost immediately dysfunctional, and consequently vulnerable to microbial colonisation, as explained in Chapter 3. When the dysfunctional zone is first formed, it usually extends along the stem or branch as far as the ends of the severed cells. Many of these cells are only a fraction of a millimetre in length, but a small proportion, particularly the early-wood vessels of broadleaved species, may extend much further: even for several metres in some cases. The nett effect is that dysfunction is mainly, but not entirely, confined to within a short distance of the wound surface in the first instance.

Following the immediate dysfunction caused by cutting, continued moisture loss and the ingress of air at the cut surface may cause the dysfunctional zone to extend further down the branch or stem. This process tends to be restricted by the active responses of living cells within the sapwood and by pre-formed barriers within the heartwood cells of some tree species (see Chapter 3). The diffusion of air and the associated growth of decay fungi may, however, become very extensive in large severed stems of species such as beech (*Fagus sylvatica*), Horse chestnut (*Aesculus* spp.) and poplars (*Populus* spp.) which contain a core of largely unresponsive and non-durable wood. It is largely for this reason that severe and often fatal dieback frequently follows the topping of old trees or the cutting of long-neglected pollard branches.

If strongly growing new shoots develop below a cut, they sometimes form a boundary beyond which the dieback of the severed parent stem or branch does not progress. There have, however, been many cases in England where old pollards have died back completely after re-cutting, even though they formed new shoots at first (Plate 155). This has happened particularly often in *F. sylvatica* and *Carpinus betulus* (hornbeam) and probably follows the colonisation of the xylem by aggressive sapwood invaders, such as *Bjerkandera adusta*. It appears likely that the new shoots are killed when fungal invasion engulfs their points of attachment to the parent stem. Decay fungi do not often grow into tissues formed after the event that initiated their colonisation, but are probably more able to do so when the new annual increments have been forming only in a localised area near the new shoots (Fig. 8.2). Such a pattern of restricted wood formation could result from a lack of photosynthetic area following cutting.

If all the new shoots are killed by an advancing column of drying or fungal invasion, the entire tree can then die very quickly. Sometimes, however, further new growth may begin closer to ground level, and this may be associated with the formation of new barriers around the remaining zones of functional sapwood. These may persist, or may in turn break down, so that the dysfunction develops in a series of steps until either a durable barrier is formed, or the tree dies.

It is clearly desirable to maintain pollarded trees by regularly cutting the pollard branches before they become excessively heavy or too old to respond successfully to cutting. Even if there has not been such a continuity of care, it is still often possible to maintain neglected pollards without either allowing them to fall apart or wounding them so severely that they die. Even a old tree, if re-cut sympathetically, may be able to use the resources remaining to it to initiate the formation of new shoots, bark and wood. These will become photosynthetically independent and, being structurally separated from the invasion pathways occupied by the decay organisms, they can survive and grow to become, in effect, a new tree surrounding a dead or decaying centre (Fig. 8.1a & b, Plate 156).

8.3.3 The importance of maintaining 'channels' of living tissue between shoots and roots

The development of dysfunctional zones in the tissues near a cut surface need not be a serious problem for the tree as a whole, provided that part of its cross-section is left intact. If, however, the entire cross-section is severed (as in the total re-cutting of a pollard), the tree's subsequent survival will depend on its ability to form new foliage which, in time, may begin to produce enough carbohydrate to maintain the function and growth of the woody cylinder. In the meantime, the maintenance of functional sapwood and inner bark will depend

Plate 155 Re-cut pollard of Carpinus betulus, *showing death of new growth due to excessive dysfunction and opportunistic colonisation by* Bjerkandera adusta; *Hatfield Forest, Essex*

Plate 156 Ancient Quercus robur *with outer shell of living wood around dysfunctional core, Dunham Massey, Cheshire*

on the availability of stored carbohydrate. This food source is also required for the growth of the new shoots.

In some trees, especially old pollards, the carbohydrate store is often inadequate to meet all the above demands. Another problem may be that new shoots fail to develop for want of dormant or adventitious buds. These problems can largely be avoided by ensuring that channels of functional tissue between roots and shoots remain when pollarded trees are re-cut. This can be achieved by retaining some of the branches, even if they are small ones which can at least connect with discrete channels of living tissue within an otherwise dead bole. Retention of living branches is particularly important for *F. sylvatica*, and for very old or weakly growing trees of most species.

It seems likely that, in the traditional maintenance of rural pollards, a proportion of branches were usually retained at each cutting cycle [62], except in the case of willows (*Salix* spp.), which have considerable ability to regenerate new shoots even from an old bole. Although parts of the stem cross-section nevertheless became dysfunctional and eventually decayed as a result of successive cutting cycles, these zones were often confined to strips of xylem and phloem associated with the individually cut branches (Plate 154).

8.3.4 The position of cuts

When pollarded trees are re-cut, it is wise to observe the usual practice of cutting the current pollard branches, rather than cutting below their points of attachment. The wood proximal to the pollard heads often contains barriers which may have remained effective for many years against the spread of dysfunction. The tree could be seriously harmed if these barriers are breached; indeed, cases have been observed in which there seems to have been extremely rapid extension of decay following the removal of pollard heads. The cross-cutting of a woody cylinder is a trauma which should in general not be suffered more than once by an old tree.

Another important consideration is that the pollard branches are usually larger in number and smaller in diameter than their parent pollard heads, so that their severance represents a more tolerable spreading of the trauma as far as the tree as whole is concerned. Also, there is evidence that carbohydrate reserves are in some cases concentrated within the pollard heads, thus providing a local resource which is needed for defence and for shoot development. Finally, as the pollard branches are younger than the parent stem, they are often more able to form new shoots after cutting.

As far as the exact position of cutting is concerned, there is a case for leaving stubs if the branches have not been cut back for many years, despite the usual arboricultural practice of cutting branches back to their bases. An important reason for retaining stubs is that they provide a better chance of bearing some viable dormant buds, which are often very scarce on old branches. One of the arguments against the retention of stubs in other kinds of arboricultural work is that they can become foodbases for decay fungi, thus favouring the progression of decay further into the tree. On the other hand, decay columns are likely to be 'compartmentalised' within a living stub, so that the main stem is then better protected from overwhelming fungal colonisation than if the branches had been cut right back.

8.3.5 The importance of moisture, shade and sunshine

The risk of old pollards dying after re-cutting appears to be aggravated by drought stress, which impairs the capacity of the xylem to maintain its water columns near the zones affected by drying from the wound surfaces. Hot, dry conditions may also lead to increased moisture loss directly from these surfaces. The loss of overhead shade due to cutting is also thought to contribute to desiccation, as it leads to increased solar heating of the bole, and perhaps also of the ground surface in the rooting zone. On the other hand, excessive retention of shade can inhibit the development of healthy new shoots. Thus, there is a delicate balance in deciding how much of the crown should be removed, even apart from considering the need to retain enough branches for maintaining continuity of the symplast and an adequate supply of photosynthetic products within the bole and roots (see Chapter 3).

In view of all the above factors, some of which run counter to each other, there is probably no simple prescription for deciding how much of the crown of a neglected pollard should be cut. However, as a general guide, it is useful where possible to retain branches at intervals all around the circumference of the bole, not only to help maintain living channels to the entire root system, but also to provide partial shading of the bole. It may be necessary to shorten the branches that are retained, or judiciously to thin the residual crown, since the re-growth may otherwise be shaded out.

The extent to which shading needs to be reduced or retained depends partly on the tree species concerned; i.e. whether it is shade-tolerant (as in the case of *F. sylvatica*) or light-demanding (as in the case of *Fraxinus excelsior*, ash). It is also very important to take account of local climate and soil conditions, and to assess the amount of shading from nearby trees. Finally, there is scope for trying out ways of ameliorating the environment, such as mulching the rooting area and providing artificial shade for trees suddenly exposed to direct sunlight, or reducing shading from the crowns of other trees.

8.3.6 Season of cutting

As far as seasonal influences are concerned, considerations for pruning (Chapter 7) also apply in most respects to pollarding, except that there is often less need to discourage the development of decay at sites where old rural pollards occur, compared with busy urban locations. Moderate amounts of decay are far from undesirable in rural pollards, in view of their importance as deadwood habitats and their relatively low safety hazard. Nevertheless, it is nearly always important to avoid causing severe dieback or death of the tree, and there is therefore a need to avoid cutting during periods of severe moisture stress or when food reserves are very depleted (e.g. for a year after a prolonged summer drought). For some species at least, the month after spring flushing has begun is a relatively poor time for cutting. Food reserves are used up by flushing and are replenished only after the leaves have matured. Autumn is also a rather poor time, since the sapwood is then at its driest in most deciduous species and therefore provides a well-aerated environment for the growth of fungi. The moisture content is replenished during the winter, but desiccation of wounded tissues can occur during prolonged frosty conditions, sometimes leading to excessive dieback of the bark and cambium around a pruning cut.

Provided that trees are not cut at times of severe drought, the summer is a relatively good time to cut them, as carbohydrate reserves have by then usually been restored following the spring flush of growth. It may well be that the practice of cutting branches for animal fodder during the hot dry summers of southern Europe [62] is not the best thing as far as moisture stress is concerned, but the branches that are then cut are usually of small diameter, so that large wounds are not created. Perhaps the best time is in late winter or very early spring, when there is no moisture stress, combined with good carbohydrate reserves [155].

8.3.7 The ability of different trees to produce new shoots after pollarding or re-cutting

Although a pollarded tree can be killed by total re-cutting of the crown, there are some species in addition to *Salix* spp. (e.g. *Tilia* spp. – limes) that often produce abundant new growth after such treatment. There are others that often respond well, but are more likely to survive if at least a few branches are retained; these include *Ilex aquifolium* (holly), *C. betulus* and *Fr. excelsior*. Oaks (*Quercus robur* and *Q. petraea*) sometimes produce healthy new growth even after the removal of most of the foliage-bearing branches, but it seems advisable to retain substantial portions of the main branches at the very least.

An interesting observation that has been made at Burnham Beeches, Buckinghamshire is that individual old pollards of *F. sylvatica* differ in their ability to produce new shoots after the cutting back of large branches. In at least some cases, this appears to relate to the growth rate of these branches when they first formed, as evidenced by the spacing of leaf and girdle scars. Branches that have grown slowly have more nodes per metre and hence more dormant buds near their bases. In the case of *Q. robur*, the genetic predisposition to form numerous epicormic shoots seems to confer an enhanced ability to recover from re-cutting or branch breakage.

Although dormant buds play a rôle in the formation of new shoots after cutting, such shoots often arise from adventitious buds. It has been observed by several practitioners that adventitious buds in some species (e.g. *Fr. excelsior*) form more readily along the torn margins of a branch break-out injury than in the vicinity of a saw cut. In some cases, owners or practitioners claim to have stimulated bud formation by bruising the bark with hammers. These methods probably depend on the tendency of adventitious buds to develop from wound callus, as occurs in some fruit trees when epicormic shoots grow at the edges of pruning wounds. It has also been suggested that injuring a thick corky layer of outer bark, if present, exposes starch-rich inner bark tissues to light and oxygen, thus stimulating bud formation. Fruit growers sometimes use plant hormones to control watersprout (watershoot) formation, and this suggests that a treatment to produce the opposite effect might sometimes be of value in pollard management.

8.3.8 Recommendations for work on old pollards

The above considerations can be translated into some tentative guidelines, but these are by no means fully tried and tested; nor are they a prescription that can substitute for individual and sensitive management based on local knowledge and on experience with particular species or provenances of tree.

1. Where possible, leave some living twigs and branches all around the bolling when re-cutting, so that well-distributed channels of functional xylem and phloem, linked to photosynthesising tissues, are retained.

These function as intact vascular pathways between the root system and generally remain free from dieback, even if this occurs within strips of tissue between them. Good crown symmetry may also be preserved in this way. (Some trees, such as *Salix* spp., may survive re-cutting well without such precautions.)

2. Except where experience dictates otherwise, cut only above a previous position of pollarding or re-cutting. The cuts should preferably be made above side-branches of the re-growth, thus retaining living shoots or channels (see previous guideline).

3. If possible, avoid cutting between the time of bud-burst and midsummer and again during autumn and early winter. Also, avoid cutting in frosty weather.

4. Avoid cutting during a drought or in the following year in severe cases, since the tree's starch reserves may be insufficient to sustain new growth. Also moisture stress may increase the drying of tissues after wounding, thus encouraging dieback and rapid fungal invasion.

5. Try to ensure that the tree continues to receive a suitable exposure to sunlight, so that there is neither excessive desiccation of the bole and surrounding soil, nor excessive shading on the re-growth. Perhaps try artificial shading if appropriate.

6. Be aware of the differing tolerances of tree species to pollarding. Species like *Fagus sylvatica*, which do not form a distinct heartwood, are more likely to decay rapidly enough to split apart than those which have a substantial decay-resistant heartwood, such as oak (*Q. robur* and *Q. petraea*). Take especial care to follow the first and second of these guidelines when pollarding species such as *Fr. excelsior* which sometimes show little readiness to produce new growth.

7. Create new pollards to help maintain the succession but start with young trees, which have a good chance of responding well to the treatment and surviving through future centuries.

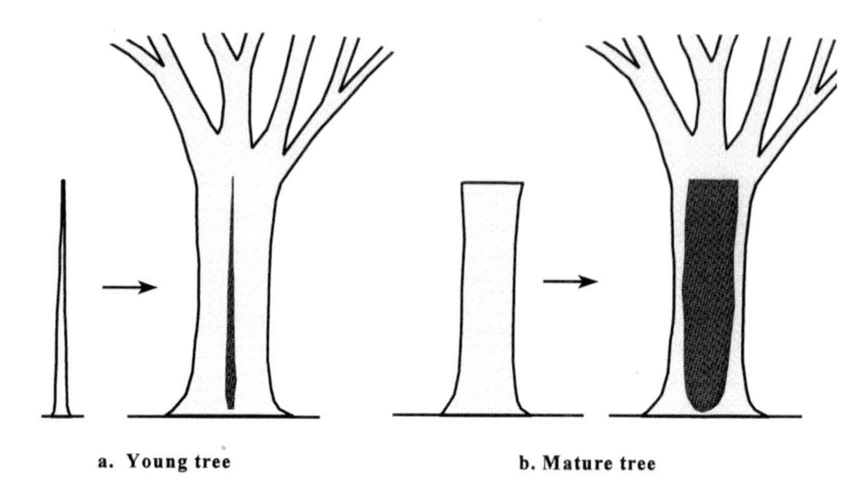

Figure 8.1 Development of xylem dysfunction and microbial colonisation, showing possible differences between the outcome of (a) pollarding a young tree and (b) topping a mature tree

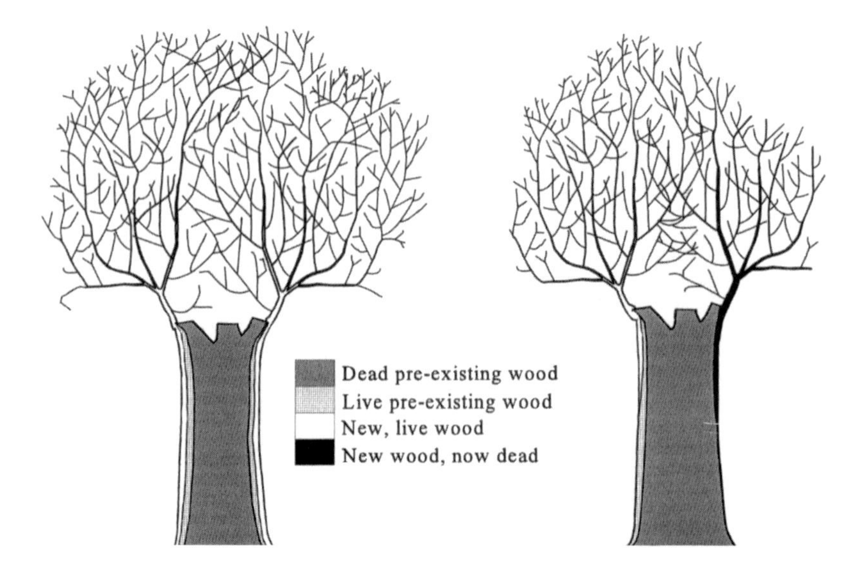

Figure 8.2 New growth following the re-cutting of neglected pollards: different outcomes involving dieback and the isolation of new xylem increments

8.3.9 Care of the rooting zone of ancient trees

Compaction is a frequent problem at sites where ancient trees stand and is almost certainly a major factor in hastening their demise. Where compaction is caused by numerous people visiting the sites, the diversion of access routes away from the area of crown spread of the trees is highly advisable. In some cases, it may even be necessary to erect barriers around trees which are especially at risk.

A particularly serious and frequent problem occurs in pastures and other areas used for agriculture, in which there is compaction from grazing animals and perhaps also from farm machinery. Although trees in permanent pastures have often co-existed all their lives with livestock, the intensification of grazing has often placed them under unaccustomed stress. As a form of natural shelter, they attract large numbers of animals, which not only cause compaction from trampling, but also deposit excessive quantities of nutrients in the form of dung and urine. Furthermore, excreted residues of anti-helminthic ('worming') drugs such as ivermectin probably interfere with the soil fauna and flora. In some cases, animals strip bark from trees, thus encouraging the excessive development of decay. It is important to consider various options, such as reduced stocking and fencing of vulnerable areas.

Ploughing around trees can be even more damaging than excessive trampling by animals, as it damages roots directly. It has probably been a major factor in the decline of rural specimens of ash, *Fraxinus excelsior,* in England [86]. While it is probably impracticable to avoid ploughing within the crown spread of all trees on farmland, protective measures should be regarded as essential for trees which have already attained veteran status and for others which are to succeed them in future years.

Literature

General references

1 Agosin, E., Blanchette, R.A., Silva, H., Lapierre, C., Cease, K.R., Ibach., R.E., Abad, A.R. & Muga, P. (1990). Characterization of Palo Podrido, a natural process of delignification in wood. *Applied Environmental Microbiology* **56**, 65-74.

2 Albers, J. & Hayes, E. (1993). *How to detect, assess and correct hazard trees in recreational areas*. Minnesota Department of Natural Resources.

3 Alexopoulos, C.J. (1995). *Introductory Mycology*, 4th edn. revd. by C.W. Mims & M. Blackwell, Wiley, USA.

4 Archer, R.R. (1987). *Growth stresses and strains in trees*. Springer-Verlag Berlin, 240 pp.

5 Bakken, S. (1995). Group-tree hazard analysis. *Journal of Arboriculture* **21**, 150-155.

6 Barrell, J. (1993). Pre-planning tree surveys: safe useful life expectancy (SULE) is the natural progression. *Arboricultural Journal* **17**, 33-46.

7 Barrell, J. (1995). Pre-developmental tree assessment. *Proceedings, International Workshop on Trees and Buildings*. International Society of Arboriculture, 132-142.

8 Barrett, D.K., & Greig, B.J.W. (1984). Investigations into the infection biology of *Phaeolus schweinitzii*. Proceedings of the 6th International Conference on Root and Butt Rots of Forest Trees (IUFRO Working Party S2-06-01), CSIRO, Melbourne, 95-103.

9 Barrett, D.K., Seaby, D.A. & Gourlay I.D. (1987). Portable 'Compression Strength Meter'; a tool for the detection and quantification of decay in trees. *Arboricultural Journal* **11**, 313-322.

10 Bethge, K., Mattheck, C. & Hunger, E. (1996). Equipment for detection and evaluation of incipient decay in trees. *Arboricultural Journal* **20**, 13-37.

11 Biddle, P.G. (1998). Tree roots and foundations. *AAIS Arboriculture Research and Information Note* **142/98/EXT**.

12 Biddle, P.G. (1998). *Tree Root Damage to Buildings*. Willowmead Publishing Ltd., Wantage, UK., 2 vols., 376 + 546 pp.

13 Blanchette, R.A. & Biggs, A.R. (eds.) (1992). *Defense mechanisms of woody plants against fungi*. Springer, New York.

14 Blanchette, R.A. (1984). Manganese accumulation in wood decayed by white rot fungi. *Phytopathology* **74**, 725-730.

15 Boddy, L. & Rayner, A.D.M. (1981). Fungal communities and formation of heartwood wings in attached oak branches undergoing decay. *Annals of Botany* **47**, 271-274.

16 Boddy, L. & Rayner A.D.M. (1983). Origins of Decay in Living Deciduous Trees: The Rôle of Moisture Content and Re-Appraisal of the Expanded Concept of Tree Decay. *New Phytol.* **94**, 623-641.

17 Bonnemann, I. (1978). Possibilities of biological and chemical control. Proc., *5th International Conference on Problems of root and butt rot in conifers*. Kassel, Germany, 322-327.

18 Bory, G. Hebert, G., Macle, N. & Clair-Maczulajtys, D. (1996). Physiological consequences of architectural pruning of trees. *Proc. Second European Congress of Arboriculture*, Versailles, International Society of Arboriculture, Sept. 1995.

19 Bradshaw, A.D., Hunt, B. & Walmsley, T. (1995). *Trees in the Urban Landscape: Principles and Practice*, Spon, UK, 272 pp.

20 Breitenbach, J. & Kränzlin, F. (1991). *Fungi of Switzerland* 3 Vols., Verlag Mykologia, Lucerne, Switzerland.

21 Brennan, G., Patch, D. & Stevens, F.W.R. (1981). (revised by D. Patch, P. Johnson & D. Marshall, 1997) Tree roots and underground pipes. *AAIS Arboriculture Research Note* **36/97/TRL**.

22 Brickell, C. & Joyce, D. (1996). *Royal Horticultural Society, Pruning and Training*. Dorling Kindersley, 336 pp.

23 Bridgeman, P. (1976). *Tree Surgery: a Complete Guide*. David & Charles, Newton Abbott, UK, 144 pp.

24 Brooks, F.T. & Moore, W.C. (1926). 'Silver-leaf disease'. *Journal of Pomology and Horticultural Science* **5**, 61.

25 Burdekin, D.A. (1979). Common decay fungi in broadleaved trees. *Forestry Commission Arboricultural Leaflet* **5**, 41 pp.

26 Butin, H. (1995). *Tree diseases and disorders*. (D. Lonsdale, R.G. Strouts., eds.), Oxford University Press, Oxford, UK, 252 pp.

27 Butin, H. & Shigo, A.L. (1981). Radial shakes and 'frost cracks' in living oak trees. *USDA Forest Service, Res. Paper* NE-478.

28 Carnell, R. & Anderson, M.A. (1986). A technique for extensive field measurement of soil aeration by rusting of steel rods. *Forestry* **59**, 129-140.

29 Carter, C.I. (1992). Lime trees and aphids. *AAIS Arboriculture Research Note* **104/92/ENT**.

30 Cartwright, K.St.G., Campbell, W.A. & Armstrong, F.H. (1936). Influence of fungal decay on the properties of timber. I. The effect of progressive decay by *Polyporus hispidus* Fr. on the strength of English ash, *Fraxinus excelsior* L. *Proceedings of the Royal Society* B, **120**, 76-95.

31 Cartwright, K.St.G., & Findlay, W.P.K. (1958). *Decay of Timber and its Prevention*, 2nd edn., HMSO, London.

32 Coate, B.D. (1993). Proactive options in urban tree hazard reduction; Part 1. *Arborist News*, June, 1993, 10-12.

33 Courtois, H. (1966). Mikromorphologische Veränderungen verholzter Zellwände durch Basidiomyceten (Braunfäulerreger). In: *Holz und*

Organismen, International Symposium, Berlin-Dahlem, (G. Becker & W. Liese, eds.) *Material u. Organismen Suppl.* **1**, 41-58.

34 Coutts, M. P. (1983). Root architecture and tree stability. *Plant and Soil* **71**, 171-188.

35 Coutts, M.P. & Phillipson, J.J. (1978). Tolerance of tree roots to waterlogging. I. Survival of Sitka spruce and lodgepole pine; II. Adaptation of Sitka spruce and lodgepole pine to waterlogged soil. *New Phytologist* **80**, 63-69; 71-77.

36 Dagley, J. & Burman, P. (1996). The management of the pollards of Epping Forest: its history and revival. In: *Pollard and veteran tree management II*, H.J. Read (ed)., Proc. meeting, Corporation of London, Epping Forest, Essex, Sept. 1993., 29-41.

37 Daniel, G., Volc. J. & Nilsson, T. (1992). Soft rot and multiple T-branching by the basidiomycete *Oudemansiella mucida*. *Mycological Research* **96**, 49-54.

38 Davies, R.J. (1987). Sheet mulches: suitable materials and how to use them. *Forestry Commission Arboriculture Research Information Note* **72/87/ARB**

39 Davies, R.J. (1987). A comparison of the survival and growth of transplants, whips and standards, with and without weed control. *Forestry Commission Arboriculture Research Note* **67/97/ARB**.

40 Davies, R.J. & Gardiner, J.B.H. (1989). The effects of weed competition on tree establishment. *Forestry Commission Arboriculture Research Note* **59/89/ARB**.

41 Davies, R.J. & Pepper, H.W. (1989). The influence of small plastic guards, tree shelters and weed control on damage to young broadleaved trees by field voles *(Microtus agrestis)*. *Journal of Environmental Management* **28**, 117-125.

42 Davies, R.J. & Pepper, H.W. (1993). Protecting trees from field voles. *AAIS Arboriculture Research Note* **74/93/ARB**.

43 Dobson, M. (1995). Tree root systems. *AAIS Arboriculture Research and Information Note* **130/95/ARB**.

44 Dobson, M.C. (1991). Tolerance of trees and shrubs to de-icing salt. *Forestry Commission Arboriculture Research Note* **99/91/PATH**.

45 Dobson, M.C. (1991). Prevention and amelioration of de-icing salt damage to trees. *Forestry Commission Arboriculture Research Note* **100/91/PATH**.

46 Dobson, M.C. & Moffat, A.J. (1993). *The Potential for Woodland Establishment on Landfill Sites*. HMSO, London.

47 Dolwin, J.A. (1996). Evaluation of internal defects in trees and the legal implications. *Arboricultural Journal* **20**, 173-178.

48 Dujesiefken, D. & Liese, W. (1990). Einfluss der Verletzungszeit auf die Wundheilung bei Buche (*Fagus sylvatica* L.) *Holz als Roh- und Werkstoff* **48**, 95-99.

49 Ellison, M.J. (1998). Quantified tree risk assessment used in the management of trees as landscape features, wildlife habitats and environmental control agents. *Journal of Arboriculture*, in press.

50 Evans, J. & Shanks, C. (1987). Treeshelters. *Forestry Commission Arboriculture Research Note* **63/87/SILS**.

51 Ferris-Kaan, R., Lonsdale, D. & Winter, T. G. (1993). The conservation management of deadwood in forests. *Forestry Authority Research Information Note* **241**.

52 Fry, R. & Lonsdale, D. (1991). eds., *Habitat Conservation for Insects: a Neglected Green Issue*. Amateur Entomologists' Society, 262 pp.

53 Gasson, P.E. & Cutler. D.F., (1990). Tree root plate morphology. *Arboricultural Journal* **14**, 193-264.

54 Gibbs, J.N. (1967). The role of host vigour in the susceptibility of pines to *Fomes annosus*. *Annals of Botany* N.S. **31**, 803-815.

55 Gibbs, J.N. (1994). De-icing salt damage to trees – the current position. *AAIS Arboriculture Research Note* **119/94/PATH**.

56 Gibbs, J.N. & Greig, B.J.W. (1990). Survey of parkland trees after the Great Storm of October 16, 1987. *Arboricultural Journal* **14**, 321-347.

57 Gibbs, J.N. & Lonsdale, D. (1998). Phytophthora disease of alder. *Forestry Practice Information Note* **FCIN6**.

58 Gibbs, J.N. & Patch, D. (1982). Decay and disintegration of dead elms. *Forestry Commission Arboriculture Research Note* **16/82/PATH**.

59 Girling, H. (1996). Personal communication.

60 Gonzales, A., Grinbergs, J., Griva, E. (1986). Biological transformation of wood into feed for cattle – "Palo podrido". *Zbl. Mikrobiol.* **141**, 181-186.

61 Gordon, J.E. (1979). *Structures, or why things don't fall down*. Penguin Books, 395 pp.

62 Green, E.E. (1996). Thoughts on pollarding. In: *Pollard and Veteran Tree Management II*, H.J. Read (ed)., Proc. meeting, Corporation of London, Epping Forest, Essex, Sept. 1993., 50-54.

63 Greig, B.J.W. (1981). Decay fungi in conifers. *Forestry Commission Leaflet* **79**, 21 pp.

64 Greig, B.W.J., Gregory, S.C. & Strouts, R.G. (1991). Honey fungus. *Forestry Commission Bulletin* **100**, HMSO, London.

65 Griffin, N. (1997). Problems from a slippery slope? *Veteran Trees and The Law*. Proc. Conf. Royal Agricultural Society of England, Stoneleigh, UK, 4 March 1997.

66 Guillaumain, J.J., Delatour, C. & Belgrand, M. (1984). Le dépérissement du chêne à Tronçais; pathologie racinaire. *Revue Forestière Française* **35**, 415-424.

67 Harris, R.W. (1992). *Arboriculture, Integrated Management of Landscape Trees, Shrubs and Vines*. (2nd ed.) Prentice-Hall Inc., NJ, USA, 674 pp.

68 Hartig, R. (1894). *Text-book of the Diseases of Trees* (translated by W. Somerville, ed. H. Marshall Ward), Macmillan, London, 331 pp.
69 Haygreen, H.G. & Bowyer, J.L. (1982). *Forest Products and Wood Science*. Iowa Univ. Press, Ames, USA, 495 pp.
70 Helliwell, D.R. (1985). *Trees on Development Sites*. Arboricultural Association, Romsey, UK, 19 pp.
71 Helliwell, D.R. (1990). Acceptable level of risk associated with trees. *Arboricultural Journal* **14**, 159-162.
72 Helliwell, D.R. (1991). Acceptable levels of risk (letter to the editor). *Arboricultural Journal* **15**, 179-181.
73 Helliwell, D.R. (1993). Water tables and trees. *AAIS Arboriculture Research Note* **110/93/EXT**.
74 Helliwell, D.R. & Fordham, S.J. (1992). *Tree roots and tree growth*. Reading Agricultural Consultants, Reading, UK, 20 pp.
75 Hendry, S.J. (1993). Strip-cankering in relation to the ecology of Xylariaceae and Diatrypaceae in beech (*Fagus sylvatica*). PhD thesis, Univ. of Wales.
76 Hepting, G.H. (1971). *Diseases of Forest and Shade Trees of the United States*. USDA Forest Service Handbook **386**.
77 Hepting, G.H. & Shigo, A.L. (1972). Difference in decay rate following fire between oaks in North Carolina and Maine. *Plant Disease Reporter* **56**, 406-407.
78 Herdt, T.H. (1997). Möglichkeiten zur Stimulierung des regenerativen Wurzelwachstums. Proc. 15th Osnabrücker Baumpflegetage, Osnabrück, Germany, Sept., 1997, Section viii, 1-13.
79 Hibberd, B.G. (1989). (ed.) *Urban Forestry Practice*. Forestry Commission Handbook **5**, HMSO, London 150 pp.
80 Hibberd, B.G. (1989). Choice of species, Chapter 5 in: *Urban Forestry Practice*, B.G. Hibberd (ed)., Forestry Commission Handbook **5**, HMSO, London, 48-71.
81 Hickman, G.W., Perry, E. & Evans, R. (1995). Validation of tree failure evaluation system. *Journal of Arboriculture* **21**, 233-234.
82 Hodge, S.J. (1990). The influence of nursery spacing on outplanting performance of amenity trees. *Forestry Commission Arboriculture Research Note* **93/90/ARB**.
83 Hodge, S.J. (1991). Improving the growth of established amenity trees: site physical conditions. *Forestry Commission Arboriculture Research Note* **102/91/ARB**.
84 Hodge, S.J. (1993). Compressed air soil injection around amenity trees. *AAIS Arboriculture Research Note* **113/93/ARB**.
85 Hodge, S.J. (1993). Using steel rods to assess aeration in urban soils. *AAIS Arboriculture Research Note* **115/93/ARB**.
86 Hull, S.K. & Gibbs, J.N. (1991). Ash dieback – a survey of non-woodland trees. *Forestry Commission Bulletin* **93**, HMSO, London.

87 Ingold, C.T. (1993). *Biology of Fungi*, 6th edn. revd. by H.J. Hudson, Chapman & Hall.

88 Jahn, H. (1990). *Pilze an Bäumen*, 2nd ed., revd. by H. Reinartz & M. Schlag, Patzer, Berlin-Hannover, 272 pp.

89 James, N.D.G. (1990). *The Arboriculturalist's Companion: a Guide to the Care of Trees*. Blackwell, 244 pp.

90 Kerr, G. & Evans, J. (1993). *Growing Broadleaves for Timber*. Forestry Commision Handbook **9**, HMSO, 95 pp.

91 King, D.A. (1986). Tree form, height growth and susceptibility to wind damage in *Acer saccharum*. *Ecology* **67**, 980-990.

92 Lane, P.B. (1990). Chemical weeding – hand-held direct applicators. *Forestry Commission Arboriculture Research Note* **53/90/WS**.

93 Learn, C.D. (1912), Studies on *Pleurotus ostreatus* Jacqu. and *Pleurotus ulmarius*. *Annales Mycologici Berlin* **10**, 542-546.

94 Liese, W. & Dujesiefken, D. (1989). Aspekte und Befunde zur Sanierungszeit in der Baumpflege. *Das Gartenamt* **38**, 356-360.

95 Liese, W. & Schmid, R. (1966). Untersuchungen über Zellwandabbau von Nadelholz durch *Trametes pini*. *Holz als Roh-und Werkstoff* **24**, 454-460.

96 Lonsdale, D. (1989). Pruning practice. Chapter 10 In: *Urban Forestry Practice*. B.G. Hibberd, (ed)., Forestry Commission Handbook **5**, HMSO, London 94-100.

97 Lonsdale, D. (1990). Treatment of storm-damaged trees. *Forestry Commission Arboriculture Research Note* **73/90/PAT**.

98 Lonsdale, D. (1992). Treatment of tree wounds. *AAIS Arboriculture Research Note* **109/92/PATH**.

99 Lonsdale, D. (1993). Choosing the time of year to prune trees. *AAIS Arboriculture Research Note* **117/93/PATH**.

100 Lonsdale, D. (1993). A comparison of 'target' pruning, versus flush cuts and stub pruning. *AAIS Arboriculture Research Note* **116/93/PATH**.

101 Matheny, N.P. & Clark, J.R. (1994). *A photographic guide to the evaluation of hazard trees in urban areas*, 2nd Edn., International Society of Arboriculture, Urbana, USA. 84 pp.

102 Mattheck, C. & Bethge K. (1992). Impulshammer zum Auffinden von Faulstellen in Bäumen. *Deutscher Gartenbau* **44**, 2683-2685.

103 Mattheck, C., Bethge, K. & Breloer, H. (1994). Allgemeinegültigkeit der Regeln zur Bewertung von Risikobäumen. *Das Gartenamt* **46**, 407-412.

104 Mattheck, C., Bethge K. & West, P.W. (1994). Breakage of hollow tree stems. *Trees* **9**, 47-50.

105 Mattheck, C. & Breloer, H. (1991-2). Die Verkehrssicherungspflicht bei Bäumen in Praxis und Rechtsprechung – der Baumbruch. *Landschaftarchitektur*, four-part series.

106 Mattheck, C. & Breloer, H. (1995). *The Body Language of Trees: A handbook for failure analysis* (Research for Amenity Trees **4**), HMSO, London, 240 pp.

107 Mattheck, C. & Schwarze, F.W.M.R. (1995). Die Holzstrahlen als getarnte I-Balken in einem mechanischen Ersatzmodell für Holz. *Allgemeine Forst und Jagdzeitung* **165**, 197-201.

108 McAvish, W.T. & Insley, H., (rev. by I. Willoughby) (1998). Herbicides for sward control among broadleaved amenity trees. *AAIS Arboriculture Research Note* **27/98/SILS**.

109 McEvoy, C. & McKay, H. (1997). Sensitivity of broadleaved trees to desiccation and rough handling between lifting and transplanting. *AAIS Arboriculture Research Note* **139/97/SILN**.

110 McLaughlin, J.A. & Setliff, E.C. (1990). *Chondrostereum purpureum* associated with decline of *Betula papyrifera* in Thunder Bay, Ontario. *Plant Disease* **74**, 331.

111 Mercer, P.C. (1987). (revd. by D. Lonsdale) The detection of decay in trees with particular reference to the use of the Shigometer. *Forestry Commission Arboriculture Research Note* **18/87/PATH**

112 Mercer, P.C., & Kirk, S.A. (1984). Biological treatments for control of decay in tree wounds. II. Field tests. *Annals of Applied Biology* **104**, 221-229.

113 Mitchell, A.F. (1982). *Trees of Great Britain and Northern Europe*. Collins, London, 288 pp.

114 Mitchell, A.F. & Jobling, J. (1984). *Decorative Trees for Country, Town and Garden*. Forestry Commission/HMSO, London, 146 pp.

115 Moffat, A.J. (1989). The new site. Chapter 5 in: *Urban Forestry Practice*. B.G. Hibberd, (ed)., Forestry Commission Handbook **5**, HMSO, London 40-47.

116 Neely, D. (1988). Closure of branch pruning wounds with conventional and 'Shigo' cuts. *Journal of Arboriculture* **14**, 261-264.

117 Nicoll, B.C. & Armstrong, A. (1997). Street tree architecture and pavement damage. *AAIS Arboriculture Research and Information Note* **138/97/SILN**.

118 Niemz, P. & Plotnikov, S. (1988). Untersuchungen zum Einfluss ausgewählter Strukturparameter auf die Ausbreitungsgeschwindichkeit von Ultraschallwellen in Vollholz und Spanplatten. *Holztechnologie* **29**, 207-209.

119 Niklas, K.J. (1994). Interspecific allometries of critical buckling height and actual plant height. *American Journal of Botany* **81**, 1275-1279.

120 Nilsson, T. & Daniel, G. (1988). Micromorphology of the decay caused by *Chondrostereum purpureum* (Pers.:Fr.) Pouzar and *Flammulina velutipes* (Curt.:Fr.) Singer. The International Group on Wood Preservation, Document No. **IRG/WP/1358**.

121 Nutman, E.J. (1929). Studies of wood destroying fungi. I. *Polyporus hispidus* (Fries). *Annals of Applied Biology* **16**, 40-64.

122 Patch, D. (1983). (revised by K. Rushforth, 1989) Tree staking. *Forestry Commission Arboriculture Research Note* **40/89/ARB**.

123 Patch, D. (1989). Stakes and ties. *Forestry Commission Arboriculture Research Note* **77/89/ARB**.

124 Patch, D. (1994). Pre-view cable TV routes. *AAIS Arboriculture Research Note* **120/94/ARB**.

125 Patch, D. & Denyer, A. (1992). Blight to trees, caused by vegetation control machinery. *AAIS Arboriculture Research Note* **107/92/ARB**.

126 Patch, D. & Stevens, F. (1991). Control of conker formation. *Forestry Commission Arboriculture Research Note* **1/91/ARB**.

127 Pearce, R.B. (1996). Antimicrobial defences in the wood of living trees. (Tansley Review No. 87) *New Phytologist* **132**, 203-233.

128 Pearce R.B. & Holloway P.J. (1984). Suberin in the sapwood of oak (*Quercus robur* L.); its composition from a compartmentalization barrier and its occurrence in tyloses in undecayed wood. *Physiological Plant Pathology* **24**, 71-81.

129 Pearce, R.B. & Rutherford, J. (1981). A wound-associated suberized barrier to the spread of decay in the sapwood of oak (Quercus robur L.). *Physiological Plant Pathology* **19**, 359-369.

130 Pepper, H.W. (1987). Plastic mesh tree guards. *Forestry Commission Arboriculture Research Note* **5/87/WILD**.

131 Perry, T.O. (1982). The ecology of tree rots and the practical significance thereof. *Journal of Arboriculture* **8**, 197-211.

132 Phillips, R. (1981). *Mushrooms and other Fungi of Great Britain and Europe*, Ward Locke, London, 288 pp.

133 Pirone, J.R., Hartmann, J.R., Sall, M.A. & Pirone, T.P. (1988). *Tree Maintenance* (6th ed.). Oxford University Press, 514 pp.

134 Potter, C.J. (1989). Establishment and early maintenance. Chapter 8 in: *Urban Forestry Practice*, B.G. Hibberd, (ed)., Forestry Commission Handbook **5**, HMSO, London 78-90.

135 Rackham, O. (1991). Introduction to pollards. In: *Pollard and veteran tree management*. H.J. Read (ed)., Proc. meeting, Corporation of London, Burnham Beeches, Bucks, March 1991, 6-10.

136 Read, H.J., Frater, M. & Noble, D. (1996). A survey of the condition of the pollards at Burnham Beeches and results of some experiments in cutting them. In: *Pollard and Veteran Tree Management II*, H.J. Read (ed)., Proc. meeting, Corporation of London, Epping Forest, Essex, Sept. 1993., 50-54.

137 Redden, G.R. (1989). The application of engineering fundamentals to arboriculture. *Journal of Arboriculture* **15**, 112-119.

138 Rishbeth, J. (1951). Observations on the biology of *Fomes annosus*, with particular reference to East Anglian pine plantations, and some factors affecting severity of the disease. *Annals of Botany* **15**, 221-246.

139 Rose, D.R. (1990). Lightning damage to trees in Britain. *Forestry Commission Arboriculture Research Note* **68/90/PAT**.

140 Rushforth, K.D. (1989). Summer branch drop. (amended by D. Patch) *Forestry Commission Arboriculture Research Note* **12/89/SILS**.

141 Savory, J.G. (1954). Breakdown of timber by ascomycetes and Fungi Imperfecti. *Annals of Applied Biology* **41**, 336-347.

142 Schacht, H. (1863). Über die Veränderungen durch Pilze in abgestorbenen Pflanzenzellen. *Jahrbücher für Wissenschaftliche Botanik*, **3**, 442-483.

143 Schröder, K. (1993). The double belt system for tree crown stabilization. *Arboricultural Journal* **17**, 375-384.

144 Schröder, K. (1994). Einsatz von Gurtsicherungssystemen. *Neue Landschaft* **6/94**, 456-464.

145 Schröder, K. (1998). Kronensicherung mit dem "Doppelgurtsystem Osnabrück". *Jahrbuch der Baumpflege* 1998, 170-183.

146 Schwarze, F.W.M.R. (1994). Entwicklung und Biomechanische Auswirkung von holzzersetzenden Pilzen in lebenden Bäumen und *in vitro*. Ph.D. Thesis, Univ. Freiburg, Germany.

147 Schwarze, F.W.M.R. & Engels, J. (1998). Cavity formation and the exposure of peculiar structures in the secondary wall (S2) of tracheids and fibres by wood-degrading basidiomycetes. *Holzforschung* **52**, 117-123.

148 Schwarze, F.M.R. & Fink, S. (1994). Ermittlung der Holzzersetzung am Lebenden Baum. *Neue Landschaft*, **39**, 182-193.

149 Schwarze, F.W.M.R. & Fink, S. (1998). Host and cell type affect the mode of degradation by *Meripilus giganteus*. *New Phytologist* **139**, 721-731.

150 Schwarze, F.W.M.R., Engels, J. & Mattheck, C. (1999). *Holzzersetzender Pilze in Bäumen*. Rombach Verlag, Freiburg, Germany.

151 Schwarze, F.W.M.R. Lonsdale, D. & Fink, S. (1995). Soft rot and multiple T-branching by the basidiomycete *Inonotus hispidus* in ash and London plane. *Mycological Research* **99**, 813-820.

152 Schwarze, F.W.M.R., Lonsdale, D. & Fink, S. (1997). An overview of wood degradation patterns and their implications for tree hazard assessment. *Arboricultural Journal* **21**, 1-32.

153 Schwarze, F.W.M.R., Lonsdale, D. & Mattheck, C. (1995). Detectability of wood decay caused by *Ustulina deusta* (Fr.) Petrak in comparison with other tree decay fungi. *European Journal of Forest Pathology*.

154 Shain, L. (1979). Dynamic responses of differentiated sapwood to injury and infection. *Phytopathology* **69**, 1143-1147.

155 Shigo (1986). *A New Tree Biology*. Shigo and Trees Associates, Durham, New Hampshire, 592 pp.

156 Shigo, A.L. (1985). How tree branches are attached to trunks. *Canadian Journal of Botany* **63**, 1391-1401.

157 Shigo, A.L. (1989). *Tree pruning: a worldwide photo guide*. Shigo and Trees Associates, Durham, NH, USA, 186 pp.

158 Shigo, A.L. (1991). *Modern Arboriculture*. Shigo & Trees Associates, Durham, NH, USA, 424 pp.

159 Shigo, A.L. & Marx, H.G. (1977). Compartmentalization of decay in trees. *USDA Forest Service, Agriculture Information Bulletin* **405**, 73 pp.

160 Shigo, A.L. & Shortle, W.C. (1979). Compartmentalization of discolored wood in heartwood of red oak. *Phytopathology* **69**, 710-711.

161 Shigo, A.L., Shortle, W.C. & Garrett, P.W. (1977). Genetic control suggested in compartmentalization of discolored wood associated with tree wounds. *Forest Science* **23**, 179-182.

162 Sinn, G. & Wessolly, L. (1989). A contribution to the proper assessment of the strength and stability of trees. *Arboricultural Journal* **13**, 45-65.

163 Skinner, D.N. (1986). Planting success rate – standard trees. *Forestry Commission Arboriculture Research Note* **66/86/EXT**.

164 Thomson, J. & Rumsey, P. (1997). Trenchless technology applications for utility installation. *Arboricultural Journal* **21**, 137-143.

165 Smiley, E.T. & Fraedrich, B.R. (1992). Determining strength loss from decay. *Journal of Arboriculture* **18**, 201-204.

166 Spiers, A.G., Brewster, D.T., Bus, V.G. & Hopcroft, D.H. (1998). Seasonal variation in susceptibility of xylem tissue of *Malus, Pyrus, Prunus* and *Salix* species to *Chondrostereum purpureum* in New Zealand. *Mycological Research* **102**, 881-890.

167 Stalpers, J.A. (1978). Identification of wood-inhabiting Aphyllophorales in pure culture. *Studies in Mycology* No. **16**, Centraalbureau voor Schimmelculturs, Baarn, Netherlands, 248 pp.

168 Sterling, P.H. (1992). The brown-tail moth. *AAIS Arboriculture Research Note* **57/92/EXT**

169 Stocker, D. & Pepper, H. (1993). Grey squirrel control using modified hoppers. *Forestry Authority Research Information Note* **232**.

170 Strouts, R.G. (1991). Dieback of the flowering cherry *Prunus* 'Kanzan'. *Forestry Commission Arboriculture Research Note* **94/91/PATH**.

171 Strouts, R.G. (1994). Fireblight of ornamental trees and shrubs. *AAIS Arboriculture Research Note* **118/94/PATH**.

172 Strouts, R.G. (1994). Personal communication.

173 Strouts, R.G. & Winter, T.G. (1994). *Diagnosis of ill-health in trees* (Research for Amenity Trees 2), HMSO, London, 308 pp.

174 Tippett, J.T. & Shigo, A.L. (1980). Barrier zone anatomy in red pine roots invaded by *Heterobasidion annosum*. *Canadian Journal of Forest Research* **10**, 224-232.

175 Wagener, W.W. (1963). *Judging Hazard from Native Trees in California Recreational Areas: a Guide for Professional Foresters*. US Forest Pacific Southwest Forest and Range Experiment Station, Berkeley, CA, *Research Paper* PSW-P1, 29 pp.

176 Waid, J.S. & Woodman, M.J. (1957). A non-destructive method of detecting diseases in wood. *Nature* **180**, 47.

177 Watson, G.W. & Himelick, E.B. (1997). *Principles and Practice of Planting Trees and Shrubs*. International Society of Arboriculture, Savoy, USA.

178 Webber, J. & Gee, C.M. (1994). Wood chips as mulch or soil amendment. *AAIS Arboriculture Research and Information Note* **123/94/FP**.

179 Webster, J. (1980). *Introduction to Fungi*, 2nd edn., Cambridge Univ. Press.

180 Wilcox, W.W. (1978). Review of literature on the effects of early stages of decay on wood strength. *Wood Fibre* **9**, 252-257.

181 Wilson, K. & White, D.J.B. (1986). *The Anatomy of Wood: its Diversity and Variability*. Stobart, London, 309 pp.

Court case references

182 British Road Services v Slater & Another [1964] Vol. 1, Weekly Law Report 493-497.

183 Caminer v Northern & London Investment [1951] AC, 88-112.

184 Cunliffe v Banks [1945] All England Law Report, 459-465.

185 Noble v Harrison [1926] 2 King's Bench 332.

186 Quinn v Scott and Another [1965] Vol. 2, All England Law Report 588-593.

187 Quinn v Scott [1965] Vol. 1, Weekly Law Report 1004-1012.

188 Sedleigh-Denfield v O'Callaghan [1940] AC 880.

189 Smith v Oliver [1989] 2 PLR 1.

190 Solloway v Hampshire County Council [1981] 79 Local Government Reports 449-461 [CA].

British Acts of Parliament and guidelines from official and professional organisations

191 *Forestry Act* (1967), as amended.

192 *Local Government (Miscellaneous Provisions) Act* (1976).

193 *Recommendations for tree work* (BS 3998), British Standards Institution, London (1989a, with 1990 amendment).

194 *Transplanting root-balled trees*. (BS 4043), British Standards Institution, London (1989).

195 *Town and Country Planning Act*, (1990), Sections 198-210.

196 *Planning (Listed Buildings and Conservation Areas) Act* (1990) [c.9].

197 *Guide for trees in relation to construction*. (BS 5837), British Standards Institution, London (1991).
198 *Building near trees*. NHBC Standard, Chapter 4.2, National House-Building Council, UK (1992).
199 FASTCo safety guides (1994-96): see Appendix 1.
200 *Tree Preservation Orders – A Guide to the Law and Good Practice*. Department of the Environment, London, 75 pp. (1994).
201 *Guidelines for the Planning, Installation and Maintenance of Utility Services in Proximity to Trees*. National Joint Utilities Group, Publication **10**, 23 pp. (1995).
202 *Generic Terms and Concepts in the Assessment and Regulation of Industrial Risks* (consultation paper). HSE Books, Sudbury, UK. (1995).
203 *Use of Risk Assessment Within Government Departments*. HSE Books, Sudbury, UK. (1995).
204 *A Guide to Risk Assessment and Risk Management for Environmental Protection*. HMSO, London, 92 pp. (1995).
205 *Guide to the Care of Ancient Trees*. English Nature, Peterborough, UK. (1996).
206 *Tree work and employing a contractor*. London Tree Officers' Association, Islington, London. (1997).
207 *Occupiers' Liability Act* (1957).
208 *Occupiers' Liability Act* (1984).
209 *Highways Act* (1980).
210 *Wildlife and Countryside Act* (1981).
211 *Ancient Monuments and Archeological Areas Act* (1979).
212 *Recommendations for maintenance of soft landscape (other than amenity turf)* (BS 7370, Part 4), British Standards Institution, London (1993).
213 *Town and Country Planning (Scotland) Act* (1997).

Glossary

(including some words not used in this book)

Abaxial pertaining to that side of a leaf or other plant organ which anatomically faces away from the axis of the parent shoot (i.e. usually the underside)

Abscission the shedding of a leaf or other part of a plant, involving the formation of a corky layer across its base (SOME TREE SPECIES SHED TWIGS IN THIS WAY.); (*see also* **cladoptosis**)

Abiotic pertaining to non-living agents; e.g. environmental factors

Acoustic of sound (also '**sonic**'); applicable to methods for tree defect detection which involve the use of hammer blows or ultrasound pulses

Adaptive growth: in tree biomechanics, the process whereby wood formation is influenced both in quantity and in quality by the action of gravitational force and mechanical stresses on the cambial zone (THIS HELPS TO MAINTAIN A UNIFORM DISTRIBUTION OF MECHANICAL STRESS.)

Adaxial pertaining to that side of a leaf, shoot or other plant organ which anatomically faces towards the axis of the parent shoot (i.e. usually the upperside)

Adventitious describing shoots, roots or other plant organs which develop other than at their normal positions of origin (e.g. shoots which do not arise from terminal or axillary buds (*see also* **epicormic** and **dormant bud**)

Aerenchyma a kind of parenchyma with extensive intercellular spaces, assisting gas exchange, and found in some plant species adapted to poorly aerated conditions

Aerobic pertaining to conditions in which oxygen is freely available, or to biochemical processes which depend on the presence of oxygen

Agarics basidiomycete fungi whose fruit bodies are gill-bearing toadstools (SOME WOOD DECAY FUNGI BELONG TO THIS GROUP.)

Anaerobic literally without air; pertaining to conditions where oxygen-dependent biochemical processes cannot occur or to processes which take place in the absence of oxygen (*related term*: **anoxic**; *cf.* **micro-aerophilic**)

Anchorage: in trees, the holding of the root system within the soil, involving the flow of forces from the stem through the branches of the root system to the cohesive root/soil interface

Ancient woodland: in the UK, a site which has been woodland for at least 350 years

Angiosperms flowering plants which bear seeds within ovaries

Anion *see* **ion**

Annual rings the annual increments of wood in a tree or shrub as seen in transverse sections of stems, branches or roots (AS THE INCREMENTS ARE THREE-DIMENSIONAL, THEY ARE REALLY CYLINDERS OR CONES, RATHER THAN

RINGS; ALSO, THEY ARE NOT ALWAYS STRICTLY ANNUAL, ESPECIALLY IN MINOR ROOTS AND IN TROPICAL SPECIES.)

Aphyllophorales basidiomycete fungi whose fruit bodies do not generally have gills (THE MAJORITY OF THE PRINCIPAL WOOD DECAY FUNGI BELONG TO THIS GROUP.)

Apoplast the non-living portion of plant tissue, comprising cell walls and associated hollow cell lumina and intercellular spaces (*cf.* **symplast**)

Arboriculture formerly, the culture of trees, especially for forestry (*see also* **silviculture**; latterly, the culture and management of trees as groups and individuals, primarily for amenity and other non-forestry purposes

Architecture: in a tree, a term describing the pattern of branching of the crown or root system

Ascomycotina (ascomycetes) one of the major taxonomic groups of fungi; their spores are borne in microscopic sacs (asci), which in some types are in turn borne on or within fruit bodies visible to the naked eye but differing from the brackets or toadstools of the Basidiomycotina

Assessment: in relation to tree hazards, the process of estimating the risk which a tree or group of trees poses to persons or property (THIS INVOLVES A VISUAL INSPECTION FOR DEFECTS AND CONTRIBUTORY SITE FACTORS, AND SOMETIMES ALSO A DETAILED INVESTIGATION OF SUSPECTED DEFECTS.)

Axial along or parallel to the axis of a structure, such as a root or shoot

Axil the angle between the adaxial side of a leaf or branch and the axis on which it is borne

Axis (*pl.* **axes**) a main stem or root, or the direction in which a structure is orientated; useful for defining the relative orientations of different parts of a tree or of cells within it

Bacteria microscopic, prokaryotic, single-celled organisms, many species of which break down dead organic matter, and some of which cause diseases in other organisms

Bark a term usually applied to all the tissues of a woody plant lying outside the vascular cambium, thus including the phloem, cortex and periderm; occasionally applied only to the periderm or the phellem

Barrier zone a layer within an annual increment of wood which contains abnormal xylem cells, laid down by the cambium in response to wounding or other trauma (THIS LAYER USUALLY FORMS A STRONG BARRIER TO THE GROWTH OF MICRO-ORGANISMS ACROSS IT.)

Basidiomycotina (basidiomycetes) one of the major taxonomic groups of fungi; their spores are borne on microscopic peg-like structures (basidia), which in many types are in turn borne on or within conspicuous fruit bodies, such as brackets or toadstools (MOST OF THE PRINCIPAL DECAY FUNGI IN STANDING TREES ARE BASIDIOMYCETES.)

Bast *see* **phloem**

Biological control agent an organism which, through artificial introduction or augmentation of its population, helps to protect a crop, an ecosystem or an individual plant or animal against a pest, pathogen or decay organism

Body language: in trees, the outward display of growth responses and/or deformation in response to mechanical stresses

Bole (trunk) the main stem of a tree below its first major branch

Bolling a term used to describe pollard heads or sometimes the entire framework of a pollarded tree

Bottle-butt an atypical broadening of the stem base and buttresses of a tree, sometimes denoting a growth response to altered stress in this region (especially due to decay involving selective delignification)

Bracing the use of rods or cables to restrain the movement between parts of a tree (*see also* **cable bracing**)

Bracket: in wood-decaying fungi, the type of fruit body produced by many species, plate-like to hoof-like in shape and with one side attached to the wood or bark

Branch a limb extending from the main stem or parent branch of a tree

Branch bark ridge the raised arc of bark tissues that forms within the acute angle between a branch and its parent stem

Branch collar a swelling at the base of a branch whose diameter growth has been disproportionately slow compared to that of the parent stem; a term applied also to the pattern in which the cells of the parent stem grow around the branch base, even if no swelling is thereby formed

Branch trace the woody connection of a branch within the parent stem

Brashing the pruning of twigs and small branches from the bole of a tree, usually in silviculture

Broadleaf, broadleaved tree a tree belonging to one of the families of angiosperms; i.e. not a conifer or other gymnosperm

Brown-rot a type of wood decay in which cellulose is degraded, while lignin is only modified (*see* Section 3.2.2.1)

Buckling an irreversible deformation of a structure subjected to a bending load

Burr a term for various kinds of atypical woody protuberances, especially those derived from the mass proliferation of adventitious buds

Butt the basal end of a trunk

Buttress zone the region at the base of a tree where the major lateral roots join the stem, with buttress-like formations on the upper sides of the junctions

Butt-rot *see* **Root- and butt-rot**

Cable bracing, cabling *see* **bracing** (When cables or ropes are used for bracing, the system is usually designed to prevent the braced parts from causing damage in the event of failure.)

Callus a term with more than one botanical meaning, especially an undifferentiated mass of cells, for example forming on the surface of wounded living plant tissue; also used to describe the fold of differentiated wood and bark forming around a tree wound (*see also* **woundwood**)

Cambial zone a meristematic layer, several cells thick, which divides to form successive increments of bark and/or woody tissues (The vascular cambial zone lays down wood on its inside and phloem on its outside. A similar meristematic layer in the bark, the phellogen,

LAYS DOWN CORKY BARK ON ITS OUTSIDE AND IN SOME CASES ALSO SECONDARY CORTEX ON ITS INSIDE.)

Cambium the single layer of cells between phloem and xylem which expands to form the cambial zone during the growing season

Canker a lesion formed by the death of bark and cambium (*see* description in Section 5.2.1)

Canopy the topmost layer of twigs and foliage in a woodland, tree or group of trees

Carbohydrate a chemical compound containing carbon, together with hydrogen and oxygen in the proportions present in water (THE MAIN TYPES OF CARBOHYDRATE IN TREES INCLUDE SUGARS, STARCH, CELLULOSE AND HEMICELLULOSES.)

Cation *see* **ion**

Cellulose a carbohydrate consisting of glucose molecules joined end-to-end, so as to form long filaments; a principal constituent of plant cell walls

Chlorosis an atypical colouring, usually yellowish, of foliage; often a symptom of mineral nutrient imbalance or inadequate root function

Cladoptosis the shedding of twigs by abscission

Column boundary layer a general term for the interface between a column of dysfunctional, discoloured or decayed wood and sound wood; applicable to a reaction zone or a barrier zone

Compartmentalisation the confinement of disease, decay or other dysfunction within an anatomically discrete region of plant tissue, due to passive and/or active defences operating at the boundaries of the affected region

Compression strength the ability of a material or structure to resist failure when subjected to compressive loading; measurable in trees using special drilling devices

Compressive loading mechanical loading which exerts a positive pressure; the opposite to tensile loading

Conifers trees, mostly with needle- or scale-like leaves, whose male and/or female inflorescences consist of cones, and whose seeds are not formed within ovaries

Conk a fungal bracket; a mainly North American term

Conservation Areas: in Great Britain, designated areas of architectural or historical interest, in which there are special procedures for planning applications and a requirement that tree work cannot generally be undertaken unless notice (currently of six weeks) has been given to the local authority concerned (*see also* **Tree Preservation Order**)

Copparding a hybrid word describing the cutting of several shoots that have arisen from a coppice stool, so that each one forms a pollard

Coppicing the cutting of a woody plant near ground level to encourage the development of multiple stems; in some regions of the UK, this term is partly interchanged with pollarding

Cortex: in trees, the parenchymatous living region of the primary bark outside the phloem (*see also* **periderm**)

Crown: in arboriculture. the main foliage-bearing portion of a tree
Crown lifting *see* description in Section 6.4.2
Crown reduction *see* description in Section 6.4.1.1
Crown thinning *see* description in Section 6.4.2.1
Cytoplasm (*adj*. **cytoplasmic**) the living contents of a cell
Damping: in mechanics, the reduction of the tendency for a structure to resonate (IN A TREE STEM, RESONANCE IN THE FORM OF SWAYING IS REDUCED BY THE LOAD EXERTED BY BRANCHES BORNE ALONG ITS LENGTH.)
Decay-detecting drill a device which allows zones of decay to be detected and mapped by virtue of their reduced resistance to penetration, compared with sound wood
Decurrent: in trees, a system of branching in which the crown is borne on a number of major widely-spreading limbs of similar size (*cf*. **excurrent**); also a term pertaining to certain fungi with toadstools as fruit bodies, whose gills run some distance down the stem; similarly pertaining to leaf bases and other plant organs which extend down the stem
Defect: in relation to tree hazards, any feature of a tree which detracts from the uniform distribution of mechanical stress, or which makes the tree mechanically unsuited to its environment
Defence: in trees and other plants, any system or process which defends tissues against damage (DEFENCES IN WOODY TISSUES MAY BE PRE-FORMED AND PASSIVE, OR RESPONSIVE AND ACTIVE.)
Delamination the separation of layers from each other, sometimes visible as longitudinal splitting in the wood of a tree
Dieback the death of part of a plant, usually starting from a distal point and often progressing in stages
Diffuse-porous one of the two main types of wood structure in broadleaved trees (*cf*. **ring-porous**), in which the diameter of the vessels decreases progressively from the early-wood to the late-wood
Disease a malfunction in or destruction of tissues within a living organism, usually not taken to include mechanical damage; in trees, usually caused by pathogenic micro-organisms
Distal: within part of a tree or other living organism, the region furthest from the main body of the organism, i.e. towards the tip (*cf*. **proximal**)
Dominance: in trees, the tendency for a leading shoot to maintain a faster rate of expansion than the lateral shoots; *also* the tendency of a tree to maintain a taller crown than its neighbours
Dormant bud an axial bud which does not develop into a shoot until after the second season following its formation (MANY SUCH BUDS PERSIST THROUGH THE LIFE OF A TREE AND DEVELOP ONLY IF STIMULATED TO DO SO.)
Drop-crotching *see* description in Section 6.4.1
Dysfunction: in woody tissues, the loss of physiological function, especially water conduction
Early-wood the wood laid down around the time of the main flush of shoot growth in the early part of the growing season (THIS WOOD IS USUALLY

MORE EFFICIENT IN WATER CONDUCTION THAN LATE-WOOD BUT IS OFTEN MORE SUSCEPTIBLE TO DYSFUNCTION AND MICROBIAL COLONISATION.)

End-loading *see* description in Section 2.2.1.1

Endophytes micro-organisms which live inside plant tissues without causing overt disease, but are in some cases capable of causing disease if the tissues become physiologically stressed, for example by lack of moisture

Energy the capacity to do work (THROUGH PHOTOSYNTHESIS, GREEN PLANTS ABSORB ENERGY FROM SUNLIGHT AND STORE IT IN THE FORM OF CHEMICAL COMPOUNDS WHICH ARE USED IN ENERGY-DEPENDENT PROCESSES SUCH AS GROWTH.)

Enzymes proteins which catalyse biochemical reactions, for example those involved in the fungal degradation of woody cell walls

Epicormic pertaining to shoots or roots which are initiated on mature woody stems; shoots may form in this way from dormant buds or they may be adventitious

Excrescence any abnormal outgrowth on the surface of a tree or other organism

Excurrent: in trees, a system of branching in which a single, distinct main stem bears a succession of branches whose diameter is progressively smaller towards the top of the tree; also pertaining to structures such as the midribs of leaves, which project beyond the lamina (*cf.* **decurrent**)

Extractives substances which, in some types of tree, are laid down in the heartwood at the time of its formation from sapwood, and which generally provide some protection against decay

Failure: in connection with tree hazards, a partial or total fracture within woody tissues or loss of cohesion between roots and soil (IN TOTAL FAILURE THE AFFECTED PART SNAPS OR TEARS AWAY COMPLETELY. IN PARTIAL FAILURE, THERE IS A CRACK OR DEFORMATION WHICH RESULTS IN AN ALTERED DISTRIBUTION OF MECHANICAL STRESS.)

Feathered tree a young tree supplied from a nursery, having a straight leading shoot and well-formed side-shoots

Felling licence: in Great Britain, a permit to fell trees in excess of a specified size of stem or volume of timber

Fibre a type of axially elongated wood cell with a narrow lumen and thick wall, providing mechanical support; *also*, a general term for the axially elongated cells in wood

Fibre-tracheid a type of wood cell intermediate in structure and function between a fibre and a tracheid

Flare *see* **root flare**

Flush-cut a pruning cut close to the parent stem which removes part of the branch bark ridge

Foodbase: in the decay of trees, a volume of woody tissue in which a fungus is established and which may supply the resources that it needs for growth into adjacent wood or for fruiting

Foreseeable: in tree hazard assessment, pertaining to failure and associated injury or damage which are predictable on the basis of evidence from a tree and its surroundings

Forestry *see* **silviculture**

Formative pruning *see* description in Section 7.6.1

"Fractometer" a proprietary device for measuring the strength and flexibility of wood samples extracted with an increment borer

Functional wood a term usually applied to sapwood which is living and conductive; more properly 'physiologically functional wood', to avoid confusion with mechanical function, which continues after death (*see also* **dysfunction**)

Fungi organisms of several evolutionary origins, most of which are multicellular and grow as branched filamentous cells (hyphae) within dead organic matter or living organisms (Wood decay fungi are specialised forms which have co-evolved with woody plants.)

Gaping a term coined for use in this book, describing the V-shaped bifurcation of the branch bark ridge, overlying a zone where the members of an acute crotch have united around a zone of included bark (*cf.* **lipping**)

Gas exchange: in woody tissues, the diffusion of gases into and out of a particular region (A high moisture content usually results in a low rate of gas exchange.)

Girdle scar a ring of numerous, minute scars, which is left encircling a shoot after the abscission of bud scales at bud-burst; useful for demarcating increments of shoot extension (The scar expands with the girth of the stem until it is obscured by rhytidome formation.)

Girdling: in woody plants, any form of damage which destroys or kills the bark and cambium all the way around a stem, branch or root, usually leading to the death of the distal portion

Girdling root a root that grows across the buttress zone or across the bases of other roots, eventually causing constriction of radial growth

Growth stresses *see* mention in Section 3.2.1

Growth substances chemicals synthesised within a plant, which influence the growth of other parts of the plant to which they are translocated

Guying a form of artificial support with cables for trees whose anchorage is temporarily inadequate (*see also* description in Section 6.5.5)

Hazard *see* definition and discussion in Chapter 1

Hazard beam: in a tree, an upwardly curved part in which strong internal stresses may occur without the compensatory formation of extra wood (Longitudinal splitting occurs in a small proportion of such cases.)

Heartwood the dead or predominantly dead central wood of various tree species whose outer living wood, sapwood, has a finite and pre-determined lifespan (*see also* **extractives**)

Heave: in relation to a shrinkable clay soil, expansion due to re-wetting, sometimes after the felling or root severance of a tree which was previously extracting moisture from the deeper layers; *also*, in relation to root growth, the lifting of pavements and other structures by radial expansion; *also*, in relation to tree stability, the lifting of one side of a wind-rocked root-plate

Helical grain (often called spiral grain) a wood structure in which the cells are aligned helically around the stem instead of running parallel to the stem axis

Hemicelluloses a diverse range of carbohydrates, each consisting of linked sugar molecules of more than one type

Hormones *see* **growth substances**

Hymenium the spore-bearing surface of a basidiomycete fruit body

Hypha one of the microscopic thread-like growths making up a fungal mycelium

Incipient failure in wood tissues, a mechanical failure which results only in deformation or cracking, and not in the fall or detachment of the affected part

Included bark (ingrown bark) bark of adjacent parts of a tree (usually in forks, acutely angled branches or basal flutes) which is in face-to-face contact, so that there is weakness due to the lack of a woody union

Increment borer a hollow auger which can be used for the extraction of wood cores for counting or measuring wood increments or for inspecting the condition of the wood

Infection the establishment of a parasitic micro-organism in the tissues of a tree or other organism

Internode the part of a stem between two nodes; not to be confused with a length of stem which bear nodes but no branches

Ion an electrically charged atom or molecule (The concentration and mobility of ions dissolved in plant sap partly determine the electrical resistance of the tissues. The charge is negative in anions and positive in cations.)

Late-wood the wood laid down after the time of the first or main flush of shoot growth in the growing season; this wood is usually less efficient in water conduction than early-wood but is often less susceptible to dysfunction and microbial colonisation

Leader: in a tree, a topmost shoot which has apical dominance

Leaf scar the slight bark ridge left by the abscission of a leaf (The scar enlarges with the growth in girth of the stem, until obscured by rhytidome formation.)

Lever arm a mechanical term denoting the length of the lever represented by a structure that is free to move at one end, such as a tree or one of its branches

Lignin the hard, cement-like constituent of wood cells (Deposition of lignin within the matrix of cellulose microfibrils in the cell wall is termed lignification.)

Lion-tailing a term applied to a branch of a tree that wholly or largely lacks side-branches, except near its tip, and may thus be liable to snap due to end-loading

Lipping a term coined for use in this book, describing the longitudinally divided appearance of a branch bark ridge in which included bark is present (*cf.* **gaping**)

Loading a mechanical term describing the force acting on a structure from a particular source; e.g. the weight of the structure itself or wind pressure

Lopping a term used generally to describe the cutting of branches from a tree, although sometimes applied specifically to the removal of large branches

Lumen (*pl.* **lumina**) in a wood cell, the space enclosed by the cell wall; this may be filled with water or gas or plugged with deposits

Maiden tree a tree grown other than from a coppiced stump and not itself coppiced or pollarded

Medullary rays: in a woody stem, the xylem rays formed in the first year of growth (Unlike rays which start to form later, they connect with the pith or 'medulla'.)

Meristem (*adj.* **meristematic**) a growing point or cambial layer in which new cells are formed by division

Micro-aerophilic pertaining to organisms or biochemical processes which are adapted to an environment low in oxygen (*see also* **aerobic/anaerobic**)

Microfibrils: in a plant cell wall, the smallest component units of a cellulose filament

Middle lamella the thin membrane joining adjacent plant cells together (In wood cells, it is often fused with the primary cell wall, forming the 'compound middle lamella'.)

Mitigation a term used in this book to describe the use of remedial action to lessen risk associated with foreseeable failure; also among other uses, a circumstance that may lessen the gravity of an offence in law

Mucilage a general term for various kinds of complex carbohydrate which are viscous and slimy when moist, and are secreted at the surfaces of many kinds of living cell

Mulch material laid down over the rooting area of a tree or other plant to help conserve moisture, suppress weeds or encourage a beneficial microflora (a mulch may consist of organic matter or a sheet of plastic or other artificial material)

Mycelium the body of a fungus, consisting of branched filaments (hyphae)

Mycology the study of fungi

Natural pruning the shedding of a twig or branch that has died back naturally and has become decayed at or near its base (often due to the activation of wood-decaying endophytes)

Negligence: as described in this book, the failure to take reasonable action to deal with tree-related hazards so as to help prevent injury to persons or damage to property

Node the point where a leaf is joined to a shoot and where an axillary bud may develop into a side-shoot

Nutrients substances which are absorbed by living organisms for the maintenance of metabolic processes; usually not regarded as including water or oxygen (GREEN PLANTS ABSORB INORGANIC FORMS OF ELEMENTS SUCH AS POTASSIUM, NITROGEN AND PHOSPHORUS AS NUTRIENTS, WHILE MANUFACTURING ORGANIC FOOD MATERIALS BY PHOTOSYNTHESIS. PLANTS ARE VITAL FOOD SOURCES FOR FUNGI, ANIMALS AND MANY TYPES OF BACTERIA.)

Occluding tissues a general term for the wood, cambium and bark that form around a wound on a woody plant (*cf.* **woundwood**)

Occlusion the process whereby a wound is progressively closed by the formation of new wood and bark around it

Parenchyma the relatively unspecialised tissue within higher plants, including the network of living cells within sapwood (axial parenchyma and ray parenchyma)

Pathogen a micro-organism which causes disease in another organism

Pectin a jelly-like carbohydrate which helps to glue plant cells together

Perennial canker a canker which develops over a number of years, causing the death of successive bands of occluding tissue, and sometimes becoming a potential fracture point

Periderm: in the bark of trees, the outermost region comprising dead, corky phellem, together with the dividing layer of cells (the phellogen) which gives rise to it by outward cell divisions (IN SOME SPECIES, INWARD CELL DIVISIONS OF THE PHELLOGEN ALSO OCCUR, FORMING A LIVING TISSUE KNOWN AS PHELLODERM OR SECONDARY CORTEX.)

Perithecium (*pl.* **perithecia**) a flask-like reproductive structure, usually less than 1 mm across, in which the asci of various ascomycete fungi are contained

Phased target pruning *see* description in Section 7.7.2.3

Phenolic pertaining to a group of chemical compounds containing the phenol unit: a benzene ring with an attached hydroxyl (OH) group (MANY PHENOLIC SUBSTANCES ARE TOXIC OR INHIBITORY TO A WIDE RANGE OF MICRO-ORGANISMS.)

Phloem the principal conductive tissue through which the products of photosynthesis are translocated in solution via specialised cells (IN THE ROOTS AND STEMS OF MOST TEMPERATE TREE SPECIES, ANNUAL INCREMENTS OF PHLOEM FORM BY CELL DIVISIONS ON THE OUTER SIDE OF THE VASCULAR CAMBIUM.)

Photosynthesis the process whereby plants use light energy to split hydrogen from water molecules, and combine it with carbon dioxide to form the molecular building blocks for synthesising carbohydrates and other biochemical products.

Pileus the expanded cap of a toadstool or toadstool-like fungus

Pith the central parenchymatous column of tissue in a plant stem or other organ

Pollard or **poll** a term for a pollarded tree

Pollard head the swollen region of a stem or branch that forms behind a pollarding cut

Pollarding the complete or partial removal of the crown of a young tree so as to encourage the development of numerous branches; *also*, further cutting to maintain this growth pattern

Pores in bracket fungi, the openings of the tubes from which basidiospores are released

Preventive action in tree hazard management, action which helps to prevent injury to persons or damage to property

Probability a statistical measure of the chance that a particular event (e.g. a specific failure of a tree or a specific kind of harm to persons or property) might occur

Progressive crown reduction *see* description in Section 6.4.3.2

Prokaryotes single-celled organisms, including bacteria, whose genetic material is not contained within a membrane-bound nucleus; plants, animals and fungi have such nuclei and are termed **eukaryotes**

Propagules a general term for the seeds, spores or other structures by which plants, fungi and some other life-forms are dispersed and perpetuated between generations

Propping *see* description in Section 6.5.4

Proximal in the direction towards the main body of a tree or other living organism (*cf.* **distal**)

Pruning the removal or cutting back of twigs, branches or roots; in some contexts applying only to twigs or small branches only, but more often used to describe all kinds of work involving cutting

Pseudosclerotial plate an impervious sheet of fungal tissue, usually dark in colour, which may develop within wood being decayed by certain fungal species; it may separate adjacent decay columns or surround an individual column

Radial in the plane or direction of the radius of a circular object such as a tree stem (*see also* **rays**)

Rams-horn: in connection with wounds on trees, a roll of occluding tissues which has a spiral appearance in cross-section

Rays radially orientated strips of parenchyma cells within wood and bark (Rays are involved in the storage and radial translocation of materials in solution and also contribute to the strength of wood.)

Reaction zone a zone, usually dark in colour, within the wood of a living tree, which forms a boundary – often a defensive one – between fully functional sapwood and dysfunctional or decaying wood

Red-rot a term sometimes applied to types of white-rot in which the inherently light colour of the decayed zone is masked by reddish pigments; not to be confused with brown-rots which sometimes also have a reddish-brown colour

Remedial action in tree hazard management, action to remove or mitigate the risk of injury to persons or damage to property

Resonant frequency in a tree or branch, the natural frequency of swaying

Resistance: in tree health assessment, the ability of a tree to withstand particular adverse conditions or attack by a specific pest or pathogen
Resistance (electrical) the ratio between voltage and electric flux in a conductor carrying a direct current (more properly impedance in the case of an alternating current); (IN A TREE, MEASUREMENT OF THE ELECTRICAL RESISTANCE OR IMPEDANCE OF TISSUES MAY AID THE ASSESSMENT OF VITALITY OR THE MAPPING OF DYSFUNCTIONAL OR MICROBIALLY COLONISED REGIONS OF BARK OR WOOD.)
Resupinate: in fungi, pertaining to a basidiomycete fruit body which grows as a layer over the host surface, as compared with a bracket or toadstool
Rhytidome the rough outer bark of many types of tree, which is formed by secondary periderms (TREES WITH ONLY A PRIMARY PERIDERM PRODUCE SMOOTH BARK.)
Rib: in tree body language, a long, narrow, axial protuberance, which often overlies a crack
Ring barking a form of girdling, involving physical damage to the bark and cambium
Ring shake a cylindrical split, formed within a tree by the separation of adjacent annual increments or of layers within an increment
Ring-porous one of the two main types of wood structure in broadleaved trees (*cf.* **diffuse-porous**), in which each annual increment includes two distinct bands when seen in cross-section; these consist of early-wood with wide vessels, and of late-wood with narrow ones.
Ripewood the older central wood of those tree species in which sapwood gradually ages without being converted to heartwood
Risk the likelihood of the potential harm from a particular hazard becoming actual harm; *also* see definition in Chapter 1
Rod bracing the use of metal rods to help restrain movement, usually of the members of a weak fork or of branches in contact (or, rarely, the opposite sides of the wall of a cavity)
Root flare the curving region where a stem base joins the main lateral roots, usually composed of individual buttresses; more or less synonymous with the buttress zone
Root-plate *see* description in Section 7.4
Root rot either a general term for any form of wood decay in roots, or a disease in which fine, non-woody roots are killed
Root- and butt-rot a form of decay in standing trees, which primarily affects the roots and buttress zone but may also extend up the stem
Rootstock or **stock** in artificial grafting, the rooted plant on to which a scion is grafted
Rotary cabling *see* description in Section 6.5.2.1
$S_{1,2,3}$ layers the three principal layers of the secondary cell wall
Safety factor *see* definition in Section 2.1
Safety standards specified standards of practice in a particular activity, such as tree management, which are intended to ensure that persons, property

or other things of value are protected from harm, beyond a minimum accepted level of risk

Sail area: in arboriculture, a general term for the wind-intercepting area of a tree's crown, which varies both with leaf cover and the orientation of leaves and twigs under different wind conditions

Sanitation: in plant disease control, the removal of material which could be a source of infection by a pathogen

Sap a general term for fluids in plant tissues, whether in living cells or in the hollow water-conducting cells of the xylem

Sapwood the living xylem of a woody plant, which either loses viability gradually over a number of years or decades or becomes converted into a distinct, largely dead heartwood

Scaffold limbs the branches which form the main framework of the crown of a tree with a decurrent growth habit

Sclerotium (*pl.* **sclerotia**) a fungal resting structure, usually an aggregation of hardened and melanized hyphae

Scion: in artificial grafting, the bud or shoot which is grafted on to the rootstock

Sealant: in arboriculture, a coating which is used to protect a wound from desiccation or infection (SOME FUNGICIDAL SEALANTS MAY GIVE PROTECTION FROM FRESH-WOUND PARASITES BUT HAVE NO PROVEN LONG-TERM VALUE FOR THE CONTROL OF DECAY.)

Selective delignification a kind of white-rot in which lignin is degraded faster than cellulose

Shake *see* **star shake** and **ring shake**

Shearing or **shear failure** the sliding apart of a structure, as in a fault-plane

Shear stress mechanical stress which tends to induce shearing

Shedding: in woody plants, the normal abscission, rotting off or sloughing of leaves, floral parts, twigs, fine roots and bark scales

Shoot: in a tree, the elongating region of a stem or branch

Shrub a woody plant which branches at or near ground level and so does not have a single trunk

Significant: in relation to health and safety, pertaining to hazards or risks which are deemed to exceed accepted standards of safety and which therefore require remedial or preventive action

Silviculture (sylviculture) the planting, tending and management of woods and forests (*see also* **arboriculture**)

Simultaneous white-rot a kind of wood decay in which lignin and cellulose are degraded at about the same rate

Sites of Special Scientific Interest (SSSIs) areas designated under UK law, at which specified activities are required, prohibited or controlled for the purpose of conserving wildlife or other natural features

Snag: in a woody plant, a portion of a cut or broken stem, branch or root which extends beyond any growing-point or dormant bud (TYPICALLY, A SNAG TENDS TO DIE BACK TO THE NEAREST GROWING POINT.)

Soft-rot a kind of wood decay in which a fungus degrades cellulose within the cell walls, without causing overall degradation of the wall

Soil heave *see* **heave**

Spores propagules of fungi and many other life-forms (MOST SPORES ARE MICROSCOPIC AND ARE DISPERSED IN AIR OR WATER.)

Staged cutting *see* description in Section 6.4.3; *cf.* **phased target pruning**

Stag-headed: in a tree, a state of dieback in which dead branches protrude beyond the current living crown

Star shake a pattern of longitudinal splitting in wood, radiating along xylem rays like the spokes of a wheel when seen in cross-section

Starch a food storage carbohydrate in plants, which is insoluble in water at normal growing temperatures

Stem: in a tree, the principal portion of the woody structure (i.e. the trunk), or one of a number of such portions with similar size and status

Stiffness the tendency of a structure or a material to resist bending; this is independent of strength

Stipe: in a fungus, the stem of a toadstool or other fruit body

Stock *see* **rootstock**

Stoma (*pl.* **stomata**) a controllable opening in the surface of a leaf or conifer needle, allowing water vapour and gases to pass between the internal cells and the atmosphere

Strain: in mechanics, the distortion in an object caused by a stress (*cf.* **stress**)

Strength the resistance of a structure or material to mechanical failure when subjected to a particular type of stress: tensile, compressive, shear, torsional etc.

Stress: in plant physiology, a condition under which one or more physiological functions are not operating within their optimum range, for example due to lack of water, inadequate nutrition or extremes of temperature

Stress: in mechanics, a force acting on an object, measured per unit area of the object (*cf.* **strain**)

Stress-notch a point where mechanical stress is locally concentrated within a structure, sometimes resulting in failure or perhaps stimulating adaptive growth in the case of a living organism

Stress-wave a pulse of sound waves of mixed frequency which is propagated through a material from a physical impact (IT IS POSSIBLE TO DETECT DEFECTS IN STANDING TREES OR TIMBER BY VIRTUE OF THEIR EFFECTS ON THE TRANSIT TIME OF STRESS-WAVES.)

Stringy white-rot the kind of wood decay produced by selective delignification

Stroma a layer of tissue which supports the fruit bodies of some types of fungi, mainly ascomycetes

Stub cut a pruning cut which is made at some distance along a branch, distal to the branch bark ridge and branch collar

Suberin a substance composed of fatty materials (lipids) and phenolics which is impervious to water and resistant to many forms of microbial degradation (IT IS THE MAIN CONSTITUENT OF CORK.)

Subsidence: in relation to soil or structures resting in or on soil, a sinking due to shrinkage when clay soils dry out, sometimes due to extraction of moisture by tree roots

Subsidence: in relation to branches of trees, a term that can be used to describe a progressive downward bending due to increasing weight

Sugars water-soluble food storage carbohydrates

Surgery: as applied to trees, a term sometimes used to describe work such as pruning or bracing

Sweep: in trees, the upward curvature of a stem with a leaning base

Symplast the living protoplasm in plant tissue, which connects adjacent cells in the form of fine strands (plasmodesmata) which pass through pits in the cell wall (*cf.* **apoplast**)

Tangential: in plant anatomy, pertaining to a plane which intersects a xylem ray at right-angles (*cf.* **radial**)

Tap-root a root formed in some types of plant which grows downwards and retains apical dominance over its side-roots (TAP-ROOTS ARE PRESENT IN YOUNG TREES OF MANY SPECIES, BUT RARELY PERSIST AS SUCH IN MATURITY.)

Taper: in stems and branches, the decrease in diameter along a given length, usually in the distal direction

Target canker a kind of perennial canker, containing concentric rings of dead occluding tissues

Target pruning the pruning of a twig or branch so that tissues recognisably belonging to the parent stem are retained

Targets: in tree hazard assessment (and with somewhat incorrect terminology), persons or property or other things of value which might be harmed by mechanical failure of the tree or by objects falling from it

Tensile stress a pulling stress

Tipping: in arboriculture, a term sometimes used to describe the shortening of branches

Topping: in arboriculture, the removal of the crown of a (usually mature) tree, or of a major proportion of it

Torsional stress mechanical stress applied by a twisting force

Tracheids narrow, tapering water-conducting cells in the wood of trees; much shorter and narrower than most vessels (THEY ARE THE PREDOMINANT TYPE OF AXIAL WOOD CELL IN CONIFERS.)

Translocation: in plant physiology, the movement of water and dissolved materials through the body of the plant

Transpiration the evaporation of moisture from the surface of a plant, especially via the stomata of leaves; it exerts a suction which draws water up from the roots and through the intervening xylem cells

Tree a woody plant which typically has a single main stem and, in maturity, attains a height of at least four metres and a stem diameter at breast height of at least 75 mm

Tree Preservation Order: in Great Britain, an order made by a local authority, whereby the authority's consent is generally required for the cutting down, topping or lopping of specified trees

Tree-pulling: in tree stability or hazard assessment, a test in which the stiffness of the stem or the firmness of the roots can be assessed by the application of a pulling force and the measurement of bending or tilting

Trunk the single main stem of a tree

Tylosis (*pl.* **tyloses**) balloon-like extensions of xylem parenchyma cells into adjoining vessels, via the pits in the adjoining cell wall (TYLOSES HELP TO SEAL OFF DYSFUNCTIONAL XYLEM.)

Ultrasound sound with a frequency above the limit of human hearing: i.e. from approx. 20 kHz upwards (AN ABNORMALLY SLOW TRANSIT OF ULTRASOUND ACROSS A TREE STEM OR PIECE OF TIMBER MAY INDICATE THE PRESENCE OF A DEFECT.)

Undercutting: in tree nurseries, the practice of cutting a seedling's roots from below, so as to encourage the development of a fibrous root system

Vascular wilt a type of plant disease in which water-conducting cells become dysfunctional

Vessels water-conducting cells in plants, usually wide and long to provide hydraulic efficiency (THEY ARE GENERALLY NOT PRESENT IN CONIFEROUS TREES.)

Veteran tree a loosely defined term for an old and valued specimen, which may have survived beyond the typical age range for the species concerned

Vigour: in tree assessment, an overall measure of the rate of shoot production, shoot extension or diameter growth (*cf.* **vitality**)

Visual Tree Assessment (VTA): in addition to the literal meaning, a system expounded by Mattheck & Breloer (1995) to aid the diagnosis of potential defects through visual signs and the application of mechanical criteria

Vitality: in tree assessment, an overall appraisal of physiological and biochemical processes, in which high vitality equates with healthy function (*cf.* **vigour**)

Volva: on a toadstool, a flask-like membrane around the base of the stipe

Welding: in trees, a term sometimes used to describe the grafting of the adjacent members of a union containing included bark

Wetwood a zone of abnormally moist wood in a standing tree, either within the heartwood or within a region of dysfunctional sapwood (ANAEROBIC BACTERIA ARE RESPONSIBLE FOR THE DEVELOPMENT OF MOST, BUT NOT ALL, FORMS OF WETWOOD. THEY GENERATE METHANE AND USUALLY GIVE RISE TO ALKALINE CONDITIONS.)

Whip a young, single-stemmed tree supplied for planting before the appreciable development of side-shoots

White-rot various kinds of wood decay in which lignin, usually together with cellulose and other wood constituents, is degraded

Wind exposure the degree to which a tree or other object is exposed to wind, with regard both to duration and velocity

Wind pressure the force exerted by wind on a tree or other object

Wind snap the breaking of a tree stem by wind

Windthrow the blowing over of a tree at its roots

Wood secondary xylem; the main structurally supporting and water-conducting tissue of trees and shrubs (*see also* **xylem**)

Wound dressing a general term for sealants and other materials used to cover wounds in the hope of protecting them against desiccation and infection (*see also* **sealant**)

Woundwood wood with atypical anatomical features, formed in the vicinity of a wound; also a term sometimes used to describe the occluding tissues around a wound in preference to the ambiguous term 'callus'

Xylem plant tissue with the special function of translocating water and dissolved mineral nutrients (The wood of trees and shrubs consists of heavily lignified xylem, laid down in radial increments, which provides structural support as well as water conduction.)

Xylem rays *see* **rays**

Appendices

Appendix 1: Some UK guides for safe working practice

FASTCo guides relevant to remedial work for tree-related hazards

(please note that FASTCo guides are not a substitute for training)

206 Brashing and Pruning with Handsaw (1994)
301 Petrol Driven Chainsaws (1998)
302 Basic Felling by Chainsaw (1995)
303 Chainsaw Snedding (1995)
304 Cross-cutting and Manual Stacking (1996)
305 Takedown of Hung-up Trees (1996)
306 Chainsaw Clearance of Windblow (1996)
307 Felling Large Trees (1996)
310 Hand Winches for Directional Felling and Takedown (1996)
401 Tree Climbing Operations (1996)
402 Aerial Tree Rescue (1998)
403 Mobile Elevating Platforms (1996)
801 Noise and Hearing Conservation (1995)
802 Emergency Planning and First Aid (1998)
803 Electricity at Work; Forestry (1996)

Appendix 2: Observations on selected tree genera and species

The incidence of various kinds of mechanical failure differs greatly between tree species and sometimes between cultivars within the same species. Much of the relevant information is, however, based on observations, rather than on scientific surveys or experiments. Indeed, for many types of tree, even anecdotal information is scarce or lacking. It is therefore important not to regard the following notes as a definitive guide on the tree genera that they mention. The notes do, however, bring together some facts and analyses of opinion which may help to make the reader aware of the hazards that may be likely to arise with particular types of tree.

The tree genera mentioned here include many of those commonly grown in the UK and the near Continent, but some are excluded due to lack of worthwhile information. Several others are excluded because they rarely, if ever, form specimens large enough to cause major safety hazards.

For each of the genera listed, there is a set of three histograms, which concern the following: the formation of forks with included bark, the failure of such forks and the failure of trees due to decay. The data are derived from an opinion survey in which twenty-nine arboricultural consultants and contractors participated. The bars represent five categories, ranging from very low to very high, and the height of each bar shows the number of respondents who provided the scores, based on their experience. In many cases, the total score is less than twenty-nine, because some respondents had insufficient experience with particular tree genera.

Although the data in the histograms are based on expert opinion, they cannot be equated with the results of a rigorously devised survey. Indeed, for histograms in which there is little difference in the height of the bars, it is reasonable to assume that opinions differed so much that not even the most tentative conclusions should be drawn. In many cases, however, there is a consistent pattern with a distinct peak. The score with the peak rating probably gives a worthwhile indication of the incidence of each of the defects within the type of tree concerned.

The histograms represent entire genera but there were cases where respondents reported large differences between species or varieties belonging to a particular genus. These differences are mentioned in the accompanying text. The text also includes other available information which is relevant to hazard assessment and management. Problems which affect a very wide range of trees, such as root killing by *Armillaria* spp. (honey fungus), are only mentioned if the type of tree concerned is affected much more than most other types. More detailed information on relevant diseases and decay fungi is provided by Strouts and Winter [173].

The scores shown in the histograms have also been used in the calculation of mean values, which are tabulated to display a ranking of genera. There are separate tables for coniferous and broadleaved genera.

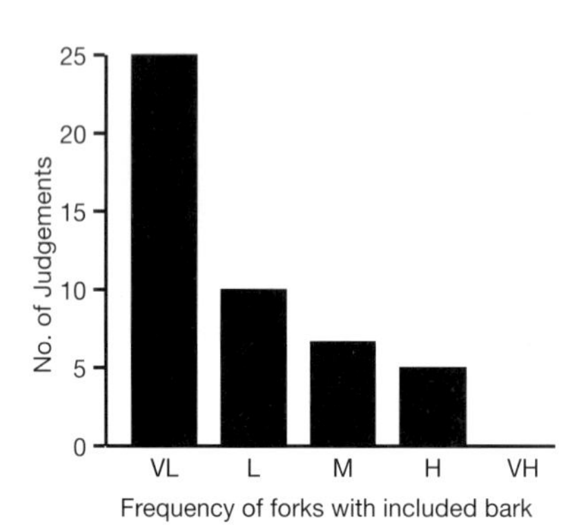

Example of a histogram. The five categories for respondents' judgement. Shown as abbreviated labels for the columns are: VL – very low, L – low, M – moderate, H – high and VH – very high.

In addition to the graphs and tables which summarise information on the occurrence of failure there are individual entries for tree genera, which provide further information. In some of these entries, additional notes concerning failure are included under the heading "mechanical characteristics".

For some genera, information about the suitability for particular types of soil or site is provided, as this is often relevant to the health or stability of trees. This advice is based partly on that provided by Mitchell and Jobling [114]. For some types of tree, there are additional comments concerning problems that may occur in urban and other intensively used sites. Some of the problems associated with such sites occur almost irrespective of the type of tree and are therefore not mentioned here. However, the problem of deicing salt damage, which can indirectly render trees hazardous due to the dieback of crowns, is much greater for some types of tree than for others. Information on the tolerance of various species and genera has been supplied by Dobson [44].

For most of the tree genera included in this Appendix, some information is supplied about the occurrence of decay fungi, but the fungi named are not necessarily the only ones that may be found. The species shown are just some of those that happen to have been recorded on living specimens. It should also be borne in mind that certain decay fungi also cause other kinds of disease, as in the case of silver-leaf caused by *Chondrostereum purpureum*.

Most decay fungi can be for convenience placed in one or other of two groups as far as their pattern of development within the tree is concerned. Those that usually begin their development either below ground, thus causing root- or butt-rots, are indicated in the following lists by the letter 'B' in brackets (denoting 'bottom rots') after the fungal name. Those that develop mainly above ground, causing 'top rots' are denoted by a bracketed letter 'T'. Other information on the significance of decay caused by many of the fungi listed below can be found in Chapter 4.

Propensity to form weak forks		Propensity for fork failure		Propensity to fail due to decay	
Genus	**MEAN**	**Genus**	**MEAN**	**Genus**	**MEAN**
CONIFERS					
Araucaria	1.05	Araucaria	1.00	Sequoia	1.04
Sequoia	1.31	Sequoia	1.19	Metasequoia	1.05
Picea	1.32	Larix	1.22	Taxodium	1.05
Larix	1.37	Metasequoia	1.27	Sequoiadendron	1.09
Sequoiadendron	1.40	Picea	1.28	Araucaria	1.11
Metasequoia	1.41	Taxus	1.29	Ginkgo	1.12
Pseudotsuga	1.46	Sequoiadendron	1.32	Taxus	1.17
Abies	1.60	Ginkgo	1.35	Pseudotsuga	1.33
Taxodium	1.70	Pseudotsuga	1.38	Thuja	1.38
Thuja	2.04	Abies	1.52	Picea	1.42
Pinus	2.11	Taxodium	1.57	Cupressocyparis	1.44
Taxus	2.21	Pinus	1.67	Abies	1.48
Ginkgo	2.52	Thuja	1.96	Pinus	1.48
Cupressus	2.74	Cupressus	2.64	Larix	1.50
Cupressocyparis	2.78	Cedrus	2.92	Chamaecyparis	1.68
Cedrus	2.96	Cupressocyparis	2.92	Cupressus	1.76
Chamaecyparis	3.17	Chamaecyparis	3.00	Cedrus	2.04
BROADLEAVES					
Platanus	1.32	Carpinus	1.32	Platanus	1.32
Carya	1.50	Alnus	1.35	Carya	1.50
Corylus	1.52	Corylus	1.44	Corylus	1.52
Pterocarya	1.57	Carya	1.60	Pterocarya	1.57
Eucalyptus	1.60	Juglans	1.62	Eucalyptus	1.60
Carpinus	1.60	Platanus	1.64	Carpinus	1.60
Zelkova	1.62	Pterocarya	1.67	Zelkova	1.62
Alnus	1.77	Magnolia	1.77	Alnus	1.77
Sophora	1.80	Zelkova	1.80	Sophora	1.80
Liquidambar	1.82	Quercus	1.81	Liquidambar	1.82
Magnolia	1.82	Pyrus	1.92	Magnolia	1.82
Gleditsia	1.91	Betula	1.93	Gleditsia	1.91
Quercus	1.93	Ulmus	2.00	Quercus	1.93
Castanea	2.00	Sophora	2.07	Castanea	2.00
Pyrus	2.12	Castanea	2.07	Pyrus	2.12
Sorbus	2.17	Prunus	2.12	Sorbus	2.17
Liriodendron	2.25	Liquidambar	2.14	Liriodendron	2.25
Ulmus	2.27	Sorbus	2.22	Ulmus	2.27
Tilia	2.32	Paulownia	2.31	Tilia	2.32
Ailanthus	2.36	Tilia	2.32	Ailanthus	2.36
Paulownia	2.42	Eucalyptus	2.33	Paulownia	2.42
Catalpa	2.44	Morus	2.43	Catalpa	2.44
Robinia	2.48	Catalpa	2.53	Robinia	2.48
Prunus	2.48	Gleditsia	2.55	Prunus	2.48
Morus	2.50	Acer	2.68	Morus	2.50
Betula	2.52	Fraxinus	2.76	Betula	2.52
Juglans	2.56	Liriodendron	2.79	Juglans	2.56
Acer	2.77	Ailanthus	3.00	Acer	2.77
Fraxinus	3.32	Robinia	3.04	Fraxinus	3.32
Aesculus	3.48	Fagus	3.54	Aesculus	3.48
Populus	3.56	Aesculus	3.54	Populus	3.56
Fagus	3.59	Populus	3.85	Fagus	3.59
Salix	3.71	Salix	3.92	Salix	3.71

Notes on individual genera: conifers

ABIES – TRUE FIRS

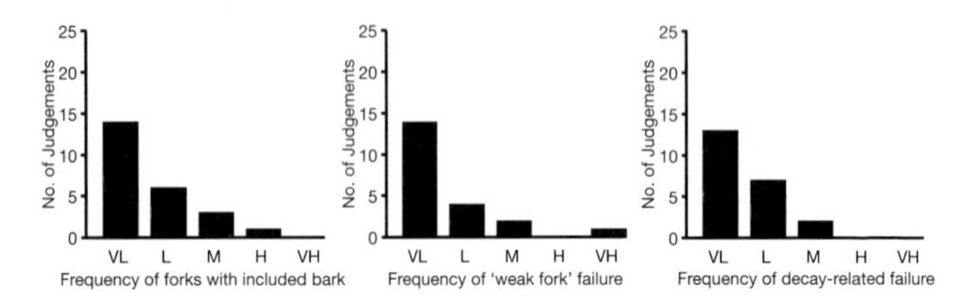

- **Fungi causing decay**. *Sparassis crispa* (B), *Phellinus* spp. (T)

- **Diseases leading to decay or other weakening**. The formation of malfunctioning xylem, induced by stem infestations of the balsam woolly aphid (*Adelges piceae*), often leads to the decline and early death of several *Abies* species in Great Britain (Strouts and Winter, 1994). The abnormal wood, known by the German term Rotholz (red wood), is also rather brittle.

- **Mechanical characteristics**. Grecian fir, *A. cephalonica*, forms heavy branches in maturity which may be quite liable to fail in storms. Grand fir, *A. grandis*, may reach a great height and is then rather vulnerable to top breakage in high winds and to lightning strike. Other species which tend to suffer wind damage or which otherwise tend to become hazardous when old include Noble fir, *A. procera*, and *A. veitchii*, Veitch's silver fir.

  Drought crack, a defect which seems to result from a check in rapid growth in various tree species, is quite common in *Abies*. Although the crack may have occlusion rolls developing at its sides, it often extends and may weaken the stem.

- **Site-related information**. The decline and premature death of *Abies* spp., mentioned above, occurs widely in Britain, but *A. alba* is said to survive relatively well in some parts of the west and north. This species is tolerant to exposure to wind and salt-laden air when well established.

ARAUCARIA – MONKEY PUZZLE, CHILE PINE

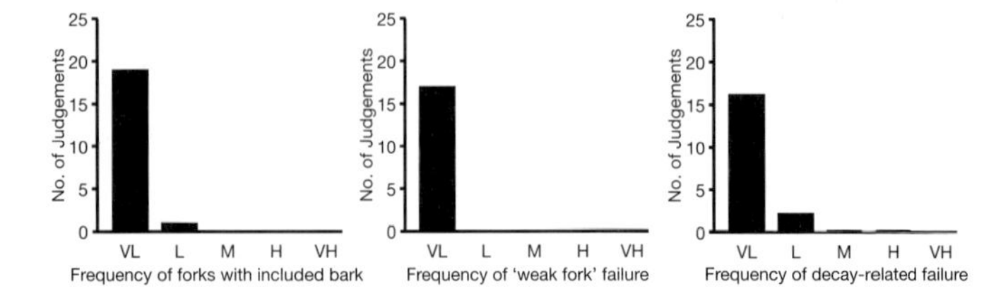

- **Fungi causing decay**. *Armillaria* spp. (B), *Ganoderma adspersum* and *applanatum* (B), *Meripilus giganteus* (B)

- **Site-related information.** *Araucaria araucana* is exceptionally resistant to exposure and is rarely blown down. It grows well on most soil types.

CEDRUS – CEDARS

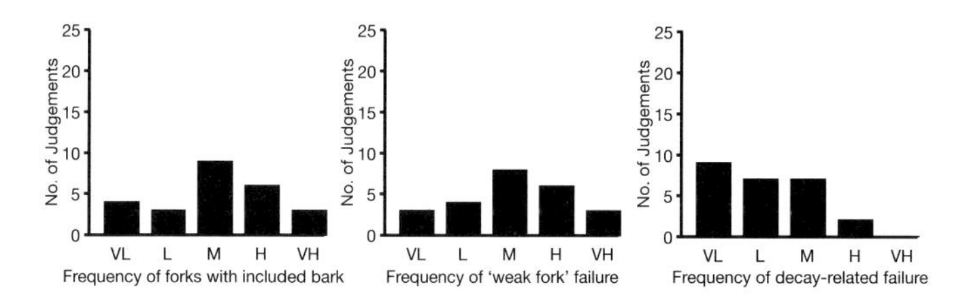

- **Fungi causing decay**. *Phaeolus schweinitzii* (B), *Sparassis crispa* (B), *Coniophora puteana* (T, but apparently only on dead wood)

- **Diseases leading to decay or other weakening**. Cankers caused by the fungus *Phacidium coniferarum* occasionally spread to large branches, which can then become brittle or decayed.

- **Mechanical characteristics**. *Cedrus* spp. tend to form heavy branches which may be liable to failure, especially the near-horizontal branches of Cedar of Lebanon, *C. libani*, which can become heavily laden with ice or snow. Branch failures in *C. libani* rarely occur at the points of attachment, but this problem is reported in the commonly grown variety of the Atlantic cedar, *C. atlantica* var. *glauca*. The Deodar cedar, *C. deodara*, may be rather unstable on sites with impeded rooting, but *C. atlantica* is relatively wind-firm.

CHAMAECYPARIS – 'FALSE' CYPRESSES

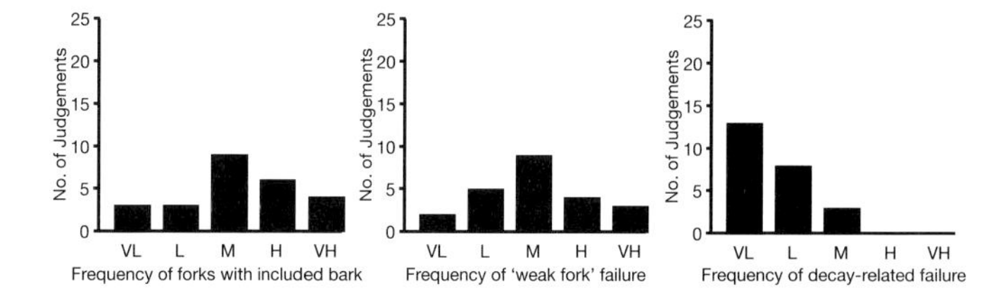

- **Fungi causing decay**. *Amylostereum laevigatum* (T), *Armillaria* spp. (B), *Heterobasidion annosum* (B)

- **Diseases leading to decay or other weakening**. Wounds, especially from topping, may allow infection by the canker rot fungus *A. laevigatum*. Phytophthora root disease is often the cause of death or serious dieback.

- **Mechanical characteristics**. There are many cultivars of Lawson cypress, *C. lawsoniana*, some columnar forms of which are prone to the splaying out of long thin branches. This species also tends to form weak forks if topped or broken when young. Windthrow tends to be a problem with old specimens of Nootka cypress, *C. nootkatensis*.

- **Site-related information**. All the species introduced to Britain thrive on a wide range of soil types and tolerate exposure well.

CRYPTOMERIA – C. JAPONICA, JAPANESE CEDAR

- **Fungi causing decay**. *Armillaria* spp. (B: also with root killing)

- **Site-related information**. *Cryptomeria* usually thrives well only in areas of high rainfall and cool summers.

CUPRESSOCYPARIS – (one named intergeneric hybrid; X *C. LEYLANDII* LEYLAND CYPRESS)

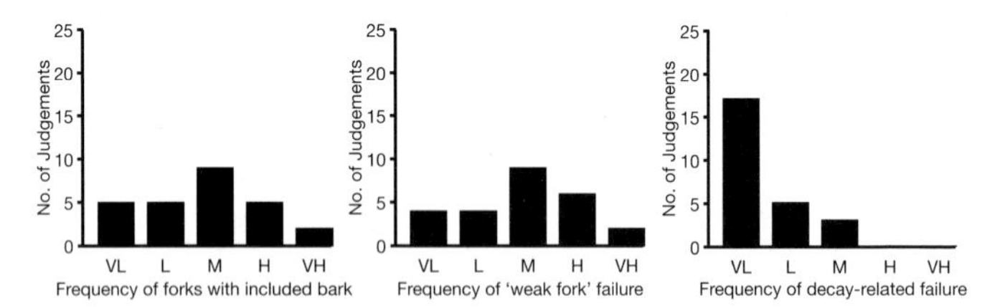

- **Fungi causing decay**. *Heterobasidion annosum* (B), *Armillaria* (B) spp., *Coniophora puteana* (T: but apparently only on dead wood)

- **Diseases leading to decay or other weakening**. This hybrid between *Cupressus macrocarpa* and *Chamaecyparis nootkatensis* can be affected by Coryneum canker (see under *Cupressus*).

CUPRESSUS – TRUE CYPRESSES

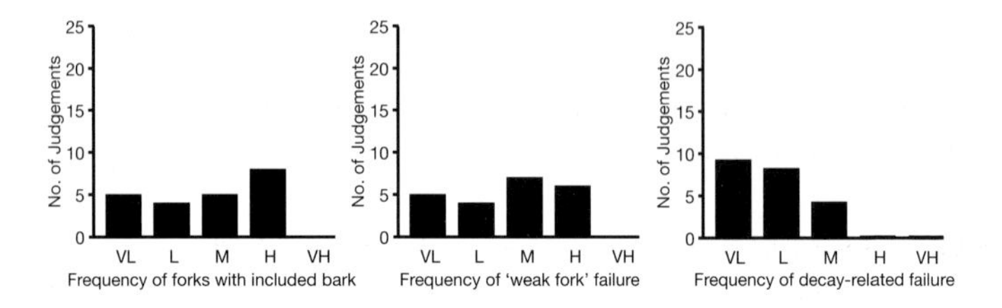

- **Fungi causing decay**. *Leptoporus ellipsosporus* (T: see Strouts and Winter, [173])

- **Diseases leading to decay or other weakening**. Various members of the Cupressaceae are susceptible to Coryneum canker, caused by *Seiridium cardinale*. This can lead to severe crown dieback in *C. sempervirens* and *C. macrocarpa*. Extension of the canker into the main stem can lead to failure due to eventual decay by other fungi. Another type of canker is occasionally caused by the fungus *Phomopsis juniperovora*.

- **Mechanical characteristics**. A high incidence of wind damage has been observed in the branches of *C. macrocarpa*, Monterey cypress, following exposure of the inner crown by pruning. Weak forks tend to form in specimens that lose their leaders when young.

GINKGO – MAIDENHAIR TREE (one species; *G. BILOBA*)

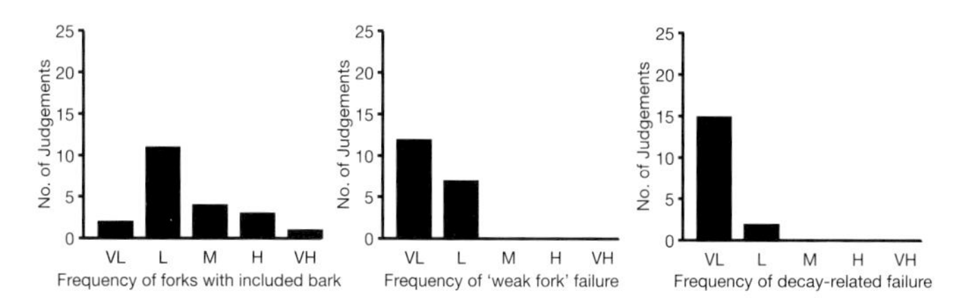

- **Fungi causing decay**. *Ganoderma adspersum* and *applanatum* (B), *Armillaria* spp. (B), *Meripilus giganteus* (B)

- **Diseases leading to decay or other weakening**. Although ginkgos may become colonised by the decay fungi listed above, they are generally disease-resistant.

LARIX – LARCHES

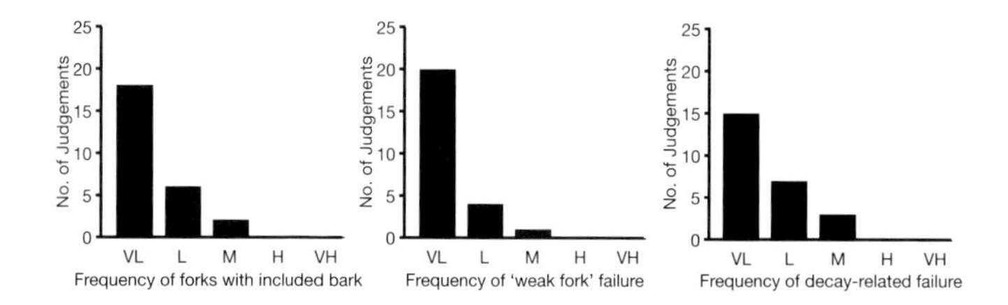

- **Fungi causing decay**. *Armillaria* spp. (B), *Heterobasidion annosum* (B), *Hypholoma fasciculare* (B), *Phaeolus schweinitzii* (B), *Sparassis crispa* (B)

- **Diseases leading to decay or other weakening**. Larch canker, caused by the fungus *Lachnellula willkommii*, can become extensive on the stems of

European larch, *L. decidua*, of certain provenances. Cankers can be caused also by *Phacidium coniferarum*.

- **Site-related information**. *Larix decidua* and, to a lesser extent, other species are rather intolerant of industrial pollution, poor drainage and heavy clay soils. Trees in generally poor health due to site conditions may become hazardous.

METASEQUOIA – DAWN REDWOOD (one species; *M. GLYPTOSTROBOIDES*)

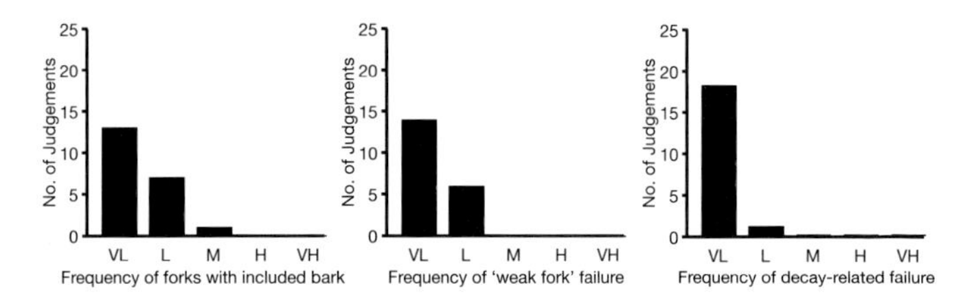

- **Fungi causing decay**. *Armillaria* spp. (B), *Heterobasidion annosum* (B)

PICEA – SPRUCES

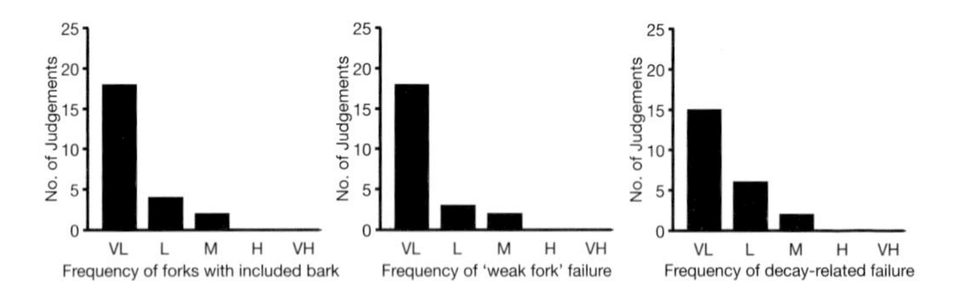

- **Fungi causing decay**. *Armillaria* spp. (B), (especially on Serbian spruce, *P. omorika*, as a primary pathogen), *Heterobasidion annosum* (B), *Hypholoma fasciculare* (B), *Sparassis crispa* (B), *Stereum sanguinolentum* (T)

- **Mechanical characteristics and site-related information**. Most species, especially Norway spruce, *P. abies*, root only into the uppermost, most highly aerated soil horizon and are therefore subject to windthrow on sites where this layer is particularly shallow. Lateral restriction of rooting and high wind exposure also increase the risk of failure. Most members of this genus are also liable to form unhealthy specimens when encountering unsuitable soils, climate and air purity.

  Drought crack has been observed in *P. abies*, as well as in other conifers, including *Abies* spp., for which some notes are included above.

PINUS – PINES

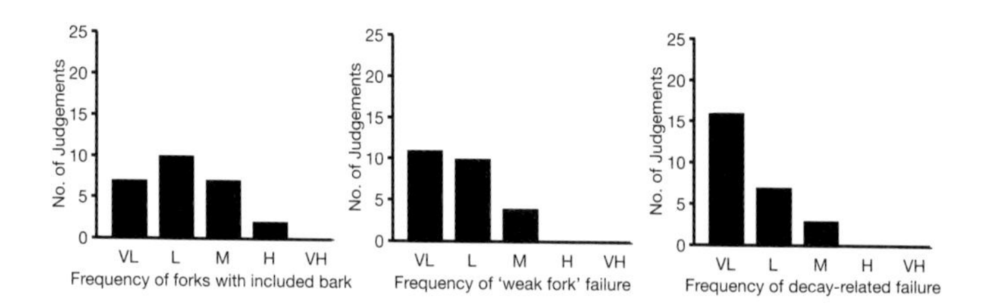

- **Fungi causing decay**. *Heterobasidion annosum* (B), *Phaeolus schweinitzii* (B), *Phellinus pini* (T), *Sparassis crispa* (B), *Stereum sanguinolentum* (T)

- **Diseases and pests leading to decay or other weakening**. In some areas of Great Britain, mainly in forest stands in East Anglia and Scotland, branch cankers caused by the rust fungus *Peridermium pini* occur and may spread to the main stem, leading to brittleness and to decay by other fungi. Weak forks can develop following the killing of young leading shoots by the tunnelling larvae of the Pine shoot moth, *Rhyacionia buoliana*. Also, older larvae sometimes feed externally on one side of the shoot, causing it to flop over and subsequently curve up so that the stem acquires a 'post horn' deformity. Below ground, mainly in forest plantations, the root-infecting fungus *Rhizina undulata* may kill young trees.

- **Shedding of heavy cones**. In common with some other conifers, pines have quite dense cones, which tend to be shed whole. The large cones of some species, such as *P. nigra*, can be hazardous close to buildings or in intensively used areas.

- **Mechanical characteristics and site-related information**. Species of *Pinus* differ so much in their suitability for various soil types and climates that no general comments are appropriate. In many species, the lower branches normally die and persist for some time before breaking. There are some reports of failure at weak forks in *Pinus nigra austriaca*, the Austrian pine, but it is not clear whether this is an inherent problem (see notes on Pine shoot moth, above). Most pines are reasonably wind-firm on a range of soil types, but the Western Yellow pine from North America, *P. ponderosa*, tends to be unstable on calcareous soils. Several other species, including Monterey pine, *P. radiata*, also dislike such soils, and may die after showing symptoms of lime-induced chlorosis.

PSEUDOTSUGA – P. MENZIESII, DOUGLAS FIR

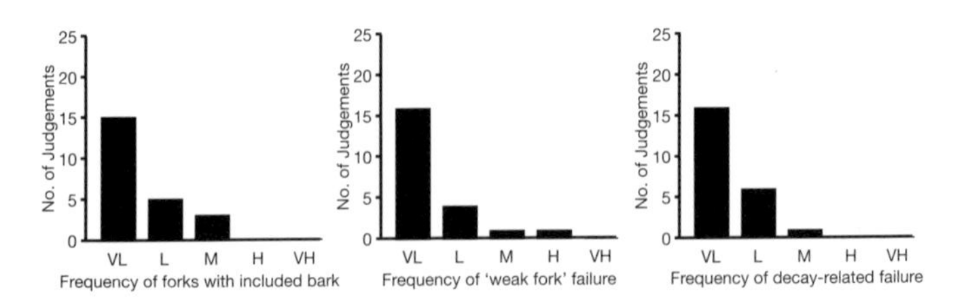

- **Fungi causing decay**. *Phaeolus schweinitzii* (B), *Sparassis crispa* (B)

- **Diseases leading to decay or other weakening**. Cankers caused by *Phacidium coniferarum* may lead to secondary decay.

- **Mechanical characteristics and site-related information**. Old specimens tend to shed heavy lower branches with foliage, and are therefore not well suited to sites heavily frequented by people. As such trees often reach over 30 m in height, their tops may shatter in high winds, except in very sheltered locations. For the same reason, the risk of lightning strikes may be rather high.

SEQUOIA – S. SEMPERVIRENS, COAST REDWOOD

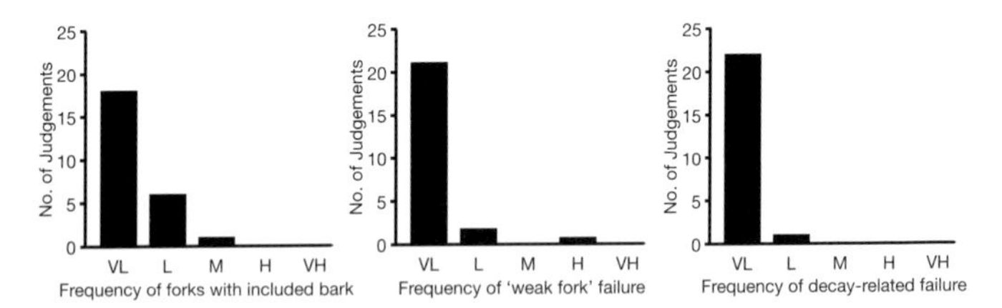

- **Fungi causing decay**. None regularly observed

- **Diseases leading to decay or other weakening**. *Sequoia* is generally free from serious diseases.

- **Lightning**. The great height that is often attained by *Sequioa* may make it a prominent target for lightning strikes.

SEQUOIADENDRON – S. GIGANTEUM, WELLINGTONIA, GIANT SEQUOIA

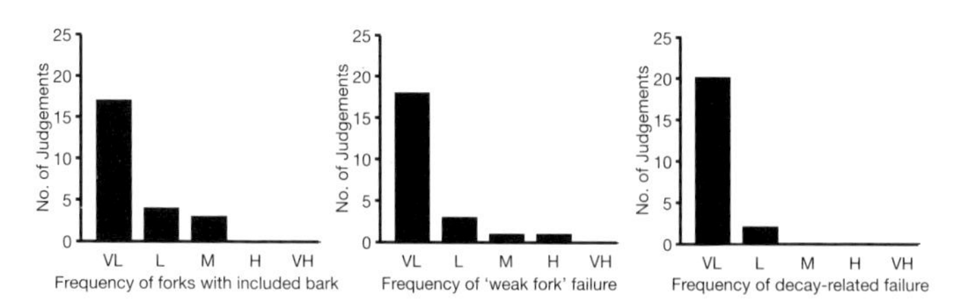

- **Fungi causing decay**. *Armillaria* spp. (B)

- **Mechanical characteristics**. This species, when well established, fails less often through wind throw or snapping of the main stem than most other tree species. Individual branches – usually of small diameter – are, however, quite often torn off by gusts of wind.

- **Lightning**. The great height that is often attained by *Sequoiadendron* may make it a prominent target for lightning strikes, as with *Sequoia*, which are thought to be the cause of the frequent death of the topmost parts of tall specimens.

TAXODIUM – DECIDUOUS CYPRESSES

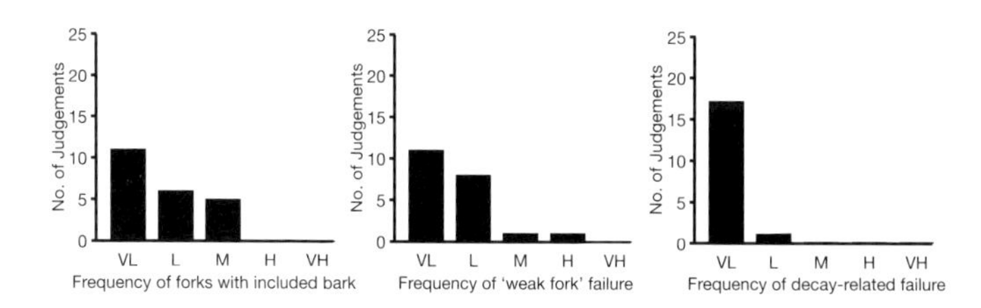

- **Fungi causing decay**. *Coniophora puteana* (T, but apparently only on dead wood)

- **Diseases leading to decay or other weakening**. *Taxodium distichum* (Swamp cypress) is a remarkably disease-free species.

TAXUS – YEWS

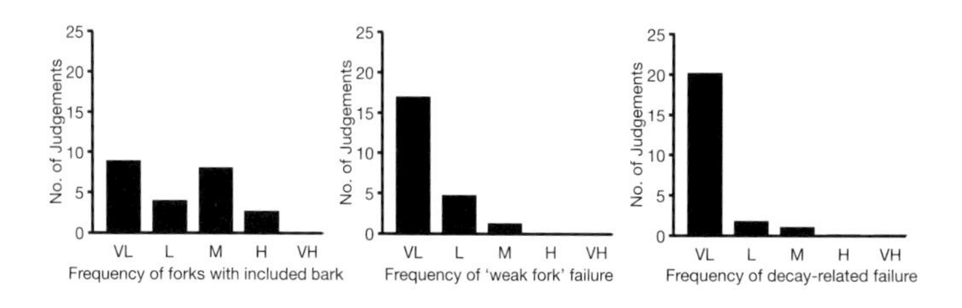

- **Fungi causing decay**. *Laetiporus sulphureus* (T), *Ganoderma valesciacum* (B), *Peniophora quercina* (B), *Phaeolus schweinitzii* (B)

- **Resistance to decay**. Most of the cross-section of a *Taxus* stem consists of a very durable heartwood, which can be decayed only by a few fungal species, and then only slowly. Even when, in ancient specimens, the main stem has become hollow, additional support is sometimes provided by roots of adventitious origin which grow into and partially fill the cavity.

- **Poisonous properties**. As most parts of the tree are poisonous to mammals, specimens with low-growing foliage are not usually allowed to remain in areas where livestock is kept. The removal of low branches usually prevents poisoning, unless animals gain access to foliage that has fallen due to mechanical failure.

THUJA – THUYAS

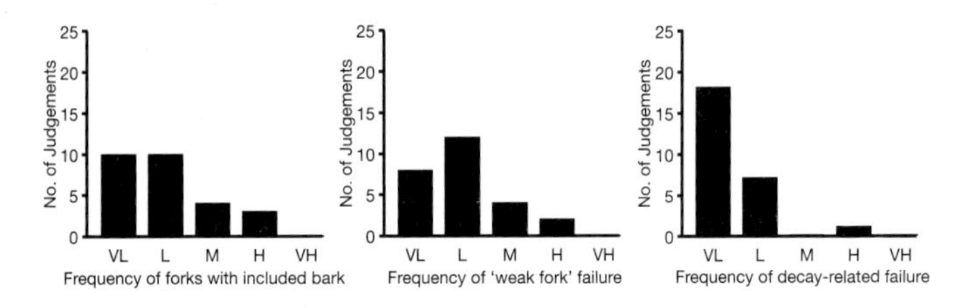

- **Fungi causing decay**. *Armillaria* spp. (B), *Heterobasidion annosum* (B), *Hypholoma fasciculare* (B)

- **Resistance to decay**. The heartwood of Western red cedar, *Thuja plicata*, is exceptionally durable.

- **Diseases leading to decay or other weakening**. As with *Cupressus* spp., *Thuja* spp. can be affected by Coryneum canker. Also, wounds may allow infection by the canker rot fungus *Amylostereum laevigatum*.

Notes on individual genera: broadleaved trees

ACER – MAPLES

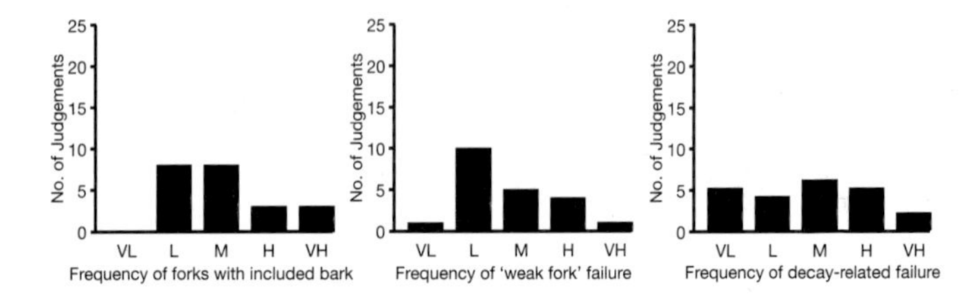

- **Fungi causing decay**. *Bjerkandera adusta* (T), *Armillaria* spp. (B, except perhaps on *Acer negundo*), *Ganoderma applanatum* (B), *G. adspersum* (B), *Inonotus hispidus* (T), *Polyporus squamosus* (T, especially in large pruning wounds or areas of crown-dieback in *A. pseudoplatanus*), *Rigidoporus ulmarius* (B), *Ustulina deusta* (B)

- **Diseases leading to decay or other weakening**. Some species of *Acer* are susceptible to fungal pathogens which rapidly invade the xylem. These include *Chondrostereum purpureum* (the silver-leaf fungus), species of *Verticillium* (a vascular wilt fungus, which is especially common on *A. platanoides*) and *Cryptostroma corticale* (the cause of sooty bark disease). Cankers, mainly caused by *Nectria* spp. are also common on species of *Acer*, and can kill branches or weaken main stems.

- **Mechanical characteristics**. *Acer saccharinum* has a reputation for failure at forks and acute branch junctions, particularly in the case of the fastigiate cultivar 'Pyramidale'. However, no differences were found between *A. saccharinum* and *A. platanoides* when the branches of several specimens of each in Ohio, USA were destructively tested by static loading.

AESCULUS – HORSE CHESTNUTS

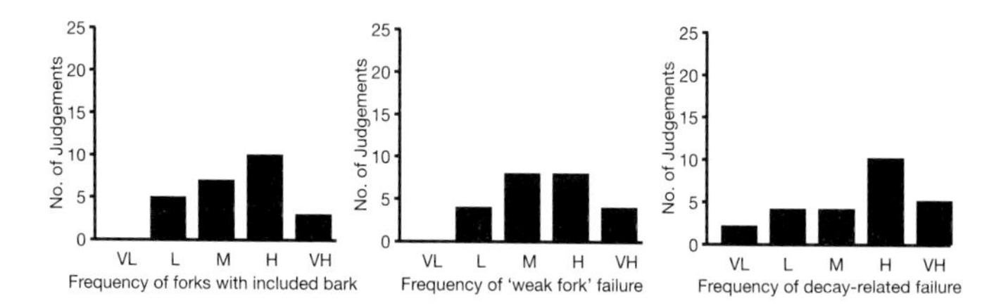

- **Fungi causing decay**. *Armillaria* spp. (B), *Ganoderma adspersum* and *applanatum* (B), *Pleurotus ostreatus* (T), *Ustulina deusta* (B)

- **Resistance to decay**. *Aesculus hippocastanum* has a soft heartwood with rather poor resistance to fungal invasion, and it is therefore particularly important to avoid inflicting very large wounds (greater than one-third of the parent stem diameter) or numerous wounds on a single stem.

- **Diseases leading to decay or other weakening**. Roots and stem bases may be attacked by species of *Phytophthora*, leading to secondary invasion by decay fungi. In *A. x carnea*, an unidentified agent induces galls through the proliferation of buds and stunted shoots. These may eventually become a seat for decay fungi.

- **Mechanical characteristics**. Summer branch drop is quite common in *A. hippocastanum*. Failure at forks is also frequent in this species, and even more so in the cultivar *A. x carnea* 'Briottii'. *Aesculus indica*, the Himalayan horse chestnut, is reported to fail less often in this manner.

- **Site-related information**. Along roads and in heavily built-up areas, the nuts of *Aesculus* spp. are sometimes regarded as a minor hazard, if only because children may endanger themselves while gathering them for 'conkers'.

AILANTHUS – A. ALTISSIMA, TREE OF HEAVEN

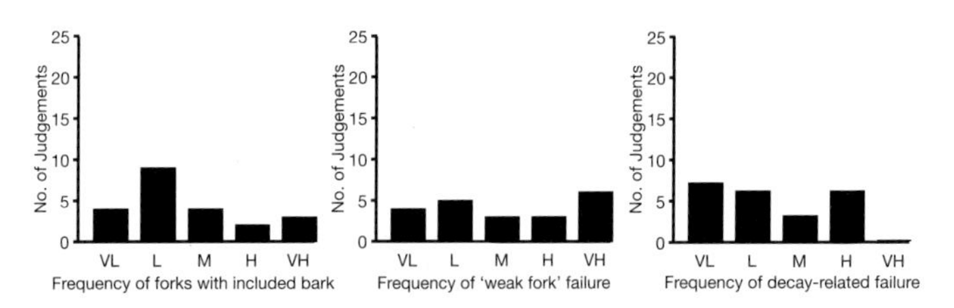

- **Resistance to decay**. The wood of this species appears to have poor decay resistance, on a par with *Aesculus*.

- **Fungi causing decay**. *Bjerkandera adusta* (T), *Laetiporus sulphureus* (T), *Pholiota squarrosa* (B)

- **Mechanical characteristics**. Some practitioners consider that this species has very brittle wood.

ALNUS – ALDERS

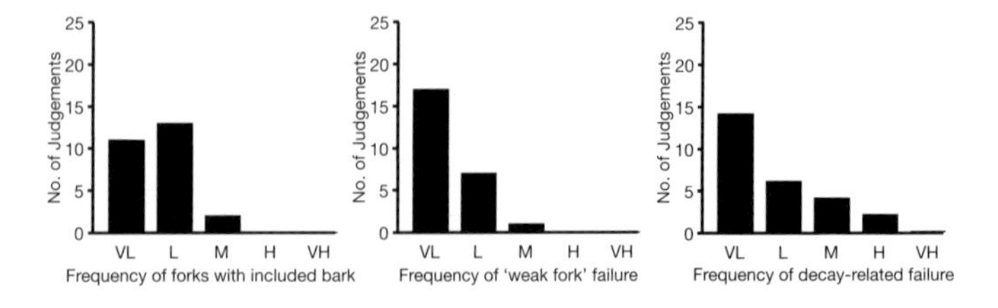

- **Diseases leading to decay or other weakening**. Following the death of trees of *Alnus glutinosa*, from whatever reason, the branches and smaller stems become brittle and liable to breakage very rapidly. Death in this species is sometimes caused by a currently unexplained disease, which involves a progressive dieback from the twigs downwards. In Great Britain, this is prevalent mainly in the north. Since the early 1990s, a previously undescribed disease caused by a species of *Phytophthora*, has also been observed on various species of *Alnus*, especially native stands of *A. glutinosa* along watercourses, which have in some cases been severely affected. The Grey alder, *Alnus incana*, frequently dies for unknown reasons before the age of forty.

BETULA – BIRCHES

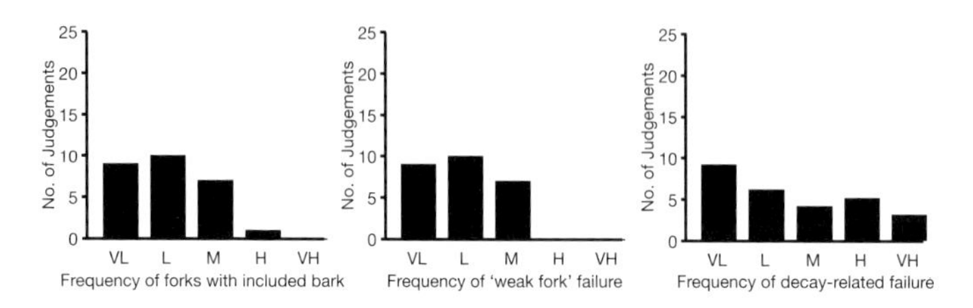

- **Fungi causing decay**. *Armillaria* spp. (B), *Bjerkandera adusta* (T), *Daldinia concentrica* (T), *Fomes fomentarius* (T: within Britain, mainly north of 54°), *Heterobasidion annosum* (B), *Hypoxylon multiforme* (T), *Inonotus obliquus* (T: within Britain, mainly in the far north), *Lenzites betulina* (T), *Phellinus igniarius* (T), *Piptoporus betulinus* (T: very common in southern Britain), *Schizophyllum commune* (T)

- **Resistance to decay**. Members of this genus generally have an exceptionally poor ability to form barriers against the development of dysfunction and decay in the xylem. There is evidence that they are highly susceptible to attack by *Chondrostereum purpureum* (the silver-leaf fungus), as well as by *Armillaria* spp. (honey fungus). Stressed or diseased trees become rapidly decayed and liable to brittle fracture. In any case, a lifespan of only 40 to 80 years is common for the Silver birch, *Betula pendula*, although slowly growing specimens in cold climates may live much longer.

  Any amount of wounding, whether from pruning or from accidental damage (e.g. abrasion from lawnmowers) should be regarded as undesirable, except for the formative pruning of twigs. Vigorously growing trees may, however, tolerate crown reduction, especially if the wounds are all small (e.g. less than 40 mm in diameter).

CARPINUS – HORNBEAMS

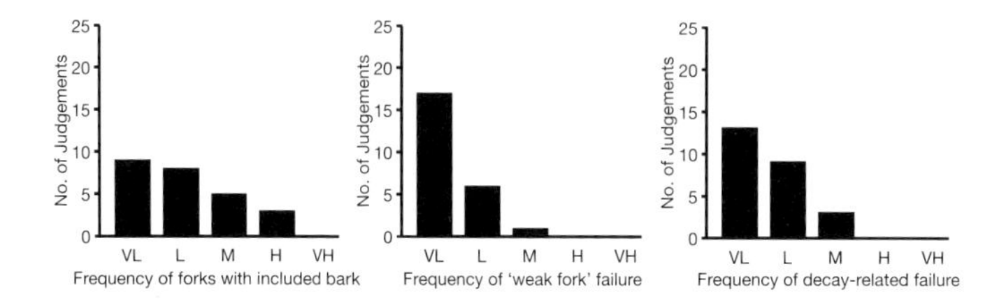

- **Fungi causing decay**. *Bjerkandera adusta* (T), *Fistulina hepatica* (T,B), *Hypoxylon fragiforme* (T), *Ustulina deusta* (B)

- **Resistance to decay**. The wood of *C. betulus* is dense and tends to decay only slowly in the standing tree. This species shows good survival as an ancient pollard, especially in Essex, although *B. adusta* has been found to invade large wounds created by the re-cutting of such trees. There are few other reports of serious decay.

- **Mechanical characteristics**. The formation of weak forks is not generally a problem in *C. betulus*, but has been reported in the cultivar 'Fastigiata' (='Pyramidalis').

- **Site-related information**. *Carpinus betulus* is highly recommended for planting on intractable clay soils, where the depth of rooting might be restricted for various other species.

CARYA – HICKORIES: see histograms only

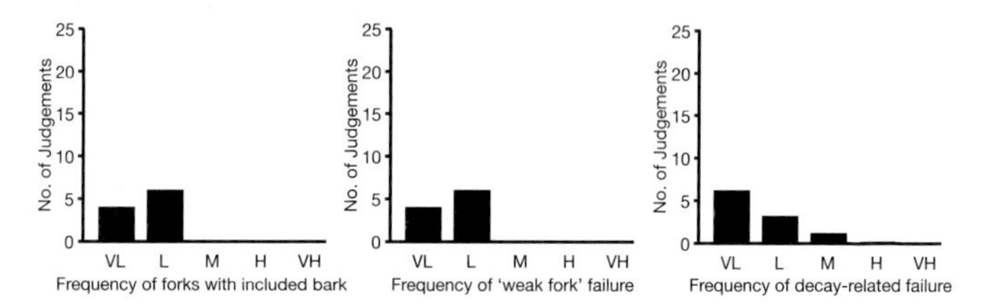

CASTANEA – SWEET CHESTNUT

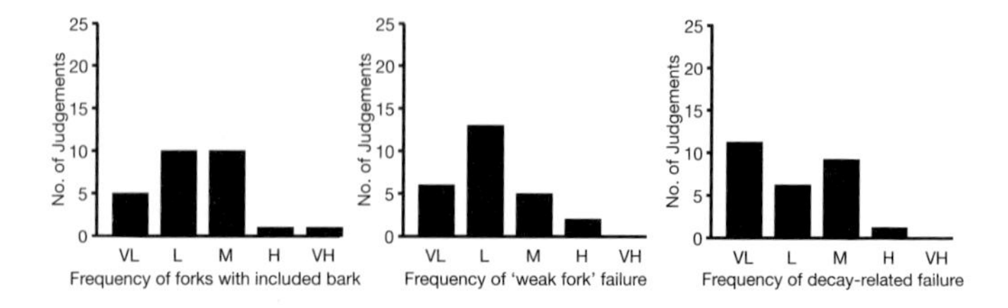

- **Fungi causing decay**. *Daedalea quercina* (T), *Laetiporus sulphureus* (T), *Hypholoma fasciculare* (B), *Fistulina hepatica* (T,B)

- **Resistance to decay**. The heartwood is very durable, and is decayed only slowly by specialised heartwood decay fungi.

- **Diseases leading to decay or other weakening**. Phytophthora root killing (ink disease), may lead to secondary decay.

- **Mechanical characteristics**. Helical grain is very common in the main stem of *C. sativa* and is occasionally associated with torsional cracking.

- **Site-related information**. Windthrow of mature specimens is liable to occur if the rooting depth is restricted by poor drainage. Also, the large fruits of this tree could cause a minor hazard in roadside locations.

CATALPA – INDIAN BEAN TREE, CATAWBAS

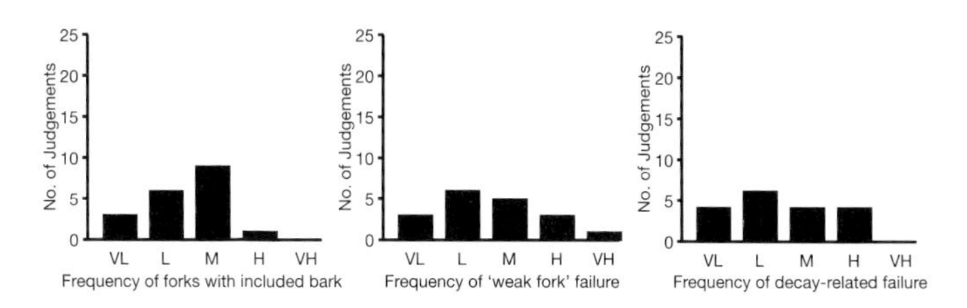

- **Fungi causing decay**. *Pholiota squarrosa* (B)

- **Resistance to decay**. *Catalpa bignonioides* appears to become susceptible to decay after the age of about 100 years.

- **Site-related information**. *Catalpa* species do not thrive in the cooler parts of the UK. Twig abscission can be heavy and could therefore be a nuisance for passers-by in built-up areas.

CERCIS – JUDAS TREES

- **Diseases leading to decay or other weakening**. Cankers, caused by the coral-spot fungus *Nectria cinnabarina*, may occur on stems and branches. A vascular wilt caused by *Verticillium* sp. may also kill parts of the tree. In either case attached dead wood may be subject to embrittlement and/or secondary decay.

CORYLUS – HAZELS

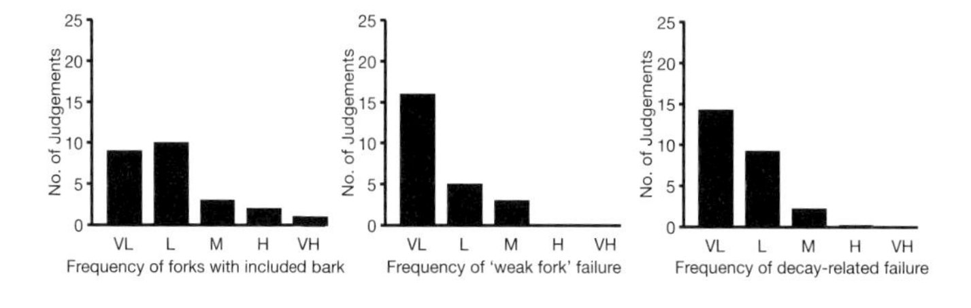

- **Fungi causing decay**. *Hypoxylon fuscum* (T), *Stereum rugosum* (T)

CRATAEGUS – THORNS

- **Diseases leading to decay or other weakening**. Phytophthora root killing may lead to secondary decay. Dieback above-ground due to the fireblight bacterium, *Erwinia amylovora*, may also lead to decay.

- **Mechanical characteristics**. Most species of *Crataegus* do not grow large enough to pose a high risk of major injury or damage in the event of failure. However, some forms of the Midland thorn, *C. oxyacantha*, grow to 10 m, while the Common thorn, *C. monogyna*, occasionally reaches 15 m, though very rarely. (*See also* under *SORBUS*, regarding the use of *Crataegus* as a rootstock)

EUCALYPTUS – GUM TREES

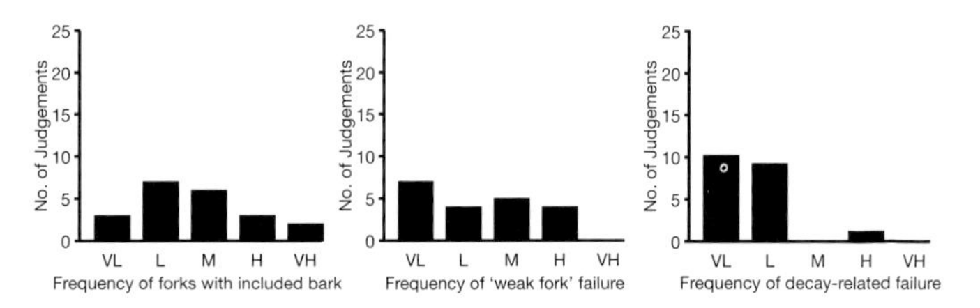

- **Fungi causing decay**. *Coriolus versicolor* (T), *Laetiporus sulphureus* (T)

- **Resistance to decay**. It is hard to generalise about this very large genus, but the wood of many species is relatively durable. Decay is quite common in native eucalypt stands in Australia, but very few primary decay problems have been reported in UK amenity plantings. The above fungi have been recorded in diseased coppice stools.

- **Diseases leading to decay or other weakening**. Silver-leaf disease, caused by *Chondrostereum purpureum*, can kill stems and branches which may fail due to decay or embrittlement. Winter cold can also kill above-ground parts of the tree.

- **Mechanical characteristics**. Inadequate root development, leading to windthrow, has been observed following the planting of pot-bound specimens of some *Eucalyptus* spp. This is, in any case, quite common amongst young specimens of *Eucalyptus gunnii*, together with top breakage.

- **Site-related information**. Under UK conditions, all eucalypts require full sun for healthy growth and many species also require a frost-free climate.

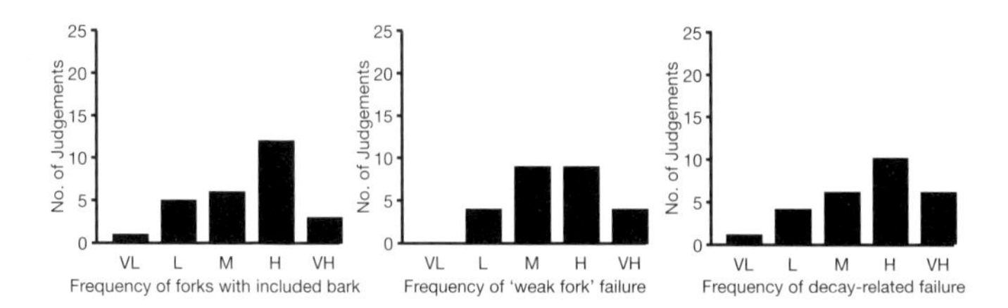

- **Fungi causing decay**. *Armillaria* spp. (B), *Biscogniauxia nummularia* (T), *Bjerkandera adusta* (T), *Chondrostereum purpureum* (T), *Coriolus versicolor* (T), *Daedaleopsis confragosa* (T), *Diatrype* spp., *Datronia mollis* (T), *Eutypa spinosa* (T), *Fistulina hepatica* (T,B), *Fomes fomentarius* (T), *Ganoderma adspersum*, (T,B), *G. applanatum* (T,B), *G. pfeifferi* (T,B), *Heterobasidion annosum* (B), *Hypoxylon fragiforme* (T), *Lenzites betulina* (T), *Meripilus giganteus* (B), *Oudemansiella mucida* (T), *Perenniporia fraxinea* (B), *Pleurotus ostreatus* (T), *Polyporus squamosus* (T), *Pseudotrametes gibbosa* (T), *Schizophyllum commune* (T), *Stereum* spp. (T), *Ustulina deusta* (B)

- **Resistance to decay**. A true heartwood is not formed in *Fagus* spp., so that the innermost wood of old specimens consists of dysfunctional sapwood which is readily colonised by decay fungi as soon as it is exposed to the atmosphere by injury or disease. The outer living sapwood is relatively resistant to many decay fungi, but may be rapidly invaded by wound rot fungi such as *Bjerkandera* and members of the *Stereum* group when injured. Dysfunction and decay induced by topping or 'tipping' wounds can become very extensive in mature or old trees, which often lack existing branches or new growth proximal to such wounds. Such damage appears to occur less in *F. sylvatica* var. *atropurpurea* than in the ordinary form of the species.

- **Diseases leading to decay or other weakening**. Below ground, Phytophthora root killing may lead to secondary decay. Above-ground, beech bark disease caused by the fungus *Nectria coccinea* on stems infested by the scale insect *Cryptococcus fagisuga*, often leads to snapping of the stem due to decay by wound rot fungi. The related fungi *N. cinnabarina* and *N. ditissima* can also kill bark, occasionally encouraging decay. Canker rot, caused by *Stereum rugosum*, also affects *Fagus* occasionally.

- **Mechanical characteristics**. Individual trees show genetic variation in the propensity to form forks with included bark. Failure at such forks and at acute branch attachments becomes common in old specimens. Widely spreading branches in such trees are rather prone to the phenomenon of summer branch drop.

- **Site-related information**. The root system of *F. sylvatica* does not develop deeply except in well aerated soil, and therefore tends to become unstable on wet, poorly drained or compacted sites. Instability may also occur on shallow soil over bedrock.

FRAXINUS – ASH TREES

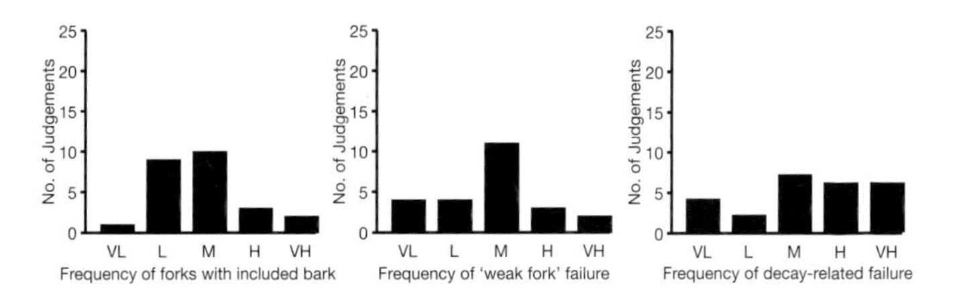

- **Fungi causing decay**. *Daldinia concentrica* (T), *Ganoderma adspersum* (B), *G. applanatum* (B), *Fistulina hepatica* (T,B), *Hypoxylon rubiginosum* (T), *Inonotus hispidus* (T), *Perenniporia fraxinea* (B), *Pholiota squarrosa* (B), *Polyporus squamosus* (T)

- **Resistance to decay**. It is thought that the relatively low moisture content of *Fraxinus* wood makes it rather susceptible to decay. Also the heartwood does not appear to be rich in pre-formed defensive substances.

- **Diseases leading to decay or other weakening**. Bacterial tumour or 'knot' of ash, caused by *Pseudomonas syringae* ssp. *savastonoi* pv. *fraxini*, and a fungal canker, caused by *Nectria* spp., can lead to secondary decay or to fracture brought about by the stress-notch effect or by associated cracking. Decay or embrittlement can also occur in trees showing the syndrome known as ash dieback, in which root damage due to agricultural and other activities seems often to play a part.

- **Mechanical characteristics**. The wood of the Common ash, *F. excelsior*, is strong and mechanically very resilient. However, its xylem rays are rapidly decayed by the commonly occurring fungus, *Inonotus hispidus*, which causes serious weakening at quite an early stage of colonisation. The cultivar *F. oxycarpa* 'Raywood' has a reputation for failure at forks. Such failure has also been reported in semi-mature ash trees that have developed a weak crown structure as a result of being 'drawn up' in partial shade. Also, if a leader dies or snaps so that an axillary shoot or pair of opposite shoots takes over, the rather large shoot angle often produces an abrupt bend at which mechanical stress may become concentrated.

- **Site-related information**. Serious root damage is very likely to occur as a result of quite superficial soil disturbance, due to the tendency of *Fraxinus* spp. to form quite large-diameter roots just below the soil surface. *Fraxinus excelsior* thrives on nitrogen-rich, moist well-drained soils. In very adverse conditions it tends to become affected by various diseases and often undergoes decay by the endophytic fungus *Daldinia concentrica*.

GLEDITSIA – G. TRIACANTHOS, HONEY LOCUST

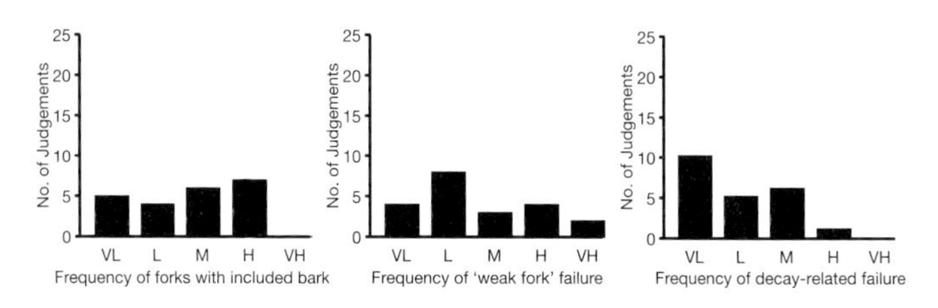

- **Fungi causing decay**. *Meripilus giganteus* (B)

- **Mechanical characteristics**. This species is reputed to be brittle when young and also after maturity. Failure at forks is not generally common, but has especially been noted in the popular cultivar 'Sunburst'.

- **Site-related information**. This species does not thrive in the cooler parts of the UK.

ILEX – HOLLIES

- **Fungi causing decay**. *Ganoderma adspersum/applanatum* (T,B), *Armillaria* spp. (B)

- **Resistance to decay**. The Common holly has hard, dense wood which appears to be relatively decay-resistant. Reports of major decay are rare.

- **Diseases leading to decay or other weakening**. Perennating cankers, caused by the fungus *Nectria galligena*, can affect the branches of *Ilex*, and it is possible that they could occasionally become infection courts for decay fungi. The rarity of root decay in Common holly may be partly due to the very low incidence of root killing by *Armillaria* spp.

- **Mechanical characteristics**. The dense wood of *Ilex* spp. appears to have considerable strength.

- **Site-related information**. The Common holly, *I. aquifolium*, is very tolerant of adverse conditions and of shade.

JUGLANS – WALNUTS

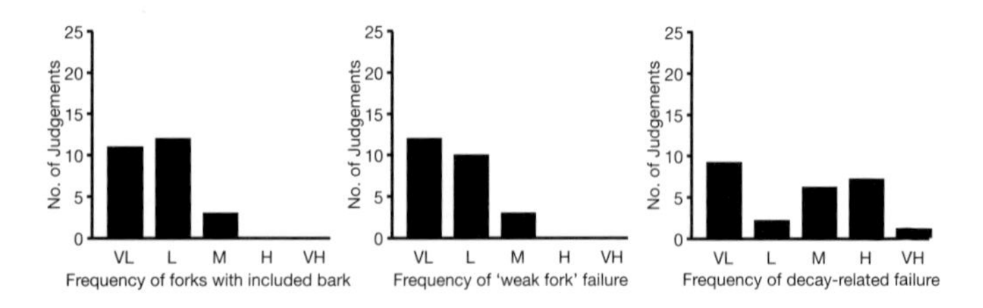

- **Fungi causing decay**. *Fistulina hepatica* (T,B), *Inonotus hispidus* (T)

- **Diseases leading to decay or other weakening**. Root killing by *Armillaria* spp. is common in English (Persian) walnut, *J. regia*, and may lead to decay. Black walnut, *J. nigra*, appears to be unaffected by this disease.

- **Diseases leading to decay or other weakening**. Cankers, caused by the coral-spot fungus, *Nectria cinnabarina*, may occur on stems and branches. General decline and dieback may also result from a viral condition, known as black line disease, in grafted specimens. In either case, attached dead wood may be subject to embrittlement and/or secondary decay.

- **Mechanical characteristics**. The wood of *J. regia* is known for its strength when used for timber. The roots of this species are able to penetrate deeply, providing very good resistance to windthrow.

- **Site-related information**. The large fruits of *J. nigra* could cause a minor hazard in roadside locations. This species is also thought to produce substances which are toxic to other plants.

LABURNUM – LABURNUM

- **Fungi causing decay**. *Perenniporia fraxinea* (B)

LIGUSTRUM – PRIVETS

- **Fungi causing decay**. *Armillaria* spp. (B), *Heterobasidion annosum* (B)

- **Diseases leading to decay or other weakening**. The shrubby species, *Ligustrum vulgare* and *L. ovalifolium* are very susceptible to root killing by *Armillaria* spp., but it is not known whether the same is true for the only tree-sized species grown in the UK, the Chinese privet, *L. lucidum*.

LIQUIDAMBAR – SWEET GUMS

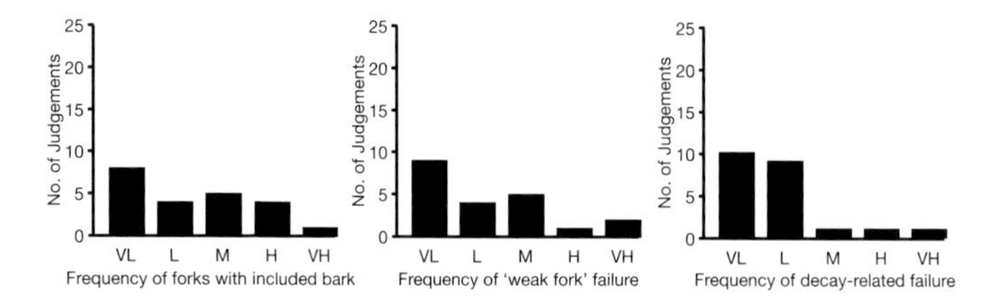

- **Fungi causing decay**. *Ustulina deusta* (B)

- **Site-related information**. *Liquidambar styraciflua* does not usually thrive in the cooler parts of the UK. Both it and the Chinese sweet gum, *L. formosana* require a fertile well-drained soil for healthy growth.

LIRIODENDRON – TULIP TREES

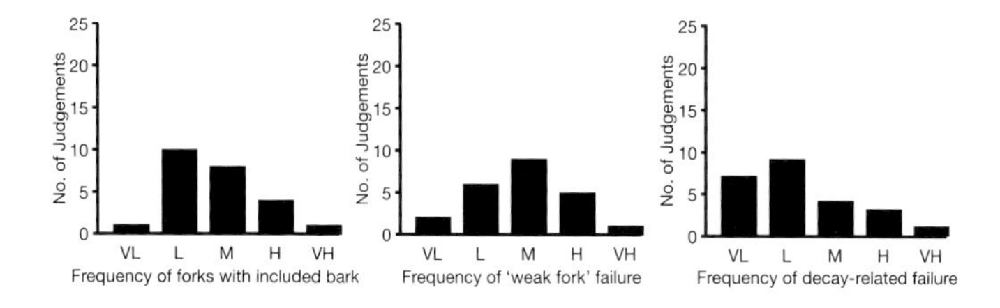

- **Diseases leading to decay or other weakening**. Root killing by *Armillaria* spp.

- **Mechanical characteristics**. Top breakage of immature specimens of *L. tulipifera* is quite common in high winds.

- **Site-related information**. Within its natural range in North America, *L. tulipifera* is noted for its intolerance to flooding and to changes in soil level.

MAGNOLIA – MAGNOLIAS

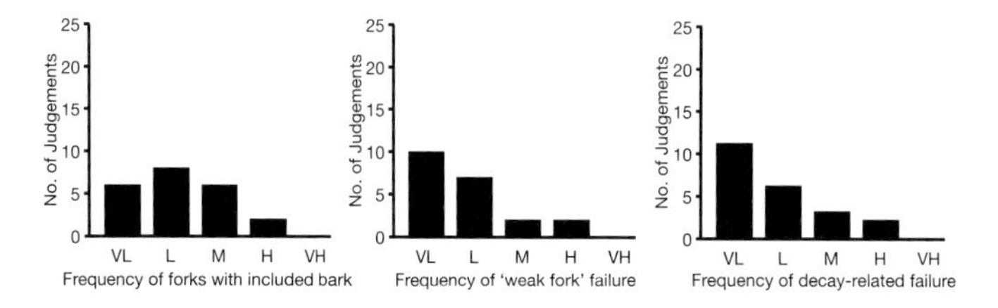

- **Diseases leading to decay or other weakening**. Cankers, caused by the coral-spot fungus *Nectria cinnabarina*, may occur on stems and branches. A vascular wilt caused by *Verticillium* sp. may also kill parts of the tree. In either case, attached dead wood may be subject to embrittlement and/or secondary decay.

MALUS – APPLES

- **Fungi causing decay**. *Armillaria* spp. (B) *Chondrostereum purpureum* (T), *Coriolus versicolor* (T), *Ganoderma* spp. (B), *Inonotus hispidus* (T)

- **Resistance to decay**. Structural pruning of fruit trees in gardens and orchards creates much dysfunctional wood, which frequently becomes decayed.

- **Diseases leading to decay or other weakening**. Parts of the tree may be killed by the silver-leaf fungus, *C. purpureum*, so that they become brittle or decayed. Phytophthora collar-rot occurs in dessert and culinary apples, and could lead to secondary decay at the stem base.

- **Mechanical characteristics**. In edible cultivars heavy loading of branches with fruit may lead to failure, especially if decay is present.

MORUS – MULBERRIES

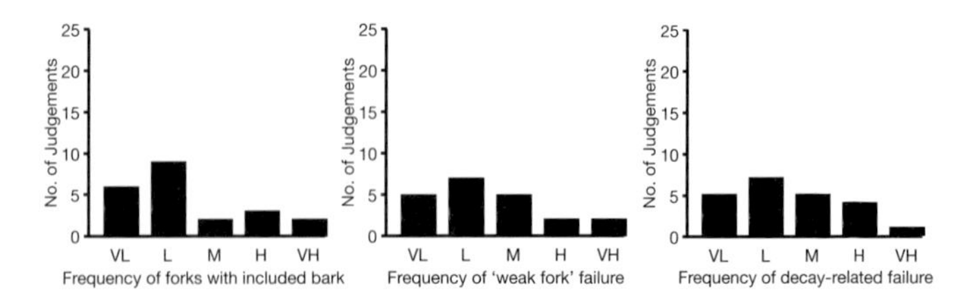

- **Diseases leading to decay or other weakening**. Cankers, caused by the fungus *Gibberella*, may occur on stems and branches. A general dieback caused by a bacterial blight has been known to kill parts of the tree. In either case, attached dead wood may be subject to embrittlement and/or secondary decay.

- **Mechanical characteristics**. Low, horizontal branches may fail, especially when laden with fruit. Also, it is quite common for the entire tree to develop a lean or to undergo windthrow. Some practitioners consider that *M. alba* is more likely than *M. nigra* to undergo failure at forks.

NOTHOFAGUS – SOUTHERN BEECHES

- **Fungi causing decay**. *Heterobasidion annosum* (B)

- **Diseases leading to decay or other weakening**. Phytophthora root killing may lead to secondary decay.

- **Site-related information**. Although most *Nothofagus* species can grow very fast in the climate of the UK, they tend to die back if subjected to spring frosts or severe wind exposure or if grown on poor soils.

PAULOWNIA – P. TOMENTOSA, FOXGLOVE TREE

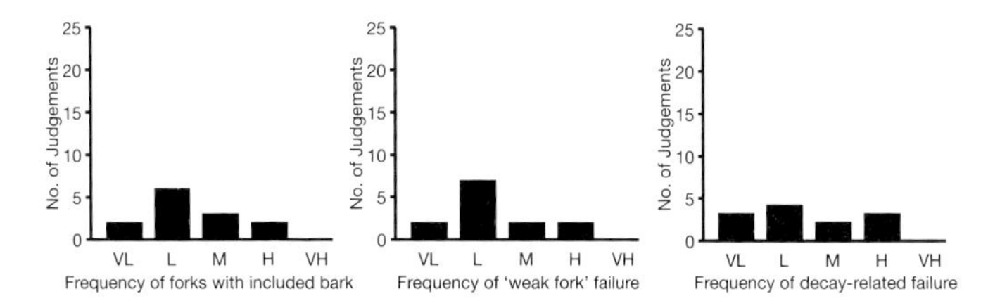

- **Resistance to decay**. *Paulownia* begins to die back and break up at a relatively young age, probably because it has rather poor defences against fungi and insects that invade the xylem.

- **Mechanical characteristics**. The branches of *Paulownia* tend to be brittle, and it is therefore best planted away from high-risk locations.

PLATANUS – PLANES

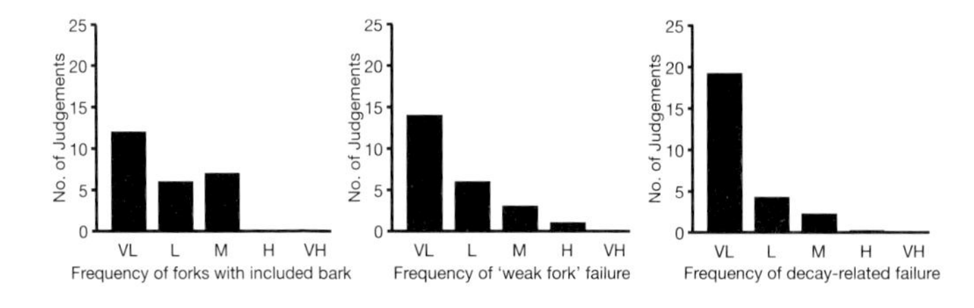

- **Fungi causing decay**. *Armillaria* spp. (B), *Ganoderma* spp. (T,B), *Inonotus hispidus* (T), *Meripilus giganteus* (B), *Perenniporia fraxinea* (B)

- **Resistance to decay**. The wood of London plane, *P. x hispanica*, seems to resist decay well, even when subjected to numerous pruning cuts. The fungus *Inonotus hispidus* is able to breach the tree's defensive reaction zones, but the strong and decay-resistant xylem rays continue to provide significant strength until a very advanced stage of decay.

- **Diseases leading to decay or other weakening**. Root killing by *Armillaria* spp. has occasionally been reported in *P. x hispanica*. Above ground, dieback can result from severe and repeated attacks on the leaves and shoots by the anthracnose fungus *Apiognomonia veneta*.

- **Mechanical characteristics**. *Platanus x hispanica* has strongly developed xylem rays, which contribute towards its considerable resistance to fracture. However, failure has occurred in specimens which were affected by end-loading due to crown lifting, and which also had large unoccluded wounds which acted as stress notches. Another exception to the excellent record of this valuable tree is the occurrence of fractures at weak forks in a particular line of nursery stock that has unfortunately been much planted in England over the last few decades.

- **Site-related information**. *Platanus x hispanica* is much planted in cities, though rarely in the cooler parts of the UK, owing to its good tolerance of atmospheric pollution. Although it is too large for many urban locations and is therefore heavily pruned, it is also tolerant of such treatment. It is, however, fairly susceptible to de-icing salt damage.

POPULUS – POPLARS AND ASPENS

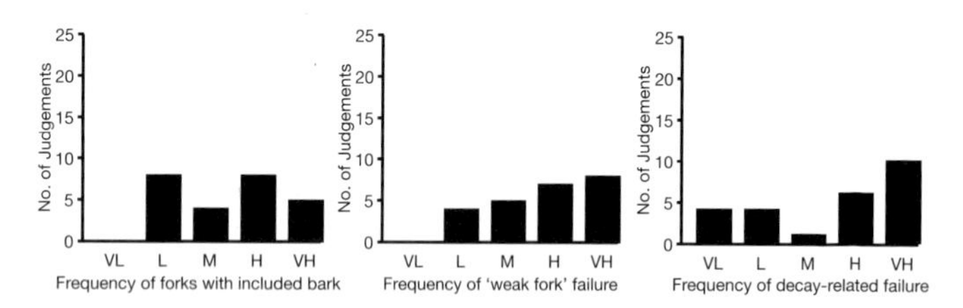

- **Fungi causing decay**. *Chondrostereum purpureum* (T), *Fomes fomentarius* (T), *Oxyporus populinus* (T), *Perenniporia fraxinea* (B), *Phellinus igniarius* (T), *Pleurotus ostreatus* (T), *Rigidoporus ulmarius* (B)

- **Resistance to decay**. The heartwood of *Populus* spp. is not very durable and is readily colonised by decay fungi when exposed by injury or dieback. In a high proportion of stems, however, it may be protected from decay to some extent by the presence of wetwood. The active responses of the sapwood to injury and fungal invasion can vary considerably between individual trees, as well as between species.

- **Diseases leading to decay or other weakening**. Members of this genus are subject to a very wide range of foliar diseases which can weaken them enough to cause dieback and susceptibility to decay. Leaf rusts (*Melampsora* spp.) and leaf spot caused by *Marssonina* spp. are of particular significance. Decay can also follow direct damage to woody parts by canker pathogens such as the bacterium *Xanthomonas populi* and the fungus *Hypoxylon mammatum*. Stems may also be weakened by the borings of various insects, such as longhorn beetles of the genus *Saperda* and the now rare Goat moth, *Cossus cossus*.

- **Mechanical characteristics**. Species of *Populus* generally have wood of low density, and many of them can reach a great size. With this combination of characteristics, specimens exposed to strong winds are often affected by the breakage of tops and branches or the development of permanent bending of the main stem. Extensive decay occurs in pollarded trees, and it is essential that these are re-cut periodically so as to prevent the development of excessively long or heavy new growth.

- **Site-related information**. Most species require abundant moisture, but also reasonably good drainage, for healthy growth and strong anchorage. Height growth may outstrip anchoring capacity on sites where there is high water table present throughout the year. Also, twig abscission can be heavy and could therefore be a nuisance for passers-by in built-up areas.

PRUNUS – CHERRIES, PLUMS, ALMONDS, PEACHES ETC.

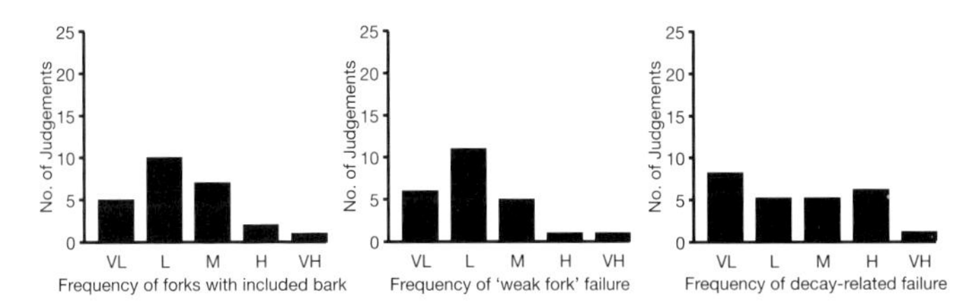

- **Fungi causing decay**. *Armillaria* spp. (B), *Chondrostereum purpureum* (T), *Coniophora puteana* (T), *Coriolus versicolor* (T), *Daedaleopsis confragosa* (T), *Ganoderma* spp. (T), *Laetiporus sulphureus* (T), *Phellinus tuberculosus* (T)

- **Resistance to decay**. The heartwood of *Prunus* spp. is fairly durable, although it may be colonised by *Ganoderma* spp. and *L. sulphureus*. The sapwood of many species and cultivars is very vulnerable to attack by *Chondrostereum purpureum* if wounded.

- **Diseases leading to decay or other weakening**. Members of this genus are very prone to canker and dieback diseases, which can lead to secondary decay. Bacterial canker, caused by *Pseudomonas syringae* pv. *mors-prunorum* is an important example in cherries, especially *Prunus avium*, as is a severe dieback disease (of unknown cause) in the ornamental *Prunus* 'Kanzan'. Below ground, Phytophthora root disease may occur.

- **Mechanical characteristics and site-related information**. The tendency to form weak forks is particularly pronounced in the cultivar *P. serrulata* "Amanagowa". The large but shallow roots of some species of *Prunus*, especially the Wild cherry, *P. avium*, often push up paving stones and other superficial structures, which can become hazardous to passers-by in built-up areas. In some species, heavy loading by fruit can lead to branch breakage.

PTEROCARYA – WING-NUTS: see histograms only

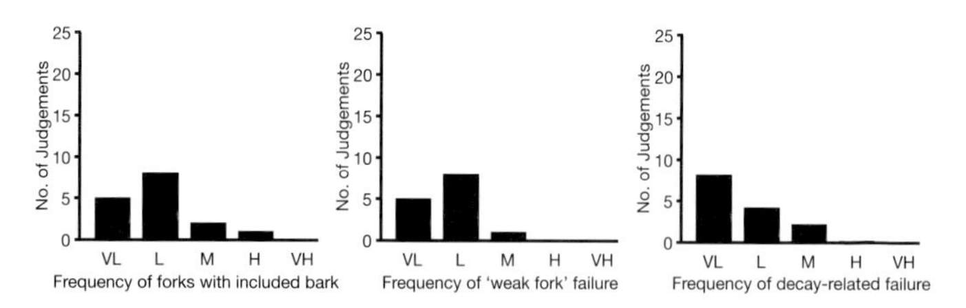

PYRUS – PEARS

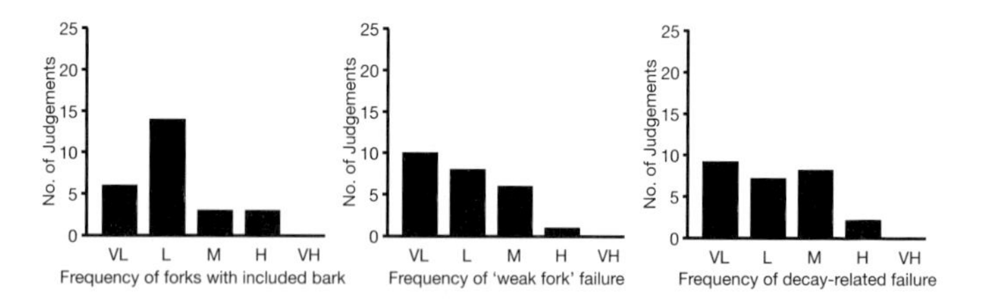

- **Fungi causing decay**. *Chondrostreum purpureum* (T)

- **Diseases leading to decay or other weakening**. There may be breakage of brittle branches following severe dieback due to fireblight, caused by the bacterium *Erwinia amylovora* or due to silver leaf caused by *C. purpureum*. Secondary decay may also ensue.

- **Mechanical characteristics**. Although most types of pear do not have much tendency to form weak forks, this can be a problem in the pyramidal cultivar *P. calleryana* 'Chanticleer'.

QUERCUS – OAKS

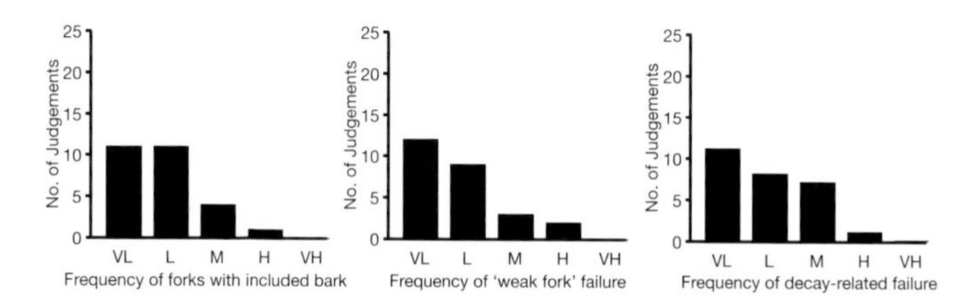

- **Fungi causing decay**. *Collybia fusipes* (B), *Daedalea quercina* (T), *Fistulina hepatica* (T,B), *Ganoderma applanatum* (T,B), *G. adspersum* (T,B), *G. pfeifferi* (T,B), *G. resinaceum* (B), *Grifola frondosa* (B), *Hypholoma fasciculare*, *Inonotus dryadeus* (B), *Laetiporus sulphureus* (T,B), *Meripilus giganteus* (B), *Rigidoporus ulmarius* (B), *Stereum* spp. (T), *Ustulina deusta* (B: mainly on the red oak group), *Vuilleminia comedens* (T)

- **Resistance to decay**. The native British *Quercus* spp. as well as many exotic ones, have a durable heartwood, which reduces the risk of extensive decay following pruning. The heartwood can, however be slowly decayed by several fungi, especially the above *Ganoderma* spp. and *L. sulphureus*. The decay caused by *F. hepatica* is especially slow in its development. The sapwood can be rapidly colonised by wound-rot fungi, but this results mainly in the death of individual branches, especially if they are stressed by shading or drought.

- **Diseases leading to decay or other weakening**. Several canker fungi, including *Stereum rugosum* and *Bulgaria inquinans* occasionally occur on *Quercus* spp., and may be accompanied by decay fungi; *S. rugosum* can cause decay in its own right. General decline of entire trees can also be caused by persistent attack by the scale insect *Kermes quercus* and by the ill-defined condition termed oak dieback.

- **Mechanical characteristics**. It is not possible to generalise about this large genus. The native British species rarely undergo failure of the main stem, and uprooting is also quite unusual, but it is not uncommon for quite large branches to be torn off in severe gales. Failures at branch junctions are generally rare, but co-dominant forks sometimes split in young specimens.

- **Site-related information**. Most species of oak can send their roots down to a sufficient depth for good stability on most soil types, but this has proved insufficient to prevent uprooting on very sandy soils during severe gales. Also, the Red oak, *Q. rubra*, does not root deeply on poorly drained sites and thus often becomes unstable before reaching maturity.

ROBINIA – FALSE ACACIAS

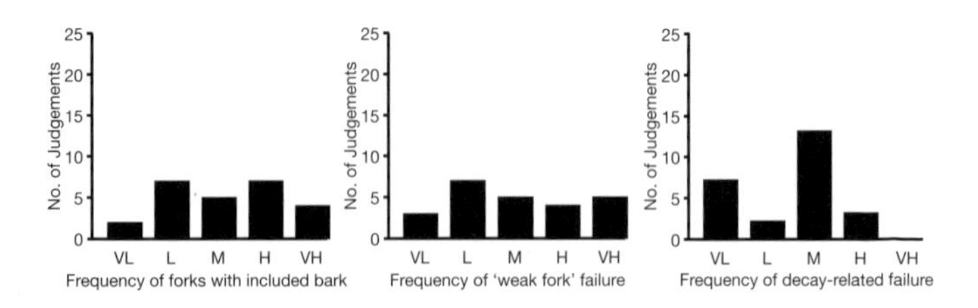

- **Fungi causing decay**. *Laetiporus sulphureus* (T), *Perenniporia fraxinea* (B) *Pholiota squarrosa* (B)

- **Diseases leading to decay or other weakening**. Branches may by killed by Verticillium wilt.

- **Mechanical characteristics**. The wood of old specimens is reputed to be brittle, and branches are sometimes torn off by high winds. It is not clear to what extent such failures are related to decay by *L. sulphureus*. Weak fork failures have been found more frequently in *R. viscosa* than in *R. pseudoacacia*.

SALIX – WILLOWS

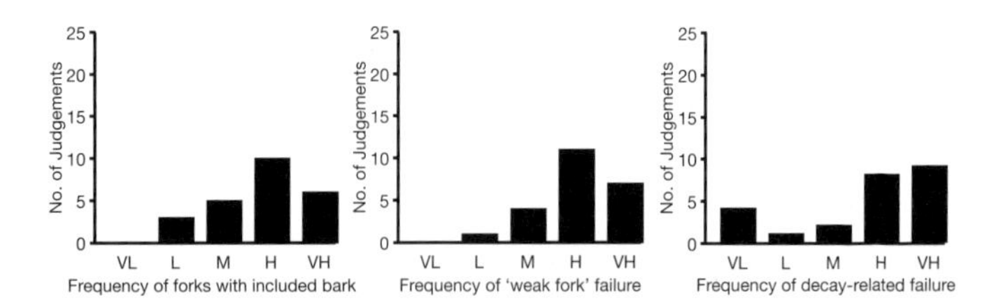

- **Fungi causing decay**. *Armillaria* spp. (B) *Daedaleopsis confragosa* (T), *Fistulina hepatica* (T,B), *Laetiporus sulphureus* (T), *Phellinus igniarius* (T), *Polyporus squamosus* (T)

- **Resistance to decay**. The wood of willows has little resistance to colonisation by most of the above decay fungi.

- **Diseases leading to decay or other weakening**. Trees may become rapidly decayed if they die back due to severe attacks by various diseases, including repeated attacks by leaf and shoot-infecting fungi, such as *Melampsora*, *Venturia* or *Glomerella*. Major dieback due to watermark disease caused by the bacterium *Erwinia salicis*, occurs in some localities.

- **Mechanical characteristics**. Some *Salix* species, especially *S. fragilis*, are rather prone to branch failure. However, this occurs less often in *S.*

alba and many of its cultivars (e.g. 'Vitellina'). The break-out of branches in pollarded willows is related to the rapid decay of the old, exposed wood. Such failure can be largely prevented by regular re-cutting of the new growth.

- **Site-related information**. Failure at the root-plate in riverside trees has been blamed on changes in water level.

SOPHORA – S. JAPONICA, PAGODA TREE: see data in histograms only

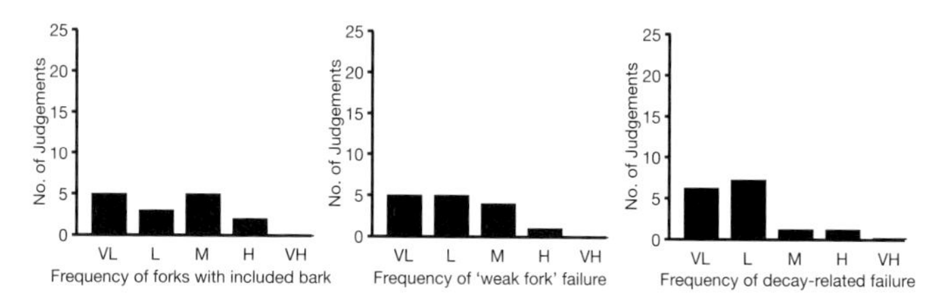

SORBUS – SERVICE TREES, WHITEBEAMS AND ROWANS

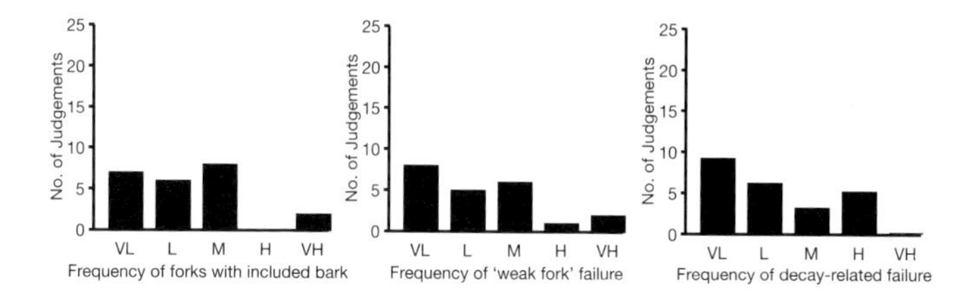

- **Fungi causing decay**. *Chondrostereum purpureum* (T) *Ganoderma adspersum/applanatum* (T,B), *Inonotus hispidus* (T), *Pholiota squarrosa* (T,B)

- **Resistance to decay**. Butt-rots are becoming quite common amongst *Sorbus* spp. planted as street trees in Britain, now that the many of these have reached maturity. Some reports indicate that the rowans may be rather more susceptible to decay than the whitebeams.

- **Diseases leading to decay or other weakening**. Embrittlement and decay may occur following dieback due to various serious diseases, including fireblight caused by the bacterium *Erwinia amylovora*, silverleaf caused by *C. purpureum*, cankers caused by *Nectria* spp. and canker and dieback caused apparently by the fungus *Valsa* (*Cytospora*) in Scotland.

- **Mechanical characteristics**. The Sargent Rowan, *Sorbus sargentii*, is often grafted on to *S. aucuparia* and the unions tend to become swollen due to incompatibility, sometimes with an associated weakness. Another point worth noting is that instability can result from the grafting of *Sorbus* spp. on to *Crataegus* rootstocks.

- **Site-related information**. *Sorbus aucuparia*, rowan, is native throughout Britain, but does not thrive in very dry areas, where it can be short-lived and consequently tends to break up.

TILIA – LIMES (LINDENS)

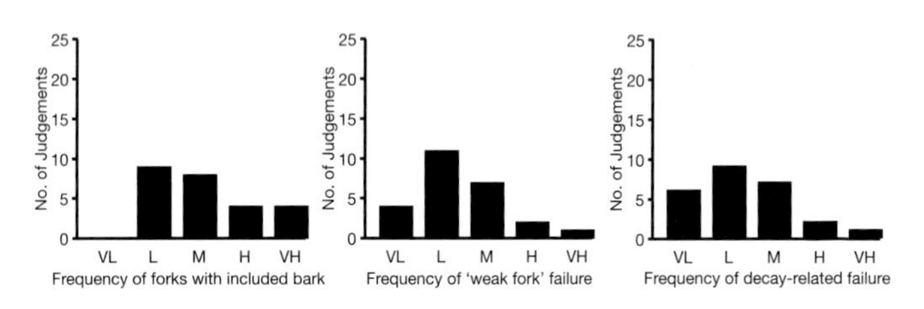

- **Fungi causing decay**. *Flammulina velutipes* (B,T), *Ganoderma adspersum/applanatum* (T,B), *Pholiota squarrosa* (B), *Polyporus squamosus* (T), *Ustulina deusta* (B)

- **Resistance to decay**. *Tilia* spp. do not have a durable heartwood, but the development of decay in their sapwood is often well delimited to small volumes of tissue.

- **Diseases leading to decay or other weakening**. Various diseases occasionally kill trees or parts of trees, which may then decay. These include Phytophthora root killing, weeping canker of *T. x euchlora* (cause unknown) and Verticillum wilt.

- **Mechanical characteristics**. The cultivar 'Greenspire' of *T. cordata* is reported to show a high incidence of weak fork formation and of resulting failure. Otherwise, failures in *Tilia* spp. appear to be confined mainly to young trees and pollarded specimens with long, crowded branches.

- **Site-related information**. In built-up areas, honeydew from aphid infestation of the Common lime, *T. x vulgaris*, can be a considerable problem, perhaps even a hazard as far as the paintwork of cars is concerned. Within the foraging range of hive bees, a toxicity hazard is thought to be caused by the nectar of the Caucasian lime, *T. x euchlora*.

ULMUS – ELMS

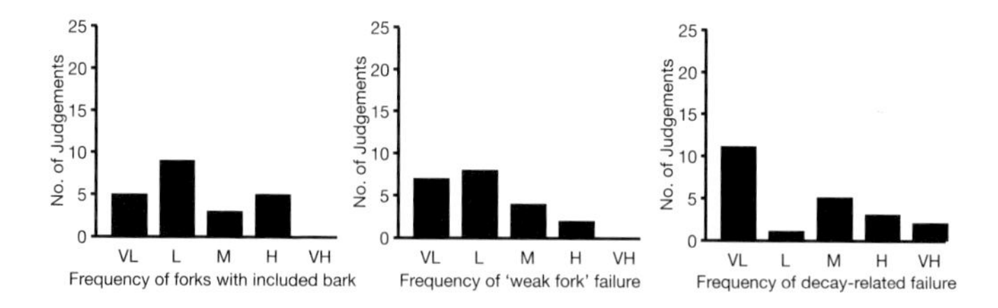

- **Fungi causing decay**. *Armillaria* spp. (B), *Fistulina hepatica* (T,B), *Flammulina velutipes* (T,B), *Ganoderma adspersum/applanatum* (T,B), *Inonotus hispidus* (T), *Perenniporia fraxinea* (B), *Polyporus squamosus* (T), *Pleurotus* spp. (T), *Rigidoporus ulmarius* (B)

- **Resistance to decay**.

- **Diseases leading to decay or other weakening**. Coral spot, Phytophthora root disease, Dutch elm disease.

- **Mechanical characteristics**. Twig shedding

- **Site-related information**.

ZELKOVA – ZELKOVA, CAUCASIAN ELM AND KEAKI

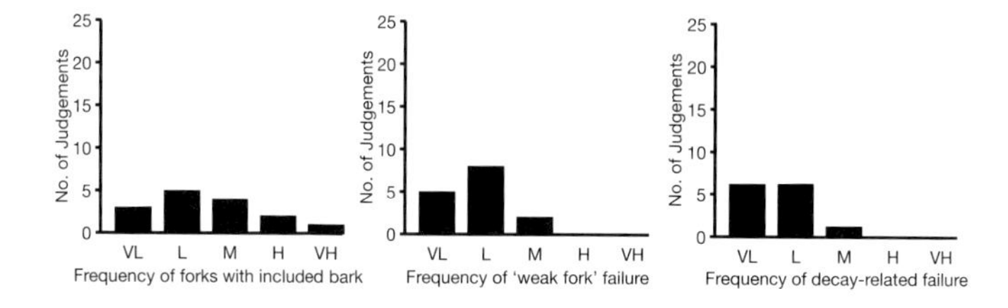

- **Diseases leading to decay or other weakening**. *Zelkova carpinifolia*, the Caucasian or Siberian elm, is susceptible to Dutch elm disease (see *Ulmus* above) but *Z. serrata*, the keaki, is said to be resistant.

- **Mechanical characteristics**. Keaki, *Z. serrata*, has an exceptionally strong and durable timber.

Appendix 3: Some examples of assessment systems for hazard or risk

1. A form for assessing risks: designed by David Lonsdale for Forest Research. (Part 2, not shown, is used if detailed inspection is required.) The numbered categories for risk of failure and for risk of harm to targets are based on the system designed by M.J. Ellison {see p.365}.

Individual Tree Risk Assessment Form completed by...

PART 1: GENERAL INFORMATION AND GENERAL INSPECTION DATA

Client's name, ref. and organisation		Tree sp. & I.D. No.		Location	Soil	Aspect	Slope
	Client no. Enq. ref.						°
		Growth stage*:	Date visited:		View conditions:		
dbh: (mm)	Basal diam: (mm)	Height: (m)	Crown spread (metres: max./min. in [..] direction.) Min. [ ] to [ ] Max. [ ] to [ ]		Lean (°) & [direction] ° [ ]		
Client's enquiry and "brief"							
General condition							
Named "targets**"							Risk of failure of 'weakest part' within 12 months (Category 1-5)
People/property risk cat. (1-6)							

General inspection data:

Remedial action: options and recommendations, or see Part 2 for detailed assessment, options and recommendations

* Juvenile, Semi-mature, Mature, Fully mature, Declining, Veteran ** Property, roads or other amenities within likely falling distance

2. A two-page form for inspection of defects and evaluation of hazard: designed by Nelda Matheny and James Clark of Hortscience Inc., Pleasanton, California, USA for the International Society for Arboriculture.

A Photographic Guide to the Evaluation of Hazard Trees in Urban Areas

TREE HAZARD EVALUATION FORM

Site/Address: ______________________

Map/Location: ______________________

Owner: public ________ private ________ unknown ________ other ________

Date: __________ Inspector: ______________________

Date of last inspection: ______________________

HAZARD RATING:

_____ + _____ + _____ = _____
Failure Potential + Size of part + Target Rating = Hazard Rating

_____ Immediate action needed

_____ Needs further inspection

_____ Dead tree

TREE CHARACTERISTICS

Tree #:______ **Species:**______________________

DBH: ______ **# of trunks:** ______ **Height:** ______ **Spread:** ______

Form: ☐ generally symmetric ☐ minor asymmetry ☐ major asymmetry ☐ stump sprout ☐ stag-headed

Crown class: ☐ dominant ☐ co-dominant ☐ intermediate ☐ suppressed

Live crown ratio:________ % **Age class:** ☐ young ☐ mature ☐ over-mature

Pruning history: ☐ crown cleaned ☐ excessively thinned ☐ topped ☐ crown raised ☐ pollarded ☐ crown reduced ☐ none

Special Value: ☐ specimen ☐ heritage/historic ☐ wildlife ☐ unusual ☐ street tree ☐ screen ☐ shade ☐ indigenous ☐ other

TREE HEALTH

Foliage color: ☐ normal ☐ chlorotic ☐ necrotic **Epicormics?** Y N

Foliage density: ☐ normal ☐ sparse Leaf size: ☐ normal ☐ small

Annual shoot growth: ☐ excellent ☐ average ☐ poor **Twig Dieback?** Y N

Callus development: ☐ excellent ☐ average ☐ poor ☐ none

Vigor class: ☐ excellent ☐ average ☐ fair ☐ poor

Major pests/diseases:______________________

SITE CONDITIONS

Site Character: ☐ residence ☐ commercial ☐ industrial ☐ park ☐ open space ☐ natural ☐ ______________

Landscape type: ☐ parkway ☐ raised bed ☐ container ☐ open ☐ ______________

Irrigation: ☐ none ☐ adequate ☐ inadequate ☐ excessive ☐ trunk wetted

% dripline paved: 0% 10-25% 25-50% 50-75% 75-100% **Lifted?** Y N

% dripline w/ fill soil: 0% 10-25% 25-50% 50-75% 75-100%

% dripline grade lowered: 0% 10-25% 25-50% 50-75% 75-100%

Soil problems: ☐ drainage ☐ shallow ☐ compacted ☐ droughty ☐ saline ☐ alkaline ☐ acidic ☐ small volume ☐ disease center ☐ history of fail

Obstructions: ☐ lights ☐ signage ☐ line-of-sight ☐ view ☐ overhead lines ☐ underground utilities ☐ traffic ☐ adjacent veg. ☐ ______

Wind (tree position): ☐ single tree ☐ below canopy ☐ above canopy ☐ recently exposed ☐ windward, canopy edge ☐ area prone to windthrow

TARGET

Use Under Tree: ☐ building ☐ parking ☐ traffic ☐ pedestrian ☐ recreation ☐ landscape ☐ hardscape ☐ small features

Can target be moved? Y N

Occupancy: ☐ occasional use ☐ medium, intermittent use ☐ frequent use

TREE DEFECTS

Rate defect severity: **S** severe defect, high potential for failure
M defect of moderate severity
L defect of low severity

LEAN: ________ deg. from vertical ☐ natural ☐ unnatural **Soil heaving:** Y N

Decay in plane of lean: Y N Roots exposed: Y N **Soil cracking:** Y N

Compounding factors: ______________________________ **Lean severity:** S M L

ROOT DEFECTS:

Suspect root rot: Y N **Mushroom/conk present:** Y N **ID:** ______________________

Exposed roots: S M L **Undermined:** S M L

Root pruned: ________ ft from trunk **Root area affected:** ________ % **Buttress wounded:** Y N **When:** ______________

Restricted root area: S M L **Potential for root failure:** S M L

CROWN DEFECTS:

DEFECT	ROOT CROWN	TRUNK	SCAFFOLDS	BRANCHES
Poor taper				
Codominants/forks				
Multiple attachments				
Included bark				
Excessive end weight				
Cracks/Splits				
Hangers				
Girdling				
Wounds				
Decay				
Cavity				
Conks/Mushrooms				
Bleeding				
Loose/cracked bark				
Nesting hole/bee hive				
Deadwood/stubs				
Borers/termites/ants				
Cankers/galls				
Previous failure				

HAZARD RATING

Part most likely to fail: ______________________________

Failure Potential: 1 2 3 **Size of Part:** 1 2 3 **Target:** 1 2 3 **Hazard Rating:** 1 2 3 4 5 6 7 8 9

HAZARD ABATEMENT

Prune: ☐ remove defective part ☐ reduce end weight ☐ crown clean ☐ thin ☐ raise canopy ☐ crown reduce ☐ restructure ☐ shape

Cable/Brace: ______________________________ **Inspect further:** ☐ root crown ☐ decay ☐ aerial ☐ monitor

Remove tree: Y N **Replace?** Y N **Move target:** Y N **Other:** ______________________

Effect on adjacent trees: ☐ none ☐ evaluate

COMMENTS

3. A system for assessing hazard and estimating risk to persons and property: designed by Mike Ellison of Cheshire Woodlands Ltd.

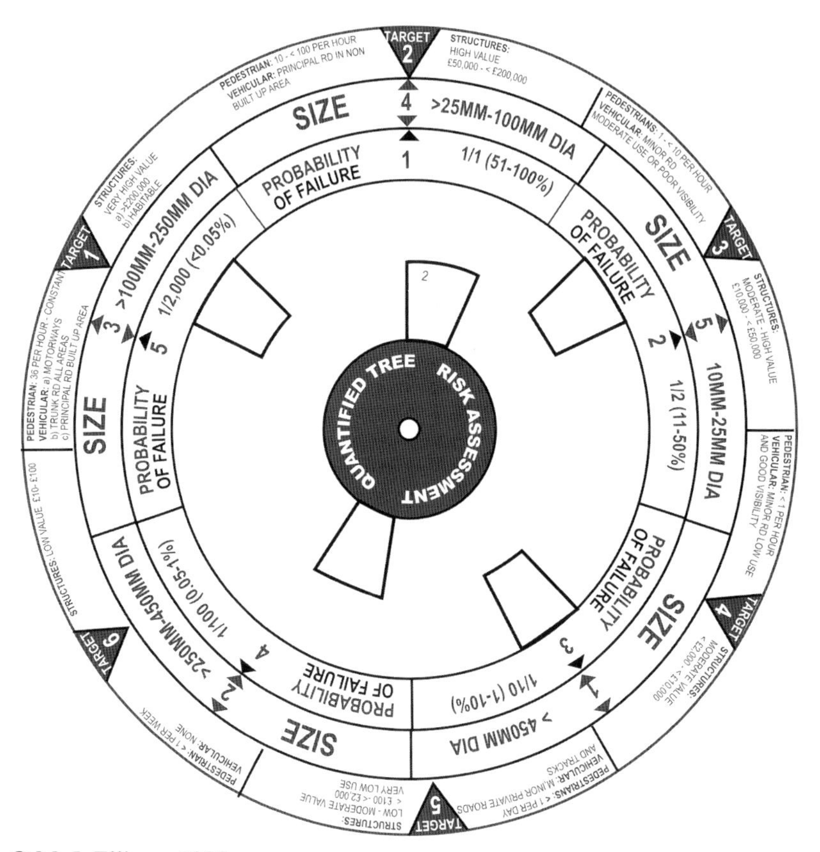

The risk assessment or 'overall probability' values displayed in the ready reckoner are based on the multiplication of three values represented by the three vanes of the reckoner. These can be rotated so as to select each value from a pre-determined range. The values are described by Ellison as 'probability ratios' and represent the following estimates:

- Size of part likely to fail: the likely potential harm, based on the diameter of the part of the tree under consideration (Five categories: 1/1, 1/1.5, 1/7.5, 1/50, 1/500)

- Probability of failure (Five categories: 1/1, 1/2, 1/10, 1/100, 1/1000)

- Target value: the nature of the target(s) – pedestrians, vehicles and structures – and the probability of impact, based on duration of occupation (Six categories: 1/5, 1/20, 1/100, 1/500, 1/10 000, 1/80 000)

Appendix 4: Diagnosis of damage to trees: possible sources of help in Great Britain

[reproduced from a list compiled by R.G. Strouts, Disease Diagnostic and Advisory Service, Forestry Commission Research Agency]

1. Diagnosis of, and general information on, tree diseases and disorders

- Forest Research, tel. Bentley, Hampshire (01420) 23000 or Edinburgh (0131) 445-2176.

- Arboricultural Advisory & Information Service, tel. Bentley, Hampshire (01420) 22022.

- Local authority arboricultural or forestry officers;

- University departments of botany, plant sciences or horticultural sciences;

- The Director, Oxford Forestry Institute, South Parks Road, Oxford, tel. Oxford (01865) 275000;

- (For members only) The Royal Horticultural Society's Plant Pathology Department at Wisley, tel. Guildford (01483) 224234;

- Some consultants registered with the Arboricultural Association {AA Secretary: tel. Romsey (01794) 368717}.

2. Identification of the larger fungal fruit bodies (e.g. toadstools and brackets).

- Forest Research (see above).

- Local natural history societies;

- The Enquiry Unit, Royal Botanic Gardens, Kew, Richmond, Surrey, TW9 3AB, tel. 0181-332-5622

3. Identification of microfungi and abnormal growths on trees

- Forest Research (see above).

- The Enquiry Unit, Royal Botanic Gardens, Kew, Richmond, Surrey, TW9 3AB, tel. 0181-332-5622.

4. Decay and Tree Safety

- Forest Research, tel. Bentley, Hampshire (01420) 23000 or Edinburgh (0131) 4452176. Arboricultural Advisory & Information Service, tel. Bentley, Hampshire (01420) 22022.

- Some consultants registered with the Arboricultural Association {AA Secretary: tel. Romsey (01794) 368717}.

- Local authority arboricultural or forestry officers.

5. Suspected malicious damage to trees

Such cases usually require an on-site inspection or consideration by a plant pathologist (see category 1, above).

Index

Please note: for tree genera, see also Appendix 2